16.99

Production and Operations Ma

Production and Operations Management

Fifth edition

Keith Lockyer
Alan Muhlemann
John Oakland

University of Bradford

PITMAN PUBLISHING
128 Long Acre London WC2E 9AN

A Division of Longman Group UK Ltd.

© K G Lockyer 1962, 1969, 1974, 1983
© K G Lockyer, A P Muhlemann and J S Oakland 1988

First and second editions published under the title
Factory Management 1962 and 1969; third edition published
under the title *Factory and Production Management* 1974;
fourth edition published under the title *Production
Management* 1983.

This edition first published in Great Britain 1988
Reprinted 1989 (twice)

British Library Cataloguing in Publication Data
Lockyer, K. G.
    Production and operations management. —
    5th ed.
    1. Production management
    I. Title   II. Muhlemann, Allan   III. Oakland,
    John S.   IV. Lockyer, K. G. Production
    management
658.5   TS155

    ISBN 0-273-02873-1

Printed and bound in Singapore

To Doris, Sheila, Sue

Contents

Section II The product

Section III The plant

distribution—factors affecting the design of the
plant/premises

Section IV The process

materials handling—the environment and efficiency—man and his dimension—man at the workplace—man and the machine—information—layout of displays and controls—man and the working environment

Section V The programmes

outline of the functions of production control—
parameters affecting the production control function—
sequence of operations—production control and the
computer

Section VI The people

the safety adviser—safety planning—the accident
prevention programme—workplace inspections—accident
or incident investigation and follow up—fire—health and
safety at work legislation

Appendices

Preface to the fifth edition

'As all experienced operations managers know, there are but two simple devices necessary to run an operating unit—a crystal ball and a magic wand. In the absence of these, the present volume is offered to those engaged in that peculiar form of juggling, known as production or operations management, in the hope that it will indicate some areas of knowledge which it may be of use to study. The text is not encyclopaedic nor is it intended to be a training manual for any of the specialist disciplines, illumination is intended to be general rather than intense.'

The above, slightly modified, paragraph opened the previous four editions and as a statement of purpose it will serve to introduce this, the fifth edition, now re-titled *Production and Operations Management*. The change in title is accompanied by a change in authorship. Keith Lockyer is now joined by his two colleagues Alan Muhlemann and John Oakland. All three have considerable P/OM teaching experience, and all have undertaken considerable research and consultancy 'at the coal face' both in the UK and internationally. This worldwide experience of the authors is reflected in the material incorporated in the book. Whilst examples are quoted throughout in pounds sterling, they could just as usefully be quoted in dollars, marks, francs . . . without affecting in any way the intrinsic value of the text.

The authors' experiences in a wide variety of industries and geographical locations has brought a realization that there are more similarities than differences in the management of the various types of transformation process, and that the management of non-manufacturing activities has only superficial differences from the management of those which create artefacts. For this reason the word 'Operations' has been added to the title.

The 5 P's model of a transformation organization—Product, Plant, Processes, Programmes and People—fits teaching and fieldwork so well that it continues to be used as the structure for this edition as it was in the fourth edition. Thus, the text divides into six sections: Section I puts P/OM into perspective, Sections I–VI deal with the 5 P's. There is also a set of appendices.

As always there is the usual conflict between cost and length, and every attempt has been made to keep the increase in length of the text to a minimum. This has resulted in the abandoning of some material, particularly that which was of interest to a limited readership. Thus 'Estimating and planning' in its previous form has disappeared altogether. Despite this, the present volume is one of the most comprehensive works dealing with production and operations management now available.

A new chapter (Chapter 5) discusses classification and coding, including bar coding, a subject which all the authors have found in their fieldwork is neglected, often to the extent that computerization of the P/OM function is impossible. Quality and reliability are extended since it is clear that the pursuit of excellence in these two fields brings with it many associated benefits. Fieldwork has also shown that work study, properly chosen and applied, is an invaluable tool for the operations manager, so that an additional chapter giving examples of use of work study has been included.

Short-term forecasting is treated more extensively than here-to-fore, and balanced discussions of the newer 'panaceas' 'OPT', 'JIT', 'MRP', 'MRP (II)' are included where appropriate. 'Linear programming' is discussed more thoroughly than in previous editions. In addition to these major changes, the whole text has been carefully scrutinized and, where desirable, re-written. Readers of earlier editions will notice that in the present edition the lists of Recommended Reading are, in some cases, shorter than previously. This comes about because economic circumstances have dictated that many specialist texts have had to be taken out of publication and not replaced.

When the first edition was published in 1962 it was possible to identify with some precision the examinations whose syllabuses had helped determine the form of the work. The enormous increase in the teaching of management at all levels now makes this quite impossible. As previously, the book covers most of the 'production' and/or 'operation' work in the Diploma in Management Studies and in the examinations of many professional bodies, including the Institute of Industrial Managers. Equally, undergraduates taking 'management', 'business' or 'administration' in their degree studies, and MSc, MTech and MBA students will also find much helpful material in the present text. It is also anticipated that this edition will continue to be as useful to the practising production, operations and general manager as previous editions are known to be.

Our thanks are due to our wives for their forbearance, and to our friends and colleagues in industry and education who have helped us so much. Probably the most helpful groups of all are the many and various students who have passed through our hands. They have been unsparing in their comments. In the past the sole author has claimed credit for errors and omissions. In the present work, any imperfections are the fault of one of the other authors.

Keith Lockyer · Alan Muhlemann · John Oakland
September 1987

Section I **Perspective**

1. *The production/operations function within the corporation*
2. *Planning*
3. *Control*
4. *Budgets and budgetary control*
5. *Classification and coding*

1 The production/operations function within the corporation

Introduction

Organizations of whatever kind are viable only if they provide satisfaction to the consumer, and this simple criterion is the only general condition for the continued existence of an organization. Such a statement, of course, raises as many questions as it produces solutions, and it is not appropriate within the present text to try to investigate this.

Two things, however, do need to be clarified:

1. That which satisfies may be either physical or intangible or both. It will here be called the product.

2. The consumer may be either outside or inside the organization: he/she may be a customer for the product or a user of the system.

What is production/operations management?

Any organization can be represented by a hierarchy of input/output diagrams. At the base of the hierarchy is a simple diagram which shows that a consumer's needs flow into the organization which then transforms them into that which satisfies the consumer (Fig. 1.1).

Since the output returns to the origin, the input/output diagram can be represented as a closed loop (Fig. 1.2).

This basic diagram may be broken down into five sequential input/output diagrams. In the first the consumer's needs are identified and translated into a statement of explicit forecasts (Fig. 1.3(i)), which in turn become the inputs to the second diagram where they are analysed and integrated to become a statement of resource plans (Fig. 1.3(ii)).

Fig. 1.1

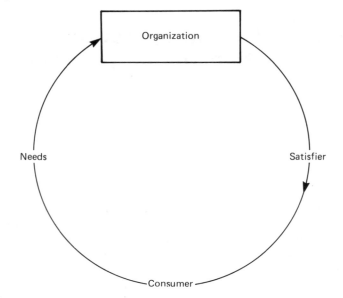

Fig. 1.2

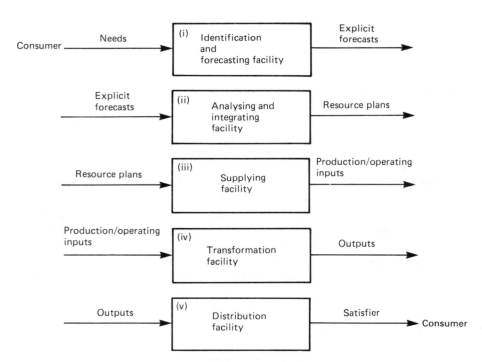

Fig. 1.3

These resource plans are satisfied from suppliers, either internal or external and generate the inputs which move into the transformation facility (Fig. 1.3(iii)), which produces outputs either physical or tangible (Fig. 1.3(iv)), which are then distributed to the consumers, providing the satisfaction originally required (Fig. 1.3(v)).

Since the output from any one diagram represents input to the next and as the last output returns to the start, the total diagram can be represented as a closed loop (Fig. 1.4).

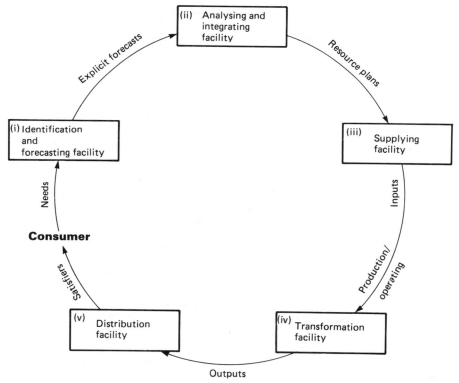

Fig. 1.4 A closed loop

This diagram is, of course, grossly simplified. For example, when forecasts are analysed it may be found that within the facilities available they are unachievable. A reverse reaction should then cause the forecasts to be modified, and a second iteration will take place. Equally, distribution facilities may be inadequate for clearing the output from the transformation facility which should cause a series of modifications in the preceding stages. A complete diagram, therefore, would not be a single circumferenced circle but a complex of interconnected stages. Eventually, however, when all signals have passed along all ganglia, a final impulse will flow around the circumference of Fig. 1.4.

The production/operations management function is that which covers the second, third and fourth of these input/output diagrams, namely the analysis, supply and transformation facilities (Figs. 1.3(ii)–(iv)). Since these are extremely closely linked it is not uncommon to regard them as one facility and the production/operations manager can then be regarded as the manager of the whole transformation process (Fig. 1.5).

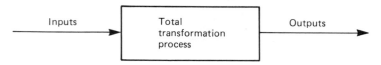

Fig. 1.5

Similarly, the identification and forecasting facility and the distribution facility are also very closely linked and may be regarded as one, the marketing facility. In some situations the distribution facility may be linked to production/operating rather than marketing; in others—for example retailing—the transformation facility may become vestigial or disappear altogether. Despite these possibilities, the fundamental tasks of any organization may be said to be 'Marketing' and 'Producing/ Operating', as shown by the two enclosing circles of Fig. 1.6.

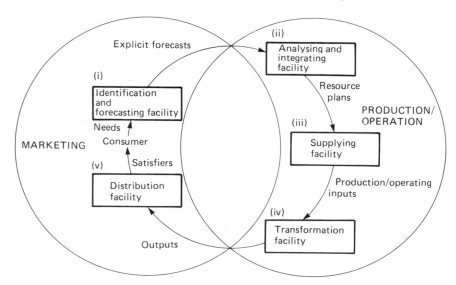

Fig. 1.6

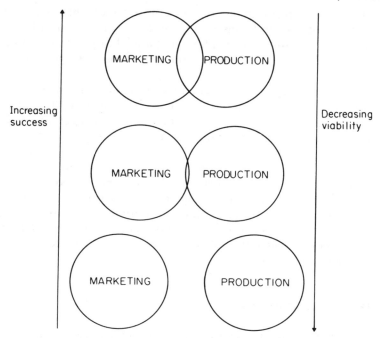

Fig. 1.7 The effects of separating the marketing and production functions

The relationship between these two functions is crucial to the success—that is, the survival—of the whole organization. The closer together they approach, the greater the likelihood of success, and it is interesting to realize that at the beginning of any organization the marketing/operations functions are usually carried out by one and the same person. Separation between these two functions or a reduction of their inter-connections increases the likelihood of disaster (Fig. 1.7).

Is there a difference between production and operations? Earlier it was stated that some of the outputs from the transformation facility might in fact be intangible. Thus, instead of being artefacts they may be something which enables the consumer to carry out that which he/she wishes to do. An example of such a situation might be a club where the needs of the consumer are that he/she shall be entertained by providing an opportunity for social intercourse. Thus the transformation process results in the provision of an ambience which will allow the social intercourse to take place. The manager of such an enterprise does, in fact, conceptually carry out the same tasks as the manager of an enterprise producing artefacts. Equally, loading jobs on to a set of machines is not significantly different from providing passenger accommodation on a range of aeroplanes. The replenishment of stock in a factory has many of the characteristics of the problems of replenishing staff in an airline. This co-existence of structure between tasks in parallel disparate organizations enables a useful study of production/operations management to be carried out.

The interesting fact which has emerged over the last few years is that the well-established tools of the production manager, that is one who produces artefacts, are equally applicable to the manager of an 'intangible' enterprise. That is not to say that every technique is applicable in every circumstance, but that there is a 'tool kit' of techniques and ideas which is available to operations/production managers, and which should be known in order to be able to choose the appropriate tool. A domestic tool kit might very well contain a range of screwdrivers of different sizes. Depending on the circumstances, the appropriately sized screwdriver is chosen. Similarly in production/operations management, the tool kit will contain techniques which are not always used but which are available to be used when appropriate.

Engineering/technology

It is important always to realize that management is not the same as engineering or technology, although there are considerable areas of common interest. Broadly, the engineer or technologist, is concerned with the *design* of physical equipment while the manager is concerned with the *organization* of the use of the equipment and other resources, e.g. men, materials and money. Equally it is important to realize that a knowledge of engineering or technology of any sort is not a necessary requirement for a production/operations manager. A similar comment applies to other sciences and engineering disciplines.

Production/operations management: a conceptual framework

Of all managerial tasks the production/operations management function is the hardest to define since it incorporates so many diverse tasks that are interdependent. To divide it up, therefore, is to destroy it, but without such division it is impossible to discuss the work of the production/operations manager in anything but the most general terms. This problem of the whole and the parts is well known to the logicians, but nevertheless it is proposed here to consider the production/operations management function under five separate headings. The division is arbitrary but has been found to provide a useful conceptual framework for consideration of the work of the production/operations manager. For simplicity, the cumbersome phrases 'production/operations manager' and 'production and operations management' will be replaced by the acronym 'POM'.

1. The product

The product is the most obvious embodiment of the interface between marketing and production, and it is not sufficient that the consumer requires the product: the organization must be capable of producing it. Agreement, therefore, must be reached between all the business functions on such matters as:

performance
aesthetics
quality
reliability
quantity
selling price or production costs
delivery dates and times

In reaching agreement on the above, cognizance must be taken of external factors, such as the needs of the market and the existing culture, the legal constraints, and the environmental demands. At the same time there are a number of internal considerations which must be examined: for example, the compatibility of a new product or service with the existing systems, facilities and traditions, and whether a new enterprise will excessively increase the variety of activities being undertaken within the organization. Variety, like entropy, tends to increase and as it does so it brings with it disorder and confusion. The temptation to increase variety is extremely great and while it must not be resisted 'at all costs' the decision to increase it must be a *conscious* one. It is not possible for the POM alone to operate a variety control policy: this must be an essential part of the corporate strategy of the organization.

2. The plant

To make the product, plant of some kind both in terms of buildings and equipment is required. This plant, which accounts for the bulk of the fixed assets of the organization, must match the needs of the product, of the market, of the operator and of the organization, and it must continue to do so for as long as the consumer need can be foreseen. The POM, therefore, will be concerned with questions such as:

future possible demands
design and layout of buildings and offices
performance and reliability of equipment
maintenance of performance
safety of installation and operation
social responsibility

These must be considered in conjunction with the financial, fiscal and political/cultural constraints imposed by the environment within which production is to be carried out.

3. The processes

The decision on product creation is made by bringing together the technical and organizational needs of the product and the organization and the people within the organization. It is extremely rare to discover that there is only one way to make something or to provide a particular service, and the ingenuity of man needs to be constrained if variety of methods is not to increase. At the same time, it is sensible to try to engage the skills, knowledge and intellect of those who are going to carry out the processes. If it were possible to harness the goodwill and good sense of *all* levels of employees, many organizations could be both more pleasant and more wealth-producing than they are today. The attitude 'we don't pay you to think but to do as you are told' may not be expressed in words, but it is often made painfully clear in behaviour.

In deciding upon a process it is necessary to examine such factors as:

available capacity
available skills
type of production
layout of plant and equipment
safety
maintenance requirements
costs to be achieved

4. The programmes

Timetables setting down the dates/times of the transfer of products to, or provision of services for, the consumer are the other visible expression of the production/marketing interface, not merely setting down dates and times but also effectively determining cash-flow, that prime controller of organizational viability. If programmes are not appropriately agreed, then programming becomes '. . . the art of reconciling irresponsible promises with inadequate resources'.

Transfer timetables generate timetables for:

purchasing
transforming
maintenance
cash
storage
transport

Although the problems of timetabling are simple to state, their resolution may be of immense complexity, involving not merely the solution of combinatorial problems, a notoriously intractable class of problem, but also the simultaneous satisfying of multiple objectives, many of which are in conflict. Unfortunately the mathematical solution is often conceived to be a complete answer to the timetabling problem. In fact, of course, the behaviour of people, both within and without the organization, can disrupt the most elegant solution in an entirely unpredictable way. Conflict will inevitably arise between the need for discipline to achieve an effective solution, and the need for freedom to meet the personal expectations of employees and consumers.

5. The people

Production, from first to last, depends upon people. Like all other products of man, man himself is variable; in intellect, in skill, in expectations. The work of the social scientist is continually enlarging our understanding of man and organizations and bringing home the fact that the 'simple' panaceas, better communications, small groups, worker participation, industrial democracy, job enrichment . . . are rarely simple, since they usually involve fundamental re-thinking of the whole organizational purpose. Despite the growth of specialized functions, the sharpest expression of personnel policy takes place within the production unit itself, since it is here that the bulk of people are employed. Again, the need for the involvement of the POM in the determination of such policy is clear—again separation and divorce increase the likelihood of disaster. The production manager should therefore be involved in discussions on:

wages/salaries
safety
conditions of work
motivation
trade unions
education and training

POM is an amalgam of all the above aspects of work (Fig. 1.8), being that ill-defined area of interest where the five sub-areas overlap. Not

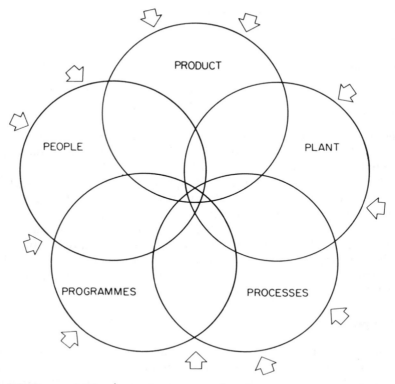

Fig. 1.8 The production/operations manager's task

merely is the area ill-defined, it is continually changing as external and internal pressures change. New legislation on, say, product liability may thrust the 'Product area' into prominence while a strike at a supplier may cause the 'Programme area' to be emphasized.

POM and corporate policy

Characteristically the transformation function will employ the bulk of the manpower, utilize the bulk of the physical assets and engage the bulk of the financial resources. Pressures for immediate solutions to transformation problems therefore are very great—a failure to deliver, an idle machine, a line of operators who are not producing, a breakdown in quality, an unsafe process or service—all *demand* attention. Without that understanding of the corporate strategy of the organization which derives from taking part in its determination, the POM will be forced to take short-term operating decisions which may generate unacceptable long-term actions by the whole organization.

It must be remembered that the determinants of a successful and continuous operation of *any* organization include:

quality
reliability
transfer   } of the product
cost
cash flow of the organization

and it is clear that these are largely determined by the behaviour of the transformation function. To try to separate POM policy from corporate policy, therefore, is an exercise which must be self-defeating. It can—it must—be an integral part of that policy and indeed it may often be the most decisive part of corporate policy. Disastrously, however, it is not uncommon to find that corporate policy has been set without adequate consideration of the abilities of the transformation function, and the consequential results frequently bring chaos and frustration. A policy on delivery (e.g. 'Company policy is to deliver within 24 hours of the receipt of order') can only have meaning if it is accompanied by policies on such matters as:

utilization of plant
utilization of labour
investment in stock
cost

and by an understanding of the technological imperatives of the product. Too often it will be found that board decisions are taken in the absence of sound transformation information, yet those decisions have to be excuted through the transformation function.

POM policy

It is not appropriate here to discuss the means by which a *corporate* policy is set, except to say that one fundamental decision has to be made, namely whether to *make* or to *buy* the products which the organization markets. Assuming that a 'make' decision is reached, the organization has a *policy for production*, and from this decision will flow the need for a *POM policy*, an integral part of corporate policy.

POM policy is the term applied to those aspects of corporate policy which particularly concern the production or manufacturing departments. Clearly this is an integral part of corporate policy and must act within, and not be independent of, it. However, corporate policy cannot set down the detail of policy, and it is in making policies and taking operating decisions within his competence that the production/operations manager effectively determines POM policy.

Failure to incorporate POM policy into corporate policy, or to exclude production considerations from corporate policy, will inevitably lead to the all too familiar conflicts with which the POM often has to deal. To be presented with policies which require

'. . . a reduction in training costs . . . a substantial reduction in error rates'

'. . . quicker delivery of special orders . . . less work-in-progress and lower material stocks'

'. . . higher plant utilization . . . and greater flexibility'

can only result in frustration and malfunction. No set of policies can be wholly consistent—'a foolish consistency is the hobgoblin of little minds'—but to operate without too many changes of direction, the wilder inconsistencies must be moderated, and some acceptable compromises effected.

Auditing the POM function

To determine policy is never simple, and to carry out this task with a multi-faceted function like production is very difficult. Before any policy can be set, it is essential to audit the situation—discover what is extant and what is desirable. Corporate strategists have long suggested that in setting up a strategy it is useful to consider the:

Strengths
Weaknesses } of the enterprise

Opportunities
Threats } offered to the enterprise

In considering any POM problem the author and his colleagues have found that it is an invaluable discipline to combine the above four considerations with the five areas of interest, producing a grid:

	Strengths?	*Weaknesses?*	*Opportunities?*	*Threats?*
Product				
Plant				
Processes				
Programmes				
People				

To illustrate the use of the POM policy grid, consider a proposal to use a computer for production control in place of an existing manual system. In this discussion only some few of the cells will be considered since space is at a premium:

Plant—Opportunities? An effective computer system offers the chance of significantly increasing utilization.

Processes—Strengths? All processes are well-defined for purposes of an incentive scheme.

Programmes—Weaknesses? The present methods of production control will not easily transfer to computerization.

People—Threats? The existing staff believe that computerization will result in the loss of jobs and a reduction in status for those remaining.

Any significant problem can be presented to the grid for systematic analysis in this way so that every facet of operational behaviour is questioned, and in so answering a sensible policy will emerge. This questioning technique is familiar to the work study engineer (Chapter 17), and its worth has there been amply demonstrated. In policy matters, too, the disciplines and illumination of a systematic question and answer method can be extremely helpful.

Opportunity cost

An important and useful concept to the POM is that of opportunity cost. As its name suggests, it is the cost of a lost opportunity. For example, if it is possible to invest in one of two alternatives, one of which will produce a return of £1,000 and the other a return of £1,050, then by investing in the first an opportunity cost of £50 is said to be incurred. A large number of the POM's decisions involve deciding between alternative opportunities and though as neat a quantification as that given above is not always possible, nevertheless it is always worth asking the question 'What is the opportunity cost of a possible action?'

Simplifying the POM task

While the life of the production/operations manager is exciting, challenging and worthwhile, it can never be said to be easy. Its multi-faceted nature, allied to the fact that the production/operations manager controls the bulk of the organization's physical and personnel resources, ensures a continual bombardment of problems which *have* to be resolved. Some method of simplifying the life of the production/operations manager is essential.

Simon makes a seminal suggestion. He distinguishes between *programmable* and *non-programmable* decisions, these being the extremes of decision types. Programmable decisions are repetitive and routine, so that a fixed procedure can be set down to solve them. Non-programmable decisions are novel, unstructured, and are often associated with people, their resolution depending upon the decision-maker's judgement, knowledge and experience. Clearly, the more problems which can be formulated so that their decisions can be programmed, the more time will be available for dealing with the non-programmable problems which are frequently the most important and subtle.

To simplify life, therefore, the production/operations manager should endeavour to set down procedures enabling programmable problems to be solved as a matter of routine. Areas of activity which lend themselves to this treatment include:

Materials management
Work methods
Maintenance policies
Timetabling
Preparation of estimates
Quality management
Safety procedures
Payment policies

In dealing with any one of these it might well be found that the programmed decision is not necessarily an 'ideal' or 'optimal' solution, but any apparent loss must be set against the benefits of releasing the manager to deal with the non-programmable problems. It is the aim of the present text to show how these programmable decisions can be made and to offer assistance in the handling of the non-programmable ones.

Recommended reading

Journals
There are a large number of current journals of interest to the production/operations manager. These include:

Business Decisions
Business Management
Factory
The International Journal of Production and Operations Management
The International Journal of Production Research
The International Journal of Quality and Reliability Management
Management Services
Management Today
Operations Research
Purchasing and Supply Management

Production and Inventory Management
The Harvard Business Review
The Journal of Industrial Engineering
The Journal of the Operational Research Society
The Production Engineer
Works Management

British Standards Yearbook, British Standards Institution, London
It is sometimes assumed that the British Standards Institution is concerned only with specifications for physical products. This is not so: there are now a substantial number of specifications dealing with production management topics. While individual specifications are identified later in the appropriate chapters, production managers are well advised to check on the existence of standards before setting up new systems or projects.
   Two BSI handbooks of particular value to production/operations managers are:

BSI Handbook 22—Quality Assurance
This brings together nine British Standards concerned with quality and reliability.
BSI Handbook 23—General Management
This brings together a number of glossaries and guides concerning work study, O & M, production planning and control, stock control, network analysis and standardization.

Textbooks
Hayes, R. and Wheelwright, S. C., *Restoring our competitive edge. Competing through Manufacturing*, John Wiley & Sons, 1984.
   A valuable book with, naturally, an American perspective. Very well referenced.
Hill, T., *Manufacturing strategy: the strategic management of the manufacturing function*, Macmillan, 1985.
   At the time of writing this is the only UK book devoted to a discussion of manufacturing strategy.
Institution of Production Engineers, *A Guide to Manufacturing Strategy*.
   While this is a 'hardware' based book, it contains much of value which can be translated into 'non-hardware' situations.
Luffman, G., Sanderson, S., Lea, E. and Kenny, B., *Business Policy—An analytical introduction*, Basil Blackwell, 1987.
   POM strategy has no meaning without reference to corporate strategy. This book is an excellent up-to-date, well-written introduction to the subject.
Simon, H. A., *The New Sciences of Management Decision*, Prentice Hall, 1977.
   A great book by a great man. Get it and read it.
Skinner, Wickham, *Manufacturing in the corporate strategy*, Wiley, 1978.
   Possibly the most seminal work on manufacturing and its strategy implications yet written. Consists of edited and sometimes modified papers written by Professor Skinner in the *Harvard Business Review*.
Skinner, W., *Manufacturing: the Formidable Competitive Weapon*, John Wiley & Sons, 1985.
   A bringing together and amplification of a number of Skinner's articles. Well worth studying.

2 Planning

The system within a system

Too often the production/operating unit is regarded as a self-contained, self-sufficient body, and its dependence upon integration with the rest of the system is recognized only when other parts of the enterprise change. The dangers of this tunnel-vision are great: for example, government legislation may force a marketing change which requires a design modification; in turn, this can alter processes in such a way that operators are displaced, with consequent redundancy and retraining problems. Had the manager looked outside the four walls of his own unit, these problems could well have been foreseen and their effects mitigated. Similarly, a board decision to change from a selling policy, where orders are *accepted*, to a marketing policy, where orders are *sought*, will inevitably demand major changes in the whole transformation system, and again, these can be foreseen if the manager looks outwards as well as inwards.

This being so, the successful manager must, therefore, plan, execute and control his work within the framework of the corporate plan. Indeed, unless the production/operations plan is *part* of the corporate plan, the *total* enterprise can only be a failure, or at best a sub-success. In a brilliant and perceptive paper, Moran expresses the resultant dilemma: 'The optimization of the total enterprise frequently requires the sub-optimization of its component divisions, but it is always difficult to get divisions graciously to accept such restraints on their objectives.'[1]

It is only when a unit is understood to be part of a whole—a sub-system within a system—that its management can be truly successful. All organizations 'maintain themselves only by carrying on active transactions with their environment', and any unit stands within two identifiable—but not independent—environments, the community at large and the parent corporation; therefore the effects of either or both must always be considered. Furthermore, *the production/operations unit itself* provides the environment for its own constituent departments, and again the inter-

---

[1] Moran's paper appears as one of the appendices to Starr's *Production Management, Systems and Syntheses*

action of the parts among themselves and with the host environment must be realized. These interdependencies produce two important consequences of high practical value:

(a) changes in the environment impose changes on the organization;
(b) changes within the organization affect the environment.

To survive, therefore, organizations must be prepared to *respond to change*, and no manager should ever believe that any decision is eternal. To construct an organization to be so rigid that it cannot accept change is to invite disaster, particularly since technological change is now accelerating at such a rate that continuous adaptation is essential for any sustained success. Clearly 'change for the sake of change' is wasteful, and piecemeal change, 'tinkering with the parts', likely to be unproductive, even counter-productive. All too often the installation of a new 'efficient' machine or system has produced no effect on the *organization as a whole*, since the necessary accompanying changes elsewhere have not been put into effect. Where cost is measured, it is the *total cost to the enterprise* that is of importance, not the unit cost of a product or a process.

While recognizing that the production/operations unit is a system within a system, it is worth pointing out that it has characteristics which distinguish it from the rest of the organization. It generally employs the bulk of the manpower, utilizes the bulk of the physical assets, requires the bulk of the financial resources and is made up of many sub-systems. This is not to suggest that the production/operations function is more important than, say, the marketing function, but to indicate that its planning is likely to be *of a different kind* from that of other functions. In particular, the weight and size of the resources involved are such that the planning must enable operating decisions to be made rapidly. The scale of resources deployed will often permit analyses within the function of a type which cannot be carried out elsewhere—but with this condition goes the danger that these analyses are carried out *for their own sake* and not for the results which flow from them.

Objectives and policies

Management at all levels is constantly required to take decisions, and in order that these will stand the test of time and advance the organization as a whole it is necessary that they should be taken logically, not arbitrarily. This is as true of the decisions taken by the most junior supervisor as of those taken by the managing director, and each in his own way requires to know:

1. *The objectives* of the organization, that is, the purpose for which the undertaking is in being.

2. *The policies* of the organization, that is, the means whereby the objectives are to be achieved.

In the absence of such knowledge, decisions can only be taken capriciously, and a short-term decision may determine some long-term action which is undesirable but inescapable. Without a clear understanding of objectives and policies a manager cannot, for example, embark upon a rational training programme, a maintenance programme or a plant replacement scheme: in fact, no decisions can be sensibly taken which are of anything but immediate value.

Planning

Taken together, the objectives and policies form a *plan* for the operation of the organization. Planning occupies a considerable portion of the manager's time, and it is worth while to try to identify those characteristics which should be found in a useful plan. Such a plan is:

(*a*) *Explicit.* Lack of clarity usually indicates a lack of understanding, of knowledge or of purpose.

(*b*) *Understood.* The recipients of a plan may not have the same technical skills as its originator, so that although it is expressed quite explicitly, there is a barrier to understanding. This is most often found in plans drawn up by specialists for non-specialist colleagues.

(*c*) *Accepted.* Any plan should be accepted by all concerned in its execution—indeed, it is desirable that a plan should be drawn up by all those who will be held responsible for its execution. Inevitably, there will need to be tactical modifications to any plan, and if it has not been both understood and accepted, then there is a very real danger that these modifications may seriously affect the ultimate achievement of the purpose of the plan.

(*d*) *Capable of accepting change.* As mentioned above, circumstances may arise which require changes to be made. Any plan which is made or presented in an unnecessarily rigid form will be of limited value in times of change.

(*e*) *Compatible with the internal and external constraints.* Cognizance must be taken of the internal limitations (men, materials, capital assets, money) and of the environment within which the company is operating.

(*f*) *Capable of being monitored.* To be able to check on the execution of a plan, it should be cast in such a form that it can be monitored. This will usually involve expressing the plan in numerical terms—in itself a useful discipline.

(*g*) *A spur to action.* Any plan which is not a very real stimulus to action is of limited value.

Is the *time scale* correct?
Has the *external environment* been considered?
Are the *internal resources* adequate?
Can it *accept* change?
Is it *explicit*?
Is it *understood*?
Is it *accepted*?
Can it be *monitored*?
Is the plan *a spur to action*?

Characteristics of an effective plan

The POM, then, to be successful, requires an unequivocal statement of the purpose of his operating unit and the means of achieving that purpose, which statement should be explicit and in writing. The act of preparation of such a statement must start from the top—the board of directors—and must spread downwards to each executive level, gaining in detail as each succeeding managerial level is reached. Thus a board should, after discussion, issue a broad directive to the manager indicating the objectives of the unit and the general policies to be carried out:

The unit will be required to produce ....
and .... and associated equipment, to be sold in the ....
price range for use in the .... market. Wherever possible ....
labour will be used, ... , ... and ....
classes of work being subcontracted. The OUTPUT will be expected
to increase by at least ...... per cent for the next .... years and
labour will be trained accordingly.

From this the manager with his senior executives can derive departmental requirements, and the following further directive could be issued:

To implement the board's decisions, the factory will be organized as follows:

Department I will be headed by Mr A, and will be required to ......
Department II will be headed by Mr B, and will be required to .....
Department III will ....

and these must be discussed and agreed between the appropriate department managers and their subordinates. This procedure will be carried out at each level, so that all concerned should know what is required and how it is expected that it will be achieved. The whole process is never 'one-way' as constraints at a lower level may require modification of requirements at a higher level. The availability of sound information concerning past performance can assist the planning process greatly, and the storage and easy retrieval abilities of the computer can help to provide historical information, analysed in a wide variety of ways.

The most succinct expression of objectives is the *marketing forecast*, which can be considered as the quantitative statement of the corporate objectives of the company. In turn this forecast is translated into policy by an *operating budget*, the quantitative representation of corporate policy. Clearly there is a very real interdependence between objectives, policies, forecasts and budgets, and it is difficult—and possibly unnecessary—to try to decide where one ends and another begins. The important requirement is that they should all be self-consistent and this may mean that the examination of a forecast may require a re-examination of either objectives or policies as the derived budget may demonstrate the impracticability of that forecast. The planning process is essentially an iterative one, and the planner will frequently need to travel up and down the chain

$$\text{objectives} \rightleftharpoons \text{policies} \rightleftharpoons \text{forecasts} \rightleftharpoons \text{budgets}$$

before a stable plan is achieved.

Forecasts

To the operating manager there are two basic forecasts without which he can only take arbitrary decisions. These are:

1. The long-term market forecast, covering the expectations of the whole enterprise for the next five (or more) years.
2. The short-term sales forecast, covering the requirements of the marketing department for the next twelve months.

The long-term market forecast
The detail of the preparation of a long-term forecast is outside the scope of the present text, since the production manager has little responsibility for it, although he must comment upon it, as far as he is able, and eventually agree with it. It should be carried out by the marketing department, backed by economic, statistical, political and technical advisers, and will be based upon information on such matters as:

1. Levels of activity, both national and international.
2. Government expenditure.
3. Labour availability.
4. Possible changes in price structure.
5. Variations in living standards.
6. Competition, both national and international.
7. Possible new products.
8. Market potentials

9. Technological changes.
10. Company resources.
11. Company history.
12. Long-term company objectives, policies and plans.

This forecast may take the form of a statement of anticipated output in monetary terms for the next five years, with notes on each year as amplification (see Fig. 2.1). A long-term forecast is particularly necessary when considerable expansion is required and when heavy capital expenditure is contemplated. In exceptional cases—for example, the building of a new oil refinery or the construction of a new leisure complex—forecasts of up to twenty years are made, although some authorities believe that in view of political uncertainties there can be little usefulness in forecasts of any kind over periods of longer than five years.

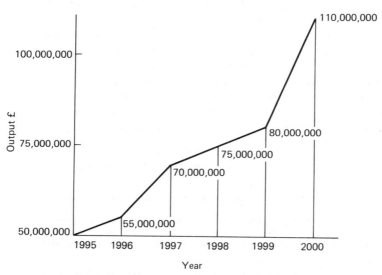

1996 Expected output £55,000,000. During this year new products A and B will be developed to be ready for marketing in 1997.
1997 Expected output £70,000,000. Products A and B will be marketed. Staff increase of 10 per cent anticipated to cope with expected increase in sales. Inauguration of work-study department.
1998 Expected output £75,000,000. Consolidation of sales targets. No increase in staff. Plans for move to new premises in 1999 to be completed.
1999 Expected output £80,000,000. Move to new plant completed. Increase in space available permits increase in development department.
2000 Expected output £110,000,000. No productive staff increases expected: increase in development and production planning staff to permit increase in productivity and range of products.

Fig. 2.1 Long-term forecast

The short-term sales forecast

The short-term forecast is the basis from which much transformation activity stems. It is a prediction covering the next budget period, usually twelve months, of:

1. the products/services to be sold, defined in as much detail as possible;
2. the prices which the market can bear;
3. the quantity;
4. the quality;
5. the reliability;
6. the required delivery dates/timings;

} of each product or service

and will be in agreement with general company policy as laid down by the board and the long-term forecasts previously made. Where a company is making items for stock the statement of the short-term forecase is quite straightforward. However, a difficulty might appear to arise in the case of a company manufacturing to customers' designs, or a company offering a service rather than a product—for example, plating, painting, repairing, packaging, computer programming. In these cases it is necessary to assume that the work done is of a foreseeable nature— should it be purely random no forecast is possible. Accepting this reservation it is then necessary to determine the product or service groups offered, defining a group as work offered having a stable and similar cost pattern. The short-term forecast will then detail:

(*a*) the product/service groups offered;
(*b*) the volume of business measured financially to be derived from each group;
(*c*) the distribution of this business throughout the year.

The procedure for setting up a forecast may be as follows:

1. A target figure for profit and/or volume for the forthcoming year is received from the board.
2. The marketing department, using information on such matters as past sales, knowledge of present trends and market research information, will set up a tentative forecast, which is submitted to the operating and finance departments.
3. The appropriate department will consider the feasibility of meeting the tentative forecast, having regard to the appropriate facilities available and obtainable. As a result of this scrutiny it might be found that one or more sections of the establishment is overloaded while others are underloaded. Modification to the draft forecast will then be suggested.
4. The finance department will then examine the amended forecast to

see if it will satisfactorily meet the company's policy on earnings and investment. This might reveal, for example, that the most readily sold item has the lowest contribution and that the marketing department, by requiring a substantial increase in the sales of this, has seriously affected the total profit yield. From considerations of this kind the finance department may propose further modifications to the forecast.

5. With the comments of the operating and finance departments available, the marketing department will produce another sales forecast which again is scrutinized. Eventually, after a series of trials, a forecast is produced which is acceptable to all concerned.

6. The final sales forecast is then submitted to the board to be approved or rejected.

The above procedure, although apparently cumbersome, must be carried out effectively if the forecast is to be stable and useful. The sales forecast *must* have the support of the marketing, operating and finance departments, and *must not* be produced by any one department in the absence of either of the other two. Equally, once a forecast has been agreed, all departments must work to it, preparing their own plans and carrying out their activities in order to achieve it.

The budget

When preparing and finalizing the sales forecasts, it will have been necessary to examine the various constraints upon the organization to ensure that the forecast lies within these constraints. In so doing, all the data necessary for drawing up a budget will have been assembled—although possibly not in the form most appropriate to budgetary control. When this crude data is broken down into responsibility areas, then a budget will have been created, and the basis for budgetary control laid down. Similarly, if the information is grouped together in cost centres around products or services, then a cost control system can follow. This subject is more fully discussed in Chapter 4.

POM policy

A budget is best considered as a statement of policy expressed in financial terms. An overall budget is therefore the corporate strategy of the organization, and from this strategy the production/operations manager must derive a POM policy. These activities are not separated—there is a two-way channel:

Corporate strategy

POM policy

through which debates pass until an acceptable stability is achieved.

It would be comforting to think that the setting of POM policy is a matter which can be programmed ('. . . follow steps 1–10 and a policy will emerge'). Unfortunately, such a routine can only be set down in specific cases: a routine for a small hand knitwear organization would be quite different to that for a complex multi-occupier holiday hotel. Experience has shown, however, that there are some useful aids to POM policy setting.

Five guides

1. *Where multiple objectives exist, it is unwise to try to satisfy them all simultaneously*. A simple example will illustrate this. A public swimming bath can be designed to satisfy at least three objectives:

(*a*) to allow divers to practice;
(*b*) to enable serious swimmers to swim;
(*c*) to let 'fun' swimmers enjoy themselves.

These three objectives do not coincide: the divers will get in the way of the serious swimmers, who in turn will interfere with the 'fun' swimmers. To try to satisfy all three groups will inevitably result in dis-satisfying them all. The local authority must decide which group of users it wishes to serve principally, and take action accordingly.

Similarly, the P/O manager may identify a number of possible objectives:

(*a*) maximum customer satisfaction;
(*b*) minimum cash flow;
(*c*) minimum scrap;
(*d*) minimum inventory;
(*e*) maximum resource utilization;
(*f*) maximum employee satisfaction . . .

These are likely to be in direct conflict with each other. What is necessary is to identify the *key* objective and plan to satisfy this in the hope that the others will be 'acceptably' achieved.

2. *The greater the diversity the greater the difficulty*. The temptation to increase diversity is great: just 'one more' of this, that or the other will

solve all problems. One more product, one more machine, one more document . . . the process is insidious. Diversity must not be resisted at all costs, but the costs of diversity must be realized when taking the 'just one more' decision.

3. *Problems become easier if broken into parts*. Some problems when first viewed seem too vast to be dealt with. Breaking the problem up can result in solving the parts which can be resolved, and thence displaying the rest in a form which indicates how they may be dealt with.

4. *Organizations should be kept as small as technology permits*. We live in an age of change, which is more rapid than ever in man's history. The larger the organization the greater its inertia and hence the slower its response to change. It should be the technology which dictates the size rather than an unsupported belief in the economies of scale.

5. *Organization structures should serve the needs of the enterprise*. Enterprises need to create that which satisfies the consumer. It is from an analysis of the needs of those 'in the front line' that a structure should be built. Building 'from the top down' can result in meaningless and costly layers of hierarchy.

---

1. Identify the key objective
2. Control diversity
3. Break problems into parts
4. Keep organizations small
5. Structure serves needs

Guides to creating policy

Three unities

In addition to the above guides, there are three unities which should be obeyed:

1. *Unity of market position*. Whatever the technology, an attempt to satisfy two significantly different market positions is doomed to failure. A restaurant renowned for its haute cuisine would be foolish to try to enter the fast food market. By doing so it would *either* change its haute cuisine to mauvaise cuisine *or* produce fast food at a high cost, or both. A common situation which arises is that there are idle resources. An attempt is made to use these by producing a cheaper product, and the skills and judgements applicable to the main product are lost.

2. *Unity of volume*. To attempt to produce high and low volume through the same plant can result in considerable organizational difficulties. The shirt manufacturer who produces in very large volume for a retail chain has the technology to produce a special, non-standard shirt— but at an excessive cost.

3. *Unity of complexity*. Simple products cannot readily be produced in organizations designed to make complex products—the infrastructure of the organization will impose enormous burdens. Imagine a sophisticated aerospace organization being asked to make a clothes peg. The whole routine of estimations, competitive buying, work study, jig and tool designers, planning sheets, inspection standards, automatic. testing . . . would swing into action. The result would probably be the finest clothes peg ever made—at a cost which could never be recouped.

---

1. Unity of market position
2. Unity of volume
3. Unity of complexity

Three unities

From the POM audit, the corporate policy, consideration of the five guides and three unities, a POM policy will emerge. To put it into practice two further steps must be taken, and the authors are indebted to Alastair Nicholson for indicating these steps as two additional P's to the 5 P's of Chapter 1.

Procedures

It is necessary to lay down procedures whereby programmable decisions can be carried out. In the absence of such procedures, decisions will largely cease to be programmable and will degenerate into a series of opportunistic statements which, sooner or later, will conflict with each other. Furthermore, the effort to make *ad hoc* decisions will reduce the effort available to deal with the really difficult 'non-programmable' decisions, those requiring experience, judgement and personal sensitivity.

Paperwork

The formal mechanism by which a procedure is implemented is some form of paperwork (although it is recognized that the medium need not necessarily be paper, but may be some form of computer input). Frequently the existence of documentation is thought of as a form of bureaucracy existing solely to occupy the time of clerical workers. Indeed, in many cases this is so: the need for a procedure and the consequent paperwork may have disappeared with changing circumstances, but the documentation itself remains. A properly controlled paperwork system, however, is as useful as the rungs in a ladder, assisting the manager to climb from one situation to another.

3 Control

The size, capabilities and complexities of even small modern organizations are such that control of the whole and of the parts must be an integral part of the organization. This is not to suggest that it is impossible to *direct*—that is to determine the use of—an organization. Far from it: the important concept here is that an organization must have control systems built as part of it, and that the control within the limits set by the directing body must come from within the functioning of the organization itself. The *purpose* of a control system is to assist in the setting *and achievement* of targets.

The thermostatically controlled room

Assume that the task is to heat a room by electricity and to control its temperature by means of a thermostat. To function satisfactorily, a calculation of the size of the heater required is necessary: too small a heater will not overcome the inevitable heat losses and the desired temperature will never be attained; too large a heater, on the other hand, will give rise to bursts of excessively hot air and a consequent blackening of the wall above it.

The active element and the level of activity having been selected, a thermostat of appropriate capacity, sensitivity and accuracy is chosen. This is then located in such a position that it can take up the room temperature and placed in circuit with the heater. A decision is made of the temperature required and the thermostat set accordingly. The system as a whole is then switched on and the room temperature increases. At all times the temperature is measured by a heat-sensitive element within the thermostat, and the temperature achieved is compared with that initially chosen.

When the required temperature is reached, a signal (SWITCH OFF) is fed back from the thermostat to the heating element and, assuming this signal is not overridden in some way (for example, by hand), the temperature will fall. Once it falls below that which is acceptable then another signal (SWITCH ON) is fed back to the heater and the temperature rises again. In this way a temperature which is sensibly constant *within the capabilities of the system* is achieved.

The essential features of control

What, in essence, has had to be done in order that the activity (in this case the heating) is in accordance with requirements? In the first place, the whole system (room, heater, thermostat, external conditions) and the level of activity desired have had to be thoroughly examined, and an appropriate PLAN made. In the course of this examination, the system initially proposed may have needed to be modified—for example, the room may have been too large for the proposed heater, the heat losses may have been excessive, and so on—so that in setting up the plan, a thorough examination of the whole system is required and a model of that system constructed. Should this model reveal that no choice of alternatives is ever possible, then no control can be exerted.

The plan having been made, it is necessary that it be set up on the thermostat—that is, it has to be PUBLISHED. When in operation, the activity has to be MEASURED—in this case the heat-sensitive element has to measure the temperature achieved. These messurements are then COMPARED with the initial plan, and finally a REPORT has to be fed back to the active portion of the system in terms which are intelligible. CORRECTIVE ACTION is then taken to restore the performance to that which was initially required.

Conditions necessary for the existence of a control system

Tocher ('Control', *Operational Research Quarterly*, Vol. 21, No. 2) has pointed out that there are four necessary conditions for the existence of a control function:

1. There must be a specified set of times at which a choice of action is possible.

2. At each time there must be a specified set of actions from which to choose.

3. A model must exist which can predict the future of the system under every possible choice.

4. There must be a criterion or objective on which the choice of action is based by a comparison of the predicted behaviour of the system with the objective.

Ideally, decisions should only be taken if all possible actions and their outcomes are explored and the 'best' selected. In practice it is often not possible to do this as either the number of alternatives is too great or some factors are difficult to determine. Hence a decision which is probably sub-optimal may have to be accepted.

Industrial control systems

It is suggested here that the features isolated above apply to all forms of control, but since the present text is concerned with industrial control systems, further examples will be taken from industrial use. For example, consider a budgetary control system. For satisfactory operation the following steps have to be taken:

1. *Planning.* A budget has to be prepared which takes into account the purpose, abilities, limitations and levels of activity of all departments to which the budget applies. It is this budget which forms the control model, and which sets forth the objectives.

2. *Publishing.* Once agreed, the budget has to be distributed to all concerned. A well-founded budget which is never disclosed to those to whom it applies is of limited value—yet it is not uncommon.

3. *Measuring.* Measurements of activity have to be obtained by means of time sheets, clock cards, material requisitions, scrap notes or any other appropriate means.

4. *Comparing.* The measurements obtained have to be compared with the levels agreed in the budget. It is probably necessary here to process the measurements in order to be able to carry out the comparison.

5. *Reporting.* Statements have to be fed back to the appropriate supervisors concerning any deviations from the budget.

6. *Corrective action.* Upon receipt of a report that performance is not in accordance with plan (that is, upon receipt of an error signal) the appropriate supervisor needs to take corrective action—either by reducing expenditure or by initiating a new plan. Note here that (*a*) if there is no ability to choose between various courses of action, no control is possible, and (*b*) the taking of the corrective action is outside the usual terms of reference of the budgetary controller.

Similarly, in a quality control system, precisely the same steps have to be taken:

1. *Planning.* Specifications ('models') have to be drawn up which take into account not only the purpose for which the product is required, but also the feasibility of meeting the specification and the cost of so doing.

2. *Publishing.* These specifications once agreed have to be incorporated in the operating information and hence communicated to the appropriate departments.

3. *Measuring*. The inspector/viewer/tester has to measure the characteristics appearing in the specification.

4. *Comparing*. These measurements are then compared with the specification. Again it may be necessary to process the measurements in order to carry out the comparison.

5. *Reporting*. Significant deviations (e.g. those which are outside 'limits' or those which appear, by their rate of change, to be drifting outside limits) are fed back to the responsible supervisors.

6. *Corrective action*. The deviations will cause corrective action to be taken which will restore the performance to its desired level. In this case the initiation of this action may take place within or without the control department, depending upon local circumstances. In process industries it is increasingly common to find that the corrective action is taken automatically upon receipt of the error signal.

Similar analyses will show that all industrial control systems exhibit the same essential features:

1. Plan
2. Publish
3. Measure
4. Compare
5. Report
6. Correct

and these seem to be inherent in any control system or mechanism. Of course, an industrial control department may have other duties laid upon it as well as the above, but this is largely a matter of organizational convenience—it does not overthrow the general hypothesis. Similarly the tasks of *planning* (except in the most mechanical sense) and *correcting* are often not carried out by the control department itself, these being frequently considered to be the duties of the administrative managerial personnel. The effect of these variations is to cause the control departments to be only part of the complete control system of the organization.

Conditions for satisfactory operation of an industrial control system

For an industrial control system to function in the manner which the originator or designer intended, it is necessary that attention should be directed towards a number of features. These include the following:

1. The purpose of the activity—its objectives—must be defined. Without such definition, effectiveness will be random.

2. Control is only possible if *choice* can be exerted. The greater the choice, the finer the possible control, but excessive choice can be expens-

ive, so that it may be desirable to restrict choice by 'fixing' some parameters or boundaries. In scheduling, for example, the number of possible schedules is often so great that some restriction is vital.

3. Any measurements must be of an appropriate precision. Thus, in a production control situation, if output is required to be held to ± 10 units, measurements to the nearest 25 units are of limited utility, while those to the nearest 1 unit, while useful, are invariably more costly to obtain and process than necessary. More than this, an over-sensitive system may record minor deviations and generate unnecessary disturbance just as an over-sensitive microphone may cause 'howl' in an auditorium.

4. The information gathered needs to be pertinent—a material control system, for example, rarely needs information on salesmen's expenses, although this would be appropriate to a budgetary control system. Feeding unnecessary information into a system may well mask the effects which the system itself is designed to detect, just as noise may prevent the ear from discriminating between two musical notes.

5. Comparisons need to be made at intervals which allow useful action to be taken. The value of knowing that stocks have fallen below the level set for re-ordering is seriously diminished if that knowledge is obtained too late to permit material to be purchased in time for it to be available when required. Such tardy information is usually termed historical—for example, historical costing—and it has use only as a guide for future action: it does not permit corrective action to be taken while the 'disturbed' situation is still in being. In some cases it is useful to use the rate of change of a characteristic as an action-sponsoring device. Thus, if the means of sets of measurements on the length of a bar being cut off were seen to rise rapidly, investigations would probably be justified even if the figures themselves were still within the limits required by the system.

6. Reports must be fed back in a form acceptable to the active department. If a material control file is expressed in dozens of parts, the information that so many standard hours' worth of parts have been delivered to stock is, at best, confusing and, at worst, useless. Care must be exercised here of course, since the processing of information may cause delays and/or distortions in the feedback line.

7. The information collected by the system must be correct, or at least consistent. The non-observance of this particular requirement has often caused a control system to be improperly discredited. Control systems do not *generate* information; they process it. An apparent shortage of material may arise from incorrect information entered on a stores requisition; a cost variance can derive from an inaccurate time sheet, and so on. The consequent errors do not arise from the control system, although it is often improperly held to be at fault. It must be recognized that the way

in which the information is collected may, by bad design, provoke the incorrect measurement or recording of data.

Where an organization has a number of control systems working, the effects of inaccuracy in any one of them may be reduced by the operation of the others: the interlinking of the various systems causes them to act as a net in which one broken strand does not destroy the utility of the net. Moreover, inaccuracies, if consistent, can be compensated for, and it may be cheaper and simpler to design a stable inaccurate system rather than one which is highly accurate.

8. The number of stages through which information is passed while being fed back from the output to the active portion of the system should be kept as low as possible. Each stage not only inevitably causes delay, but will also generate distortions, the correction of which may well be difficult, costly and time-consuming.

---

1. Purpose must be defined
2. Choice of action must be present
3. Information should be appropriately precise
4. Information should be pertinent
5. The speed of response of the system should be fast enough to permit *useful* action to be taken
6. Information should be presented in the correct units
7. Reports should be accurate, or of consistent inaccuracy
8. The number of stages in the feedback loop should be as few as possible

---

Requirements for the installation of a control system

Advantages of an explicitly designed control system

The above discussion suggests that at least one control system is inevitable in the running of an organization. This, of course, is not necessarily so: organizations can be 'regulated' by means of random ON–OFF switches, just as the temperature of a room can be 'regulated' by arbitrarily switching the heater on and off by hand. This type of regulation is all too common, and possesses all the disadvantages of manual temperature control such as violent 'swings' in activity, irrational changes and lack of delicacy. It does, however, provide a considerable element of surprise when results are obtained ('. . . after a year's trading I find we have made a loss').

It is sometimes argued that any situation will have within it a number of regulators, irrespective of the intention of the designer. While this may be so, it would seem likely that a control system explicitly designed to be an integral part of the situation has a number of very real advantages.

These include the following:

1. The formulation of the plan itself, if carried out with due responsibility, will require the detailed consideration of the complete system. When trying to govern the temperature of a room, it was necessary to ask the purpose for which the room was being heated, whether the heater was big enough, the thermal insulation of the room good enough, the thermostat capable of carrying the current, the location of the thermostat correct, and so on. Similarly, when drawing up a budget, the objectives and the tasks to be performed must be clearly known and understood, and the material, plant and personnel to fulfil the tasks must be estimated. This will inevitably cause an examination both of the task itself (for example, is the sales forecast achievable?) and of the various resources (are ten chargehands necessary?—are more progress chasers needed?—can another cleaner be afforded?—must cash be raised from the bank?). In the course of this examination, the tasks and the resources may require modification. Thus, the plan itself is an organizational tool of considerable and unique value.

2. Once set up the plan will give prior knowledge of the achievable performances of the system. This is obviously so with a budget, but may not appear to be so with other control systems, yet in all cases it applies with equal force. For example, if a quality control system in its operation requires a dimension to be held to ± 0.01 mm, then implicit in this is not only the statement that this accuracy is desirable, but also that it is economically achievable.

3. By deriving information from the system as it is functioning, it is possible to correct the behaviour of the system and modify the effects of any distortions. This is shown most spectacularly in the case of statistical quality control, where the reductions in rejects can be dramatic. Thus, control must be realized to be constructive, not restrictive.

4. By signalling only deviations from a plan, management is released from the necessity of examining all data, and can examine only those which require action.

---

1. The system is an organizational tool
2. Prior knowledge of achievable performance is obtained
3. Corrective action can be taken while such action is useful
4. Only 'trouble' areas are examined

Advantages of an explicitly-designed control system

4 Budgets and budgetary control

One of the most powerful tools for planning and control available to the manager is the *budget* which, if properly prepared and used, has all the advantages of an explicitly-designed control system. Furthermore, since most activities can be expressed and measured in financial terms, a *financial budget* can assist in displaying all the activities of an operating unit in a common language.

The preparation of a budget must start with a *forecast* of intended activity, and it may well be that the first forecast is modified several times when *intent* is offered to *ability*. The more closely the various functions can come together, the more rapidly will an agreed forecast and a subsequent agreed budget be prepared. It cannot be emphasized too strongly that unilateral decisions anywhere will result in stress and possibly dysfunction.

Preparing the budget

Given a forecast, the operations manager can use it as a basis from which to prepare his various budgets. These are usually expressed in financial terms, since all activities are capable of being so expressed, and hence a budget covering many different activities will be homogeneous. The method of preparing an operating budget may be as follows:

1. From the forecast an estimate is made of:
(*a*) the material content,
(*b*) the direct labour content in operator-hours of the required tasks.
2. From the direct labour estimates, estimates are made of:
(*a*) the direct labour: requirements for each of the departments—that is, the direct labour force required in each department;
(*b*) the supervisory labour necessary to control the direct labour in each department;
(*c*) the ancillary labour required to support the work of each department.

3. From the above estimates and the forecast the service and control staffs (for example, the maintenance, quality assurance, wages, costing, accounting, production control, technical, design and development, and managerial staffs) required to achieve the forecast are estimated.

4. From the long-range forecasts and the general objectives and policies of the company an estimate is made of any other indirect staff—(for example, research and training) which may be required to be employed during the current financial year, but whose efforts will not produce revenue during that time.

5. Calculations of general expenses—rent, rates, insurance, tax, heating, lighting and so on—are made.

6. All the above are then consolidated into an estimate of what the total expenditure will be during the financial period under consideration.

7. The difference between the total estimated expenditure and the total revenue is the profit which should be achieved.

8. This profit, added to the estimated expenditure, gives the operating budget for the financial year.

The budget is clearly a very complex statement, embodying both policy decisions (for example, those concerning the methods of depreciation to be used) and organizational assumptions (for example, those concerning the acceptable levels of support staffs). None of these can be justified except on pragmatic grounds, and it is therefore impossible to produce a budget which is clearly 'correct': what is required is an *acceptable* budget, that is one which does not conflict with *any* of the corporate objectives. It is unlikely that such a document will be produced at a first attempt, and it is usually necessary to make a series of drafts, starting with one in fairly broad terms, and amending and refining it successively until acceptable results are obtained.

It must be stressed that the budget should be an *agreed* document representing a consensus of the views of all whom it directly concerns. The executive who co-ordinates the drawing up of the budget must actively involve the appropriate supervisors in the preparations, discussions and analyses required in preparing it. The budget is not an *order-giving* but a *situation-displaying* document, and the manager needs '. . . to unite all concerned in a study of the situation, to discover the law of the situation, and obey that' (M. P. Follett, *The Giving of Orders*).

The importance of the preparation of a budget cannot be stressed too greatly, since it results in management knowing *in advance* the activities to be undertaken in the budget period and their probable results. Beside this very obvious benefit, the act of preparation itself produces other gains—notably it requires that the organizational structure and the staff required should be carefully considered. Without a budget a decision concerning the employment of, for example, extra staff can only be made on the grounds of immediate expediency. On the other hand, the budget will show immediately what effect the extra expenditure will have on the year's trading, and whether the benefits to be gained justify that expenditure. The structure discussed and agreed when preparing the budget will also result in a clarification of the duties of each individual so that each person can know what is expected of him. Furthermore, the act of being involved in the preparation of a budget—that is, in policy-making—can be a potent motivating force; equally, the *imposition* of a budget can be inhibiting or destructive.

During the initial stages of a company's existence, the preparation of a budget is difficult, and the results inaccurate. But, as information is accumulated, a budget becomes both easier to prepare and much more accurate. Thus early difficulties must not be allowed to prevent the preparation of the budget—it is one of the most important weapons in the armoury of the manager. Furthermore, once the budget is prepared it can be used as a very simple, yet accurate, means of monitoring activity by continually comparing budgeted with actual performance. Finally, should circumstances change during the year, the budget can be used to show what steps need to be taken to compensate for the altered circumstances.

The capital expenditure budget

From the preparation of the operating budget, and knowing the long-term requirements of the company, the production manager will build up a list of new plant and equipment required. This will be cast into the form of a capital expenditure budget which, when ratified by the board, will permit the purchase of the new equipment. Subsequent purchasing will depend upon the cash resources of the company, and the actual placing of an order for such items is usually authorized by the financial accountant, who will verify that the placing of the order at that time will not prove embarrassing.

The break-even chart

The derivation of a break-even chart from a budget enables rapid assessments of the effect of variations in the budget factors to be made, and thus increases the overall value of the budget. In its simplest form it consists of the graphical representation of costs at varying levels of activity shown on the same chart as the variation of income with the same variation in activity. The point at which neither profit nor loss is made is known as the 'break-even' point, and is represented on the chart by the intersection of the two lines. On Fig. 4.1 the line OA represents the

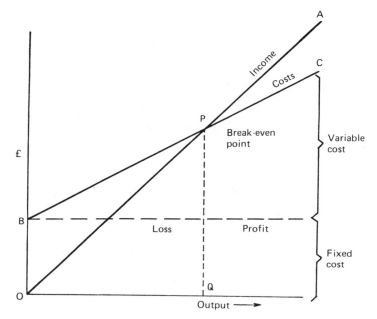

Fig. 4.1 Break-even chart

variation of income with output, and BC the variation of costs with output. At low output, costs are greater than income; while at high output, costs are less than income. At the point of intersection P, costs are exactly equal to income, and hence neither profit nor loss is made. If the budget figure for output is below the break-even point (i.e. less than OQ) then the organization is said to be budgeted for a loss. A more usual situation is for the budget figure to exceed the break-even figure (i.e. to exceed OQ), when the organization will be budgeted for a profit.

Variations in either income (i.e. from sales) or costs will result in the slopes of the respective lines varying, causing the break-even point to slide up and down. Fig. 4.2 shows the same organization as in Fig. 4.1, the costs being assumed to remain constant. With the income as in Fig. 4.1, the income line OA intersects the cost line at P. Assuming that the selling prices are increased (i.e. the income increases) the income line intersects the cost line at X, which is lower than the original break-even figure, while if the sales prices are decreased (i.e. the income decreases) the break-even point slides up to Y. A similar set of graphs will show the effect of a variation in costs, and by combining the two effects a rapid assessment of the effect of any course of action can be made.

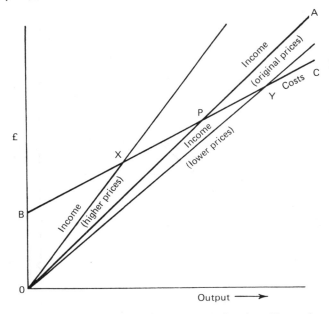

Fig. 4.2 Break-even chart showing effect of variation in selling price

The margin of safety

In practice, it is clearly desirable for budgeted income to exceed break-even income by as large an amount as possible—working at or near the B/E point is very difficult as the ability to accept changes is small. A measure of this ability is given by the *margin of safety*: the ratio of the amount by which budgeted income exceeds B/E income to the budgeted income itself:

$$\text{Margin of safety} = \frac{\text{Budgeted income} - \text{B/E income}}{\text{Budgeted income}} \times 100$$

For example, if:

Budgeted income = £200,000
Break-even income = £160,000

then:

$$\text{Margin of safety} = \frac{200,000 - 160,000}{200,000} \times 100$$

$$= 20\%$$

Clearly, the smaller this percentage becomes, the more the company is at risk. (*Note*: some workers refer to the difference between budget and break-even—£40,000 above—as the margin of safety. As this is only significantly meaningful if it is related to the budget or the break-even, the above ratio is probably more useful.)

An alternative expression for the margin of safety is the *percentage of capacity* figure. Here it is assumed that the budgeted volume employs all the capacity available, and that at the B/E point, capacity is used in direct proportion to the volume made, therefore:

$$\text{Percentage of capacity} = \frac{\text{B/E income}}{\text{Budgeted income}} \times 100$$

which would give, using the above figure:

$$\text{Percentage of capacity} = \frac{160,000}{200,000} \times 100$$
$$= 80\%$$

The implication that capacity is fully utilized at the B/E point is, of course, misleading and this expression is probably best avoided.

Drawing a break-even chart

Trading expenditure can be considered in the short term to be made up of two parts, the *fixed* costs and the *variable* costs. The fixed costs are those which do not change with variations in output within a relevant range and include such items as rent and rates. Variable costs on the other hand are the costs which do change in the short term and within a relevant range with variations in output, and these include labour and material costs, insurance, supervision and similar items. Together they form the total cost: the difference between the *income* and the *variable costs* being the *contribution*. These are shown diagrammatically in Fig. 4.3, where the fixed cost OB is represented by a line BF parallel to the abscissa, the variable cost by the line OV which passes through the origin and income by the line OA, which also passes through the origin. The total cost is the result of adding the fixed and variable costs, and its variation with output is shown by the line BC. This can be considered to be drawn either by *first* setting off the fixed cost (OB) and then drawing the variable cost through B at the correct slope, or by drawing the variable cost through the origin and then drawing a line parallel to it, spaced by a value equal to the fixed cost.

The distance between the income and variable cost lines is the contribution, and at the break-even point the contribution PT is equal to the fixed cost OB; that is to say:

at break-even, contribution = Fixed cost

This gives a simple method of calculating the break-even point. For

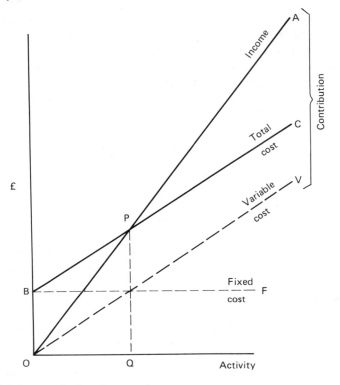

Fig. 4.3 Make-up of a break-even chart

example, in a company whose income is £100,000, the profit is 10 per cent and the fixed cost is £15,000. What is the break-even point?

Income	= Variable cost + fixed cost + profit
i.e. £100,000	= Variable cost + £15,000 + £10,000
∴ Variable cost	= £75,000
	= 75 per cent of income

At break-even:

Contribution	= £15,000
Income	= Variable cost + contribution
Income	= 75 per cent income + £15,000
∴ 25 per cent income	= £15,000
∴ Income	= £60,000

The same result is obtainable in a number of other ways: the choice of method is dictated by the circumstances.

Margin of safety (£) = £100,000 − £60,000 = £40,000

$$\text{Percentage of capacity} = \frac{60,000}{100,000} \times 100 = 60\%$$

$$\text{Profit/volume ratio} = \frac{10,000 + 15,000}{100,000} \times 100$$

$$= 25\%$$

It is sometimes useful to express contribution in terms of total profit and fixed cost.

Total profit   = Total income − Total cash
                          = Total income − (fixed costs +
                            variable costs)
∴ Total profit + Fixed cost = Total income − Variable cost
                          = Contribution

The profit graph and the profit/volume ratio

In place of the B/E chart, *a profit graph* may be drawn which relates profit earned to output (see Fig. 4.4). At outputs below B/E costs exceed incomes, and negative profits, that is losses, are made, so that the profit graph is on the negative side of the output axis, while at B/E neither profit nor loss is created, and the graph crosses the output axis. Above

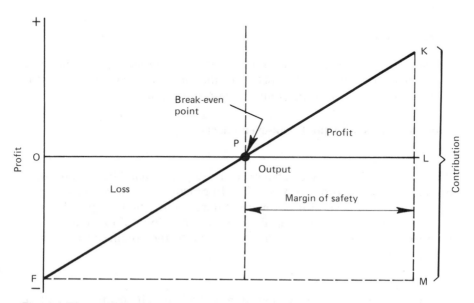

Fig. 4.4 The profit graph

B/E, profit appears and the graph rises above the axis. The increase in profit for a unit increase in output is said to be the profit/volume ratio (P/V ratio), and is the slope of the profit graph; that is, it is the ratio:

$$\text{P/V ratio} = \frac{KM}{FM}$$

where M is the budgeted output. KM is the sum of KL (the profit generated at the budgeted output level) and LM, which is equal to OF, the loss at zero output, that is, the fixed cost. Hence:

$$\text{P/V ratio} = \frac{KL + LM}{M}$$

$$= \frac{\text{Profit} + \text{Fixed costs}}{\text{Output}} \times 100$$

Alternatively:

$$\text{P/V ratio} = \frac{KL}{PL} = \frac{\text{Profit}}{\begin{array}{c}\text{Margin of safety}\\\text{(expressed in £)}\end{array}}$$

Using the same figures as previously:

$$\begin{array}{l}\text{Margin of safety}\\\text{(as a \%)}\end{array} = \frac{100{,}000 - 60{,}000}{100{,}000} \times 100$$

$$= 40\%$$

Marginal cost

While the profit/volume ratio is the increase in *profit* per unit increase in output, another useful concept is the *marginal cost*, which is the increase in *variable cost* per unit increase in output.

Some problems with the break-even charts

Variety of products
As drawn and discussed above, it is implied that the organization produces only one product or service. In practice, of course, most organizations produce several if not many different outputs. One possible way to deal with this is to consider all outputs as multiples of one output, and then to deal with the relationship of income to the volume of this surrogate product.

Analysis of costs
It is assumed in what has been written that all costs be neatly categorized into 'fixed' and 'variable', and that costs vary linearly with volume. In

practice, the initial division may contain elements of arbitrary decision, while costs may change abruptly in a 'step' fashion. While some workers try to incorporate these step changes on the chart, it is probably better to draw and use the chart over a short range, one where the changes are of no significance.

Budgetary control

Once a budget has been drawn up it can be used as an instrument of control by continually comparing actual with budgeted performance. Since all activities are ultimately capable of being expressed in financial terms, the breadth of control possible is very great. This comparison is known as *budgetary control*, and the essential features of this, like any other control system, are:

1. *Planning*, that is, the preparation of the budget. This is discussed briefly in Chapter 2. In general there is a master budget which summarizes a number of detailed or departmental budgets. The departmental budgets are produced first, then amalgamated into the master budget which will need to be compared with the directives issued by the board. The reconciliation of master budget, departmental budgets and board directives may well require several iterations. Drawing up a budget in the absence of past information is difficult, but the act of preparation *forces* consideration of organization and potential.

2. *Publishing*, that is, informing each executive of that which is expected of him. This is often done implicitly in the very act of planning a budget, but once the whole budget is complete an explicit statement should be made. This 'selling' of the budget is most important, since no system is able to work unless the people concerned with it understand it and are prepared to make it work. At the initial inception of a budgetary control system there is always great reluctance on the part of a departmental manager to co-operate, and a fear that 'they' are going to show him how to do his job.

3. *Measuring* results; this is always a difficult task since technologists, for example, who are quite used to measuring artefacts, suspect the measurement of output, wages or other similar features. It is necessary of course that the items being measured are those which appear in the budget, and that they are measured in the same units as those originally used.

4. *Comparing* the results with the budget. The measurements taken above, while being significant in themselves, have a much greater significance when compared with a budget. The difference between actual and budgeted expense is sometimes called the variance, although this term is strictly applicable only to deviations from standard. Confusion may also

arise here in that 'variance' is a term used in statistics for the square of the standard deviation.

5. *Reporting* the results of the above activity. This is done by means of budgetary control statements, which enable the manager, and such of his subordinates as are necessary, to know whether the objectives set out in the budget are being fulfilled and, if not, in which areas attention should be concentrated.

6. *Correcting* the behaviour of the system or modifying the plan itself. As pointed out earlier, the responsibility for taking the corrective action often lies outside the 'control' department, being the responsibility of the departmental manager or supervisor. The budget, and the budgetary control statements, must be *tools* to assist the manager, not *weapons* to assault him.

Preparation of budgetary control statements

The preparation of a budgetary control statement requires care, and the following points should be observed:

1. *Information should be accurate*, or at least of a *known* inaccuracy. If it is known that inaccuracies are present then consistency of measurement and presentation are vital. The basing of action upon incorrect data may lead to incorrect action being taken, which will bring the whole scheme of budgetary control into disrepute. An unwarranted air of accuracy is sometimes given by quoting figures to too many significant places. For example, if the number of hours worked is 123, and the wages earned are £742.50, and it is known that both the hours' and wages' figures are in error, there is no point in calculating that the average rate (that is, wages ÷ time, or £742.50 ÷ 123) is 603.6585p an hour. Even if the initial figures were correct and the 0.6585 correct, it is difficult to conceive of any circumstances when it could be useful. The uncritical use of the pocket calculator or computer can often lead to an excessive number of figures being quoted.

2. *Information should be pertinent*, and no information should be presented to an executive concerning matters over which he has no control. The simpler the control statement, the more use will be made of it. Two sources of useless information are: (*a*) the recording of expenditures which are fixed, such as rent and insurance; and (*b*) the presentation of information to one departmental executive of expenditure incurred in another department.

3. *Information should be adequate.* Nothing is more frustrating than the inability to make a decision because some information is missing. This can lead to the collecting of excessive data, and a balance must be struck between 'too little' and 'too much'. Probably the only useful test which

can be applied here is that of *usefulness*. Will the operating manager *use* the information? Clearly, the detail required varies with hierarchical level: information needed in one position will probably be excessive in a superior position and madequate—but too broad—at a subordinate one.

4. *Information should be up-to-date*, so that useful action, if required, can be taken. The presentation of data concerning matters over which, by virtue of the time which has elapsed, nobody has any control, is of little more than historical interest, and as such can only be useful as a guide to future action. The frequency with which statements should be issued depends very much on local circumstances: usually monthly is adequate in stable organizations although weekly may be necessary in times of rapid change. A useful criterion concerning the frequency of reporting is given by Antony, who suggests that a useful measure of the time interval is 'the shortest period of time in which management can usefully intervene and in which significant changes in performances are likely'.

1. Accurate
2. Pertinent
3. Adequate
4. Up-to-date

Information requirements for a budgetary control system

Example of a budgetary control statement

A possible form of budgetary control statement which might be supplied to a POM appears below. All fixed budget items are excluded from the statement since no control can be exerted upon them. The others are presented in a form as shown in Table 4.1. This shows immediately that the actual output of £1,212,500 is below budget by some £125,000, yet the direct wage bill is effectively as planned, and the direct material usage is high. The only figure which may be of significance is that of indirect labour in the production department. The manager would probably call first for a statement of the work-in-progress and the scrap generated. Should these figures indicate that there was no apparent pilfering, but that the productivity was low, giving an excessive direct labour cost for the output, and that excessive scrap had been produced, he would then call for an analysis of the production department's indirect labour costs. These would already have been prepared and submitted to the production manager in a form similar to Table 4.1, and would reveal a shortage of fitters, an understaffed production control department and a severe shortage of supervision on the production floor itself.

Table 4.1 Budgetary control statement for week 26

Item	Amount this week	Total to date 26 weeks	Budget 26 weeks	Budget comparison Above	Below
	£	£	£	£	£
Output	47,000	1,212,500	1,337,500		125,000
Small tools and tool maintenance	910	2,200	2,000	200	—
Telephones	1,200	3,200	3,300	—	100
Travelling and entertaining	90	2,000	2,100	—	100
Canteen	40	1,000	1,000	—	—
Staff advertising	1,100	3,000	2,500	500	—
Welfare	30	700	750	—	50
Bank charges	40	900	850	50	—
Cleaning materials	50	1,350	1,350	—	—
Insurances	40	1,110	1,110	—	—
Printing and stationery	200	5,000	3,700	1,300	—
General expenses	50	1,250	1,300	—	50
Indirect wages:					
Accountancy costing	950	22,000	24,000	—	2,000
Personnel	1,040	22,000	20,000	2,000	—
Engineering	540	14,000	14,500	—	500
Inspection	1,820	47,000	47,500	—	500
Production	10,000	240,000	291,000	—	51,000
Holiday pay	580	15,000	16,500	—	1,500
NHI	1,260	33,000	34,250	—	1,250
Pension fund	270	7,000	8,000	—	1,000
Direct labour	15,600	410,000	411,550	—	1,550
Direct material	10,000	260,000	253,210	6,790	—

In the absence of a budget, the lack of output might well be noticed, but the probable causes—that is, the lowered productivity due to shortage of service, control and supervisory staff—could not be *known*, and great reluctance might have been felt in employing more charge-hands in the situation as outlined. In practice, of course, the statement shown would have been one of a series which would have shown the trends developing, and remedial action would have been taken before. The manager would have been in a position earlier to discuss his problems authoritatively with his superior by virtue of the accumulation of information.

Three points must be borne in mind when operating a budgetary control system:

(*a*) Budgets are only useful if the managers are *committed* to them, and commitment is best achieved by involving the manager concerned in the preparation of the budget. A budget imposed without discussion will be, at best, feared; at worst, ignored.

(*b*) Budgets, and the derived control documents, are *tools* of management, not punitive weapons. They should exist to help the manager, not to punish him.

(*c*) No budget should ever be considered to be fixed and immutable: differences between performance and budget (the cost accountant's 'variances') may arise from changes in external circumstances, and if these are significant, then the budget must be revised.

Value added

Contribution has been defined above as the difference between the income and the variable costs, that is, it is that portion of the income which contributes to non-variable, non-assignable charges such as rent, rates, insurance, supervising and managerial salaries, design costs, taxation, and disposable profit. A different relationship between income and expenditure is given by *value added*, the most generally accepted definition of which is:

Value added = Income − Expenditure on materials and services

Value added therefore represents the sum of money available to the organization from which its internally incurred costs (rent, rates, insurance, depreciation, design costs, taxation, disposable profits *and direct labour*) must be met.

Various VA ratios may be defined—for example, VA/employee, VA/£ paid in direct wages—which have the advantage that they are free from any particular set of financial conventions. Clearly VA and the various VA ratios can be increased by:

1. increasing income: that is, by increasing selling prices;
2. reducing expenditure on purchased materials and services.

Changes in the key ratio

$$\frac{\text{Value added}}{\text{Wages and salaries}}$$

indicate the effectiveness with which labour is being deployed *provided* that sales income and all other factors remain effectively constant. This ratio is sometimes used as the basis for financial incentive schemes.

Recommended reading

Dyson, J. R., *Accounting for non-accounting students*, Pitman, London, 1987,

Specifically written for those who are not accountants but need to use accounting techniques and conventions. Clear and up-to-date, it is wide enough to be worth a place on every POM's shelf.

Glautier, M. W. E., Underdown, B. and Clark A. C., *Basic Financial Accounting*, Pitman, London, 1985.

Well written and well produced. Principally useful for specialists.

Knott, G., *Understanding Financial Management*, Pan Books, London, 1985.

Inexpensive, well written, very useful.

5 Classification and coding

One of the most fruitful activities which a chief executive can set in train is that of installing and maintaining satisfactory classification and coding systems within an organization. A sound system will be invaluable in: variety control, materials management, cataloguing, production control, material control. If any or all of these are to be computerized, then it is essential that some sound coding be available.

The need for a classification system is very easily demonstrated. For example, a pile of 250 books is only a pile of books until they are classified in some way, when they can become a working tool. Similarly, if the items served by a restaurant appeared on a menu in random or alphabetical order, customers would have difficulty in constructing a meal. Items on offer, then, are classified in some way which will be helpful to the user—for example, into soup, fish, meat, dessert, beverages. The more items being dealt with, the more comprehensive the classification system needs to be. To consider another example, an operations manager may classify documents into five categories:

Products
Plant
Processes
Programmes
People

Soon, however, it will become obvious that this classification is too coarse, and sub-classifications will be created. This division can continue virtually indefinitely until it calls for a file which depends upon the colour of the ink of the document's signatory. Such a sub-division would be absurd because:

(a) It serves no useful purpose.
(b) The colour of ink changes with time and light.

The purpose of a classification system

Essentially, a classification system should exist to aid the user of the system. The problem which then arises is that an organization may have within it different users who have different needs, and a whole series of different classification systems may exist side by side and chaos will ensue. For example, the packing department may wish to classify packages by the length of the major dimensions, since it is this which determines the size of the packing paper. On the other hand, the post room may wish to classify packages by weight, since it is this which determines postal charges. The solution to this dilemma is to create a two-stage classification system, the first part of which defines the needs of the first department, the other the needs of the second. The basic requirements of any classification system are that it shall be comprehensive enough to serve the needs of the user, and that all categories should be mutually exclusive. The decision on the form of a classification system is of enormous importance to the organization since it can significantly affect the effectiveness of operation. An incorrect or inadequate system will hamper the organization, and be very difficult to replace.

Coding

A code is an assembly of letters and/or numbers designed to serve some purpose. When used in conjunction with a classification system, a code replaces a word description and, in so doing, liberates the user from the meanings imposed upon words by everyday usage. Brisch, probably the most important worker in the field of industrial classification, quotes in a seminal paper ('Maximum ex Minimo', *Proc. I Prod. E*, June 1954) a case where a simple pin was 'separately designed, produced and stored' under 38 different names, ranging from 'arbor' to 'distributor drive plain pin'. Had a code been assigned to the part, this enormous duplication of effort could have been saved.

Characteristics of a satisfactory classification and coding system

It would seem that the characteristics of a satisfactory classification and coding system are:

1. Any 'code name' should indicate only one item.
2. Any item should bear only one 'code name'
3. Coverage should be comprehensive and adequate for as far ahead as it is possible to foresee.
4. All code names in a system should be of constant length.

5. A code name should not be excessively long.
6. The simpler the item, the simpler the code name.
7. Classification should be by permanent features.

One simple yet effective system is the two-field Family name–Given name method. In this, the whole range of items available or likely to be available is considered and grouped into families, the families having some strong similarities in some important, permanent characteristic. Each member of the family is then given a second code, differentiating it from its fellows. If now it is believed that a new item should be introduced into the organization, an examination of the information concerning the family into which it would fit would soon reveal if an item already existed which could be employed without introducing a new one. The original definition of families needs to be done very carefully and the definitions written down, that is a dictionary must be formed.

As an example, reference is made to a company with which one of the authors was associated. There were some 3,000 drawings extant which had been drawn over the course of some fifteen years. The number chosen for any drawing was the next number in the series of natural numbers, so that the twenty 'pointers' used, for which tools and drawings existed, had numbers spread at random throughout the number series. Thus, if a pointer were designed it would be given a number—say 2948. The next item to be designed might be a bracket, which would have the number 2949 and so on. To identify all the pointers, therefore, it was necessary to search through all the drawings—a virtually impossible task. It was then decided to re-number all drawings in accordance with a family name–Christian name technique. Sixty-four families were identified, and in order to allow for expansion these were numbered 000 upwards, pointers being numbered 012. A four-figure number was assigned to each member of the family since it was felt unlikely that there would be more than 10,000 drawings in any one family. All the pointers then carried numbers as follows:

```
012    0000
012    0001
012    0002
012    0003
012    0004
```

These were then filed together, and when a pointer was required, reference had only to be made to the 012 file, and a search carried out among twenty drawings only.

The changing of all numbers to a logical system showed that some items had been drawn three, four and in some cases five times under different numbers. When the items were stored according to drawing numbers (so that the drawing number became virtually a stores location number) all similar items were grouped together physically. Other departments rapidly became familiar with the various 'family names' and it was found that, in the cost department for example, errors in pricing became more readily noticed since all 012 . . . components had similiar prices and those which were substantially incorrect were very easily observed.

More fields will be needed if the information to be coded is complex. Consider a travel company which wishes to code its holidays. It will possibly need five fields:

1. *A location field*. If the company currently has a dozen countries in which it organizes holidays, and it wishes to divide each of these countries into nine regions, N, NE, E, SE, S, SW, W, NW, Central, then the first field could be a three-number field:

00 representing A-land
01 representing B-land
02 representing C-land
and so on.

The third number need only be a single number or letter, for example:

0 represents North
1 represents North-East
2 represents East
and so on.

2. *A hotel classification field*. The company may have five classifications of hotel so that a single number or letter would suffice:

0 represents outstanding
1 represents very good
2 represents good
3 represents acceptable
4 represents rustic

3. *A hotel size classification*:

0 represents a hotel with less than 49 bedrooms
1 represents a hotel with between 50 and 99 bedrooms
2 represents a hotel with between 100 and 249 bedrooms
3 represents a hotel with between 250 and 499 bedrooms
4 represents a hotel with between 500 and 999 bedrooms
5 represents a hotel with 1,000 or more bedrooms

4. *A hotel location field*. For example:

0 indicates a location within walking distance of a beach
1 indicates a location requiring transport to a beach

2 indicates an inland location
3 indicates a mountainous location
and so on.

5. *A hotel name field*. Here the hotels in the situations defined by the previous four fields are given some sort of identifier.

If it is now necessary to find a holiday in the west of C-land in a good hotel with between 50 and 99 located inland, all that is necessary is to retrieve all hotels with an 02/6/2/1/2 code.

An example of an international code is provided by the ISBN (International Standard Book Numbering) system. This is a four field code:

First field: group—0 indicates the UK and the other English-speaking countries which have joined the scheme, 2 indicates France, 9 Germany and so on.
Second field: specific publisher—273 Pitman Publishing Ltd.
Third field: title and edition of book.
Fourth field: a check number to eliminate errors. The present edition of this book thus has an ISBN 0 273 02873/1.

Bar coding

A code, whether numeric or alpha-numeric, can be converted into a 'bar code', that is an assembly of elements, an element being either a bar or a space. An element may be either wide or narrow and the information embedded in a bar code is obtained by translating both the bar data and the space data. The construction of a bar code (the symbology) depends upon the use to which it will be put, but no newcomer to bar coding should ever try to invent a new bar code—there are ample already available. If the product being made will eventually find its way into the retail trade, it is almost certainly better to use the EAN code (the International Article Number, originally the European Article Number). This is used in most European countries and in Japan, South Africa, Yugoslavia, Australia, New Zealand and Czechoslovakia. In the USA and Canada, the UPC code is employed, but apparatus designed to read the EAN symbol will also read the UPC code, so that companies which export to

PROD + OPS MNGMNT 5E

ISBN 0-273-02873-1

9 780273 028734

the USA may prefer to use the latter. ISBN numbers are translated into bar codes using the EAN symbology. Another code which is quite widely found is the 'Code 3 of 9' or 'Code 39' wherein each character contains nine elements of which three are wide.

Reading a bar code

Bar codes are read using 'readers' which comprise a light or weak laser source which is shone on to the code and its reflection picked up by a receiver which enters it into a computer where it is translated into a form appropriate to the use required. A reader may be static, fixed in one position, and the coded item is moved across the reader, or it may be in the form of a wand which is stroked smartly across the code.

Advantages of bar coding

Bar coding has two substantial advantages over other means of data collection:

1. It is fast. A complex description can be read and put into a computer in about two seconds.
2. It is accurate. Transcription errors disappear if the reader is kept clean and the symbols themselves are not degraded.

Recommended reading

There are no texts currently in print devoted to this subject. Much assistance, however, can be obtained from the manufacturers of bar coding equipment, printers of bar codes and institutions devoted to controlling them. The author of this chapter has found the following organizations very helpful:

The Article Number Association
6 Catherine Street
London
WC2B 5JJ
Tel. 01-836 2460

Bar Code Systems Ltd
5 Observatory Road
London
SW14 7QB
Tel. 01-878 9688/9

Aim UK
The Old Vicarage
Haley Hill
Halifax
HX3 6DR
Tel. (0422) 59161

Computype
Oslo Road
Sutton Fields
Hull
HU8 0YN
Tel. (0482) 835366

Section II **The product**

Section 1 The product

6 Control of variety

Within any organization, variety is inevitable. It will exist in the products made and the services offered, in the methods used, in the materials employed and in the organizational and operating techniques. While some variety is desirable, as variety increases so organizational problems and costs will increase. Thus, for example, an increase in the number of materials stored will increase the storage room required, increase the difficulties of stock recording, increase the number of orders placed and so on. As variety increases, controllability decreases. Control of variety is essential and the task of *reducing* variety with subsequent control of the remaining variety is one of the most fruitful tasks which can be undertaken by any organization.

Variety control a managerial responsibility

Increase of variety is insidious, new parts, plants, methods, materials often being introduced for reasons valid only for a short time. Variety control is a matter for management as a whole, and must become part of the tradition of the company. This is not to imply that no changes should ever take place, but that the widest possible view should be taken of all changes, and their *total* effect on the organization considered. As has been truly said, change is not necessarily progress. Equally truly, the job of the operating manager is to achieve the maximum result with the minimum effort.

1. Minimum variety of products and services
2. Minimum variety of parts
3. Minimum variety of materials
4. Minimum variety of processes
5. Minimum variety of people

Aims of a variety control programme

A variety control programme

Variety control can be undertaken in three ways:

(a) *Simplification*—'the reduction of unnecessary variety' (*Brisch*);
(b) *Standardization*—'the control of necessary variety' (*Brisch*);
(c) *Specialization*—the concentration of effort on undertakings where special knowledge is available;

all of which combine to reduce and control variety. A programme can start in any one place in an organization, or it can proceed on a number of fronts simultaneously. It is a continuing process and, though certain techniques will prevent the spread of variety in some fields, in all there must be a continual awareness of the dangers of uncontrolled diversity: habits must be formed which will build up safeguards.

Benefits of variety control

These can be considered under three main headings as follows:

1. *In marketing*
A wide variety of products or services reduces the 'selling' which can be done at any one time. Reduction of this variety must not be carried to such extremes that the genuine needs of the customer are not satisfied, but care must be taken to avoid those 'marginal' products or services which are so often provided in small quantities to suit (possibly irrational) customers' tastes and yet are not charged at prices high enough to recover their costs. The argument is often put up that this 'special' will bring with it a flood of other work, yet all too often the sprat catches no mackerel. A wide diversity of products or services is often characteristic of a young company, a declining one, or one which has no need to control costs. Fierce competition brings with it a reduction in the number of products and a consequent intensification of selling effort.

The following comments illustrate this point. In the *Daily Telegraph* of 24 January 1981, the Business Correspondent discussed the very serious effect of Japanese action on British bearing production in the UK. He pointed out: '. . . The Japanese "attack" has been concentrated on a narrow front. The NSK Peterlee plant produces only six ranges of bearings, against 12,000 different types and sizes made by Ransome.' Similarly, in *On a clear day you can see General Motors*, J. Patrick Wright states: 'Control of manufacturing was impeded by the almost senseless proliferation of car models, parts and optional equipment. We made a study which showed, for instance, that 67 per cent of all engine combinations went into only 1 per cent of the cars we built. So we could eliminate two-thirds of all of our engine combinations and face the prospect of losing only 1 per cent of our sales potential.'

In cases where an after-sales service must be provided, the more concentrated the output the better the service can be and, since the number of spare parts which must be kept is reduced, the less the cost of the service. This can be a very potent selling factor and can often 'clinch' a sale, as well as build up the goodwill which brings with it repeated orders.

2. *In design*

The fewer the number of designs, the greater the productivity of the technical departments. It is frequently found that a part will be designed which could be identical to, or is replaceable by, an existing part. This wastes not only design effort but subsequent production, production control and operating effort. Often minor modifications to existing parts will render it useful for a number of functions other than that for which it was first designed. At first this might appear to impose restrictions upon the designer which might inhibit his creative ability, yet in fact it will release him from the drudgery of detailed designing. No designer calls for special screws, nuts, wire diameters, sheet metal thickness—standardization is accepted here, yet the variety of products which can be made from these items is infinite.

Concentration upon a limited field allows a designer to build up a body of knowledge which will permit him to answer questions within that field very much more rapidly than if his interests ranged over a wide area. This again does not produce stagnation, since the concentration brings with it a deepening of knowledge and a more fundamental understanding of the problems within that field of limited study. This is generally recognized, so that there are now no individual designers responsible for, say, the complete design of an aeroplane; there are design teams, each member of which specializes upon a few aspects. (See also Chapter 10.)

3. *In operation*

If one part can be used in place of two, operating runs will be longer, and ancillary time (setting, breaking down) will be reduced, both absolutely and when 'spread'. Fewer production aids will be required, and there will be a higher utilization of special plant. Variety reduction generally will reduce stocks by the reduction in the number of different items held, and by the lower minimum (insurance) stocks resulting from the merging of parts, and stores space will be more fully utilized. The cost of stock control and stock-taking will be correspondingly reduced. The larger quantities and the fewer products or services produced simplify the production control problem and ease the difficulties of the buyer in that he has fewer orders to place, and those he does place are for larger quantities.

The success of fast food operations derives largely from the very small variety of products offered.

1. Intensification of selling effect
2. Better after-sales service
3. Greater technical productivity
4. Better understanding of technical problems
5. Larger runs
6. Less ancillary time
7. Fewer operational aids
8. Higher plant utilization
9. Reduction in total stocks
10. Greater use of stores space
11. Easier stock control
12. Quicker stock-taking
13. Simplification of production control
14. Reduction in buying effort

Benefits of variety control

Variety control in the final product

When considering variety control in the final product or service, two aspects of the range offered to the market must be investigated simultaneously:

(*a*) how much income does each item produce?
(*b*) how much contribution does each item generate?

where

Contribution = Selling price − Direct costs.

To illustrate the need for both aspects to be investigated, consider this simplified and somewhat exaggerated example:

Item	Income produced	Contribution
A	6,210	700
B	2,415	607
C	8,895	513
D	778	350
E	585	233
F	346	117
G	97	− 23
H	391	− 47
J	204	− 59
K	1,142	− 82
	21,063	2,520 − 211
		= 2,309

If these are ranked in order of (*a*) income and (*b*) contribution, the following results will be obtained:

(*a*)   *Rank by income*:

			Income
Rank	*Product*	*Unit*	*% of total*
1	C	8,895	42.2
2	A	6,210	29.5
3	B	2,415	11.4
4	K	1,142	5.4
5	D	778	3.7
6	E	585	2.8
7	H	391	1.9
8	F	346	1.6
9	J	204	1.0
10	G	97	0.5
		21,063	100.0

See Fig. 6.1.

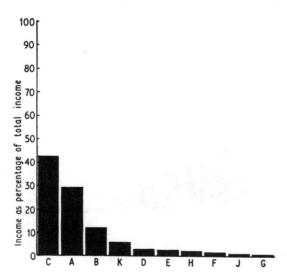

Fig. 6.1 Products ranked by income

(*b*)   *Rank by contribution*:

		Contribution	
Rank	*Product*	*Unit*	*% of total*
1	A	700	30.3
2	B	607	26.3
3	C	513	22.2
4	D	350	15.2
5	E	233	10
6	F	117	5
7	G	− 23	− 1
8	H	− 47	− 2
9	J	− 59	− 2.5
10	K	− 82	− 3.5
		2,520 − 211	100.0
		= 2,309	

See Fig. 6.2.

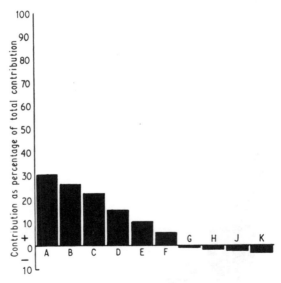

Fig. 6.2 Products ranked by contribution

To consider either of these in the absence of the other could readily lead to incorrect conclusions: for example, Product K which is ranked fourth by income actually makes a loss, and Product A, which produces most contribution, does not produce most income. It is not unusual to find that it is most easy to sell that product which is severely under-priced.

One common approach to variety control at this stage is to consider first the items, ranked by income, and to subject all low-income items to a very close scrutiny. It may be that some of these have not yet achieved sales maturity, or they may have prestige value. In the absence of any such good commercial reasons these low-income items should be considered as prime candidates for abandonment.

The second analysis—that of contribution for each item—is most usefully considered after the income for each item has been examined. Of the items remaining after the pruning already suggested has been carried out, it may well be found that the contribution provided by some products is either low or negative, and items F, G, H, J, K should again be subjected to a very close scrutiny to determine whether sales can be increased, or whether a cost-reduction programme should be initiated.

The income-contribution chart

Another approach, which virtually enables the above two stages to be coalesced, is to plot an income-contribution chart. In this the abscissae are the income ranks, and the ordinates the contribution ranks. Thus, product A has an income rank of 2, and a contribution rank of 1, and A is represented by the point (2, 1)—see Table 6.1. All the points are plotted on the income-contribution chart (Fig. 6.3): ideally, volume and contribution ranks should correspond, giving a straight line at 45° to either axis. Points lying *above* this line should be tested as follows:

Can costs be reduced?
Can prices be increased?

while points lying *below* this line should be tested:

Can sales volume be increased?

Table 6.1 Income-contribution ranks

| Product | Rank by | |
	Income	Contribution
A	2	1
B	3	2
C	1	3
D	5	4
E	6	5
F	8	6
G	10	7
H	7	8
J	9	9
K	4	10

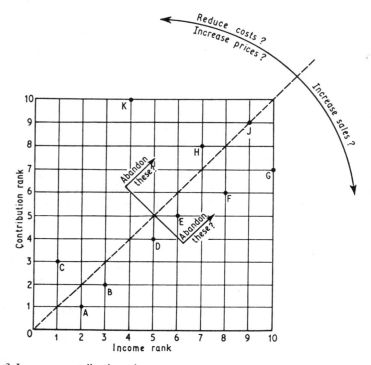

Fig. 6.3 Income-contribution chart

Neither of the above approaches in itself can determine the action which must be taken, but they can provide excellent guidance. Both, of course, demand good recording and costing procedures. Where there are a large number of items on offer, the procedure described may become unwieldy and costly. In this sort of situation, initial consideration of only the high-income, high-contribution items (the 'A' items in both sets of ranking—see Appendix 1) is recommended.

One large firm of manufacturing chemists reduced its product range from 1,500 to 221. This was done by:

(*a*) Eliminating all products whose sales were less than 0.01 per cent of total annual turnover;

(*b*) Examination of all products whose gross profit was below a certain level;

(*c*) Detailed consideration of the sales trends of each remaining product.

To assist their customers, whose goodwill might have been jeopardized by the abandoning of certain products, they negotiated the transfer of orders for discontinued lines to other firms in the same field who were still making these lines. This drastic reduction of range was accompanied by a reduction in the total number of orders received, but the size of the orders received increased, and there was, in fact, an expansion in total turnover.

Making to customer's specification is a much more difficult task, since each customer will require a different product. Here the marketing department can proceed in two ways:

(*a*) Set up a range of stock items which can be offered to the customer in place of the customer's own design. If a substantial saving in price or excellence in delivery can be shown, the customer will often be prepared to forgo some of his individuality.

(*b*) If the above is not possible, to try to guide the customer into preparing designs which employ parts which are already designed and for which equipment and instructions already exist. If these do not affect either the appearance or the performance of the product into which they are incorporated, there is a good chance that the customer will accept them, particularly if other advantages accrue.

Variety control in the components used

Most products are built up from a number of parts and, if the final product or service cannot be standardized, then it may be possible to standardize some of the parts. This can usually be done most easily in the unseen or invisible components—for example, interlinings and pockets in men's wear—but in order to be able to do it at all it is necessary to identify *readily* any component. Even a relatively small company will have a large range of parts—almost certainly over 2,000 if the company is well established.

Should a new part or constituent appear to be necessary, there must be some simple way of discovering whether one which is acceptable already exists. This can be attained by using mechanical sorting devices, and small needlesort cards are available. Even better, of course, is a computer. Many micros now have ample capacity for this purpose. However, when the storage and sorting of numbers is carried out, a very effective technique which simplifies work of the designer/stock controller/operations manager is to number all drawings and documents in such a way that the number itself identifies the part or constituents.

A discussion of the desirable properties of an effective coding system appears earlier and there is no doubt at all in the author's mind that the long-term benefits of a good coding system will considerably outweigh its installation costs. Care must be taken to ensure that the system is fitted to the user organization: an unnecessarily complex scheme can be expensive, and the simpler the scheme the better. However, *ample provision must be made for expansion*: the costs and inconvenience of changing from one scheme to another can be high. (See page 51 *et seq.*)

Variety control in purchased items

Wherever goods are purchased from outside suppliers, they should be appropriately and adequately defined. This will either be done by drawings made internally, and covered by a logical numbering system, or specifications laying down the salient factors concerning the item. Such specifications must, wherever possible, be industry-approved specifications—for example, that issued by the British Standards Institution. Use of such specifications will not only ensure that items are to a uniform and known standard but also that the goods concerned are most likely to be made in quantity by a number of manufacturers, thus being cheaper and more readily available than specially designed parts. Should any doubt be felt on this score, the reader is advised to purchase first a quantity of screws to a British Standard Specification and then the same quantity of a similar size screw to a special design.

Variety in raw material will lead not only to complexity in the raw material stores itself but also to possible variation in the subsequent product. This in turn will be felt throughout the whole operation, causing variations in equipment and processes. This is particularly significant in flow production, where the effects of variation can be very serious, but it must not be ignored in batch production, where variations do not make themselves felt so immediately.

Variety control in operation

Throughout any organization there will inevitably be a number of similar processes, or processes which, while not being similar in themselves, produce similar results. In may be possible to modify some or all of these and create a single process which will perform all that is required at an acceptable level of efficiency. This may apparently increase the *unit* cost of some processes, but it will reduce the *total* costs to the organization. The reduction in the variety of methods used will result in a greater flexibility of labour, a higher possible utilization of plant, and a simplification of the organizational task. Thus, if two different products are made in the same way, the setting-up time of the plant involved can often be substantially reduced. Similarly, if one equipment can be used in place of two, the maintenance problem is considerably eased. The gains in this field are likely to be greater in small-scale rather than large-scale operation.

Just as an analysis of finished goods is likely to show that the bulk of income is derived from a comparatively small part of the product range, so an analysis of operating processes is likely to show that, of the total capability, an extremely small part produces the bulk of the workload. Thus, Dr Opitz, in an investigation of manufacturing in twenty-five German companies, found that 80 per cent of all turned jobs had diameters of less than 200 mm, despite the fact that the permissible turning diameters of the machine tools were greatly in excess of 200 mm. Similarly, while nearly all turning machines have facilities for thread cutting, only 25 per cent of the jobs examined used these facilities. Later work by FERA (Production Engineering Research Association) in the UK has produced similar results, and these *component statistics* indicate that considerable savings can be achieved both by reducing the variety and complexity of equipment being used and by grouping together components with common technological needs so that groups of components can be produced in one batch, rather than in several separate batches. This gives rise to an organizational system known as 'Group Technology', which is more fully discussed later (Chapter 16).

---

1. Use industry-agreed standards if possible
2. Use company-agreed standards if possible
3. Standardize raw materials
4. Standardize parts
5. Simplify identification of raw materials and parts
6. Standardize methods
7. Standardize routes
8. Standardize plant and equipment

Steps towards a variety control programme

7 Control of value

Value analysis is a cost-reduction and control technique which operates by attacking the basic design of the product or service, rather than—as is done in work study—by improving the way in which the product is made or the service offered. The explicit statement of a value analysis is comparatively recent, being first put forward by L. D. Miles in the late 1940s and early 1950s. In an ideal world, where all designs were as economical, simple and elegant as possible, value analysis would have no place; or, it could be argued, it had been carried out at the conception and design of the product or service. In the present, imperfect world in which most managers find themselves, value analysis can provide a disciplined way of attacking cost.

Value analysis is 'an organized procedure for the efficient identification of unnecessary cost . . . by analysis of function . . .', *function* being 'that property of the product which makes it work or sell'. The essence of value analysis, therefore, is first to identify the function of the product and then to examine alternative ways in which this function can be achieved, finally choosing that which involves least cost. To do this, a routine has been evolved which, if followed, is likely to produce acceptable results.

The identification of function

The first, and most important, step in value analysis is to make a formal statement of the function of the product or service, and in itself this is valuable and often surprisingly difficult. Most investigations of problems start with questions. The work study engineer asks 'What is the purpose of this operation?', the marketing manager 'What shall we sell?' and the value analyst 'What does it *do?*'

It is important that the question of function should be answered explicitly and in writing. One authority suggests that the answer should be recorded in two words, a verb and a noun; for example:

'gives light' for a lamp;
'supports weight' for a beam;
'transmits force' for a shaft.

This isolation of function is a 'process of deletion'. For any statement of function the question can be asked:

'What can be discarded without diminishing the statement?'

and steadily, redundant words, ideas, concepts are jettisoned until the most economical statement is obtained.

Rarely is there only one function; there are usually several, and all need to be identified and stated. Of the various functions, one is usually of more importance than the others, and this, the *primary* function, is examined first.

Value

Value may be equated with *price*, which is that which '. . . must be given, done, sacrificed . . . to obtain a thing', and any product will have several different values:

(a) *Exchange value*, which is the price a purchaser will offer. This, the conventional purchase price, is the sum of two parts: the value due to usefulness and the value which ownership itself bestows. These are often referred to as:

(b) *Use value*, the price the purchaser will offer in order to ensure that the purpose (or function) is achieved.

(c) *Esteem value*, the price which is offered beyond the use value.

Exchange value = Use value + Esteem value

The exchange value is set by the market and is influenced by the usefulness and esteem in which the product is held. In purchasing it is useful to try to express these values in monetary terms, in order to assess their acceptability. Thus, consider two items, A and B, carrying out different tasks, both of which can be purchased for the same price (100p). By comparing these with others and with the tasks which have to be carried out, valuations can be made:

'It is worth 60p to get function A completed.'
'It is worth 10p to get function B completed.'

	A	B
Exchange value	100	100
Use value	60	10
Esteem value	40	90

Thus, the questions which now can be posed are:

'Is A desired so much that 40p must be paid in excess of its usefulness?'

'Is B desired so much that 90p must be paid in excess of its usefulness?'

Of course, use value is a subjective judgement, but it is one which most people make ('I reckon that is worth . . .' is a common enough remark) and by setting it down in numerical terms, a measure—albeit an imprecise one—is provided. In some cases, when design work is being carried out, the use value is determined effectively by the target cost which should appear as part of the design specification.

When an organization produces something for its own use—for example, for incorporation into a marketable product, or for marketing as a complete entity—a fourth value can be recognized:

Cost value (sometimes called the *cost price* or *intrinsic value*), which is the sum of all the costs incurrred in providing the product.

The difference between the cost value and the exchange value is the profit, and in most situations it is the profit which must be increased, and the task of the value analyst may be said to be that of decreasing the cost value while maintaining or increasing the use and esteem values.

Carrying out a value analysis exercise

Value analysis may be applied to any product or any procedure, but some exercises are likely to be more rewarding than others. In general, multi-component hardware will generate savings more readily and quickly than single-component products or administrative procedures, although startling results have been recorded on the value analysis of a single pin, and on the analysis of an organization. Clearly, that which is to be analysed must be one where worthwhile savings are possible.

The value analysis team

Many—possibly most—of the successes of value analysis derive from the fact that a problem is attacked by a number of people simultaneously. Whether these people should constitute a permanent team, or be called together, is open to discussion. Probably the best solution is to have a *small* permanent core of experienced people who co-opt as many of their colleagues as seems desirable. Certainly those immediately concerned *must* be present, and where purchased parts are concerned, a representative from the supplier will attend. It will always be found useful to invite intelligent 'laymen' to join, 'laymen' in this context implying those who have no special case to plead or cause to defend. The size of the team is important—too large and it will become unwieldy and impossible to convene, too small and it will be too inward-looking. Between six and ten members appears satisfactory.

Gage's twelve steps

In the carrying out of a VA exercise, twelve steps have been identified by Gage:

1. *Select the product to be analysed*
Here the problem is to identify the product or service which will give the greatest return for the costs incurred in the analysis itself. Rules are obviously impossible to lay down, but the following indicate situations likely to produce worthwhile results:

  (*a*) a multiplicity of components
  (*b*) a large forecast usage
  (*c*) a small difference between use value and cost value
  (*d*) considerable market competition
  (*e*) a long-designed product
  (*f*) the generation of considerable documentation
  (*g*) the creation of organizational complexity.

2. *Extract the cost of the product*
The cost required here is the marginal or out-of-pocket cost (see Chapter 22). An absorption cost would involve decisions on the apportioning of overheads which could easily distort any apparent cost savings. The calculation of marginal costs is not always easy, and it is here that companies first experience difficulties in value analysis. At this stage, details of individual components are not required.

3. *Record the number of parts*
In general, the larger the number of parts, the greater the chance of cost reduction.

4. *Record all the functions*
This forces consideration of the purpose of the product or service. Many serve more than one purpose and all the functions should be stated here, preferably in verb–noun form.

5. *Record the number required currently, and in the foreseeable future*
This gives magnitude to the effort which can be expended, and the costs incurred in the analysis.

These five questions are 'fact-finding'—they firmly establish the bases upon which all further work is created.

6. *Determine the primary function*
While a number of functions may be present simultaneously, it is not possible to consider them all at the same time—some order of priority must be established. This is done by reconsidering the list prepared in step 4 and deciding which would be the primary function in the view of the purchaser/user of the product.

7. *List all other ways of achieving the primary function*
It is here that value analysis requires the presence of a number of people, the value analysis team. Ideas are obtained by means of a 'creativity' or 'brainstorming' session at which ideas are generated and advanced by means of a free flow of ideas. It involves a relaxed atmosphere with an absence of criticism and a desire to contribute something by all present. The purpose of the leader is to stimulate these contributions and to create the freedom of thought and behaviour which are essential. Judgements on ideas are withheld until a later date—the more outrageous the idea, the more welcome it should be both for itself and as a stimulant.

Many UK managers reject the idea of brainstorming, since the thought of 'making an ass of myself' is anathema to them. Care must be taken, therefore, in setting up and running the session to see that no criticisms of any ideas are made, and that when the sifting of ideas is carried out later, it is done on objective grounds. Follet's Law of the Situation ('. . . accept the orders given by the situation') is as valid in value analysis as in other areas of management.

8. *Assign costs to all the alternatives*
To avoid losing the momentum of the brainstorming session, costs must be assigned to the various alternatives as rapidly as possible, but it is better not to try to assign these costs during brainstorming or the free flow of ideas will be dammed. It is probably desirable to adjourn the VA meeting and reconvene it later when the costs are available. To avoid too much delay, 'order of magnitude' costs are acceptable.

9. *Examine the three cheapest alternatives*
Steps 7 and 8 allow the three cheapest alternatives to be selected and examined for feasibility and performance. The design of the new product will begin to emerge at this stage.

10. *Decide which idea should be developed further*
From step 9 and the examination carried out there, a decision is taken upon which idea should be developed further.

11. *See what other functions need to be incorporated*
Re-examination of step 4 will show which other functions have not already been incorporated in the suggestions in step 10.

The above six steps may produce a complete solution, or it may be that further detailed work needs to be carried out to finalize the new design. Here check lists of ideas may usefully be produced. The precise list will depend on the organization, but the common feature is the question:

'Does its use contribute value?'

Every addition, whether it be an extra component, tolerance, hole, bend, document, form . . . should be examined against this question. Equally useful is the inverse:

'Can anything be removed without degrading the product?'

While the 'new' product is being developed, the value analysis committee can undertake the final step.

12. *Ensure that the new design is accepted*
Conservatism, the principle of 'worry-minimization' and sheer inertia will all combine to resist new ideas. To forestall this, the VA team should consider the ways in which the new idea can be 'sold'. This will almost certainly require:

(*a*) a model
and statements of:

(*b*) anticipated savings,
(*c*) anticipated capital expenditure,
(*d*) improvements in value,
and a proposed plan in terms of:

(*e*) critical path analysis network.

The above twelve steps are incorporated in Gage's twelve questions:

1. What is it?
2. What does it cost?
3. How many parts?
4. What does it do?
5. How many required?
6. Which is the primary function?
7. What else will do?
8. What will *that* cost?
9. Which three of the alternative ways of doing the job shows the difference between 'cost' and 'use value'?
10. Which ideas are to be developed?
11. What other functions and specification features must be incorporated?
12. What is needed to sell the ideas and forestall 'road-blocks'?

Gage's twelve value analysis questions

Value engineering

The application of VA techniques—and particularly those concerned with the isolation of function—to the design stages of a product or a system is clearly most desirable. Greater savings, though probably less identifiable, can be made, and for 'one-off' and short- run tasks, only prior value studies are possible. The term 'value engineering' is often reserved for this 'cost prevention' exercise.

Recommended reading

Miles, L. D., *Techniques of Value Analysis and Engineering*, McGraw-Hill, New York, 1972.
   This is not only the first text on value analysis, it is the only one still in print which the authors can find. Written by the 'originator' of VA, it is stimulating and useful if a little dated.

8 Quality

This chapter discusses the general issues concerned with the management of quality, the policy and systems that are required. Chapters 20 and 21 deal with the techniques used in the actual control of quality.

The management of quality

The reputation attached to an organization for the quality of its products is accepted as a key to its success and the future of its employees. To prosper in today's economic climate, any organization and its suppliers must be dedicated to never-ending improvement, and more efficient ways to obtain products or services that consistently meet customers' needs must constantly be sought. The consumer is no longer required to make a choice between price and quality, and competitiveness in quality is not only central to profitability, but crucial to business survival. In today's tough and challenging business environment, the development and implementation of a comprehensive quality policy is not merely desirable—it is essential.

Quality is not a property which has an absolute meaning: a high-quality pair of beach shoes can well be a very low-quality pair of walking shoes, a low-quality billiard cue can be a very high-quality pea-stick. The quality of a product or service has meaning only when related to its *function*—'that which makes it work or sell'—and the isolation of function is rarely simple. A useful and succinct definition of quality then is:

Quality is fitness for function or purpose.

This definition requires that both the needs of the customer *and his belief in his needs* are explored. Frequently a choice of product is made upon apparently irrational grounds: identical products, presented in different ways, will sell in vastly different quantities, and will have different qualities ascribed to them. Similarly, a quality judgement is often related to the price paid without any regard to the discernible properties of the item being purchased. The detergent which sells better in a blue box than a red one, the analgesic which is 'more effective' when sold under a proprietary name than when sold as a British Pharmacopoeia product, are well known. The reasons for the purchase may be difficult to identify, yet their reality must not be denied.

The quality of products and services is important not only for users but also for suppliers. For manufacturers, quality deficiencies result in additional costs for inspection, testing, scrap, rework, and the handling of complaints and warranty claims. In the so-called service industries, errors, checking, enquiries and complaints account for losses in efficiency and productivity. Repeat sales and future market share will also be affected, with significant effects on profitability and survival. Quality must, therefore, be taken into account throughout all the areas of marketing, design, purchasing, production or operations, and distribution. It must be controlled in all these functions, and their activities co-ordinated to achieve a balanced corporate quality performance. Quality performance will not just happen, effective leadership and teamwork is the only sure recipe for success. Real understanding and commitment by senior management, together with explicit quality policies, lead to an improvement throughout the entire organization, which in turn generates a momentum for the improvement of products and performance.

The quality of a product should stem from a managerial decision, a decision as complex and as important as any which directors are called upon to make. It must be based upon consideration of both the external environment and the internal resources: the identification of the customer's perception of function must be matched by the ability to produce a product which will be recognized as satisfying that perception, and in the event of a conflict between these two determinants, the intended market segment may have to be changed, or the internal resources may have to be increased. Thus, if a soundly based market investigation reveals that a product requires a quality which cannot be economically achieved with existing equipment, the company must either change its intended market or improve its production facilities. A word of warning: the customer's perception of quality changes with time and the company's attitude to quality must, therefore, change with this perception. The skills and attitudes of the producer are also subject to change, and failure to monitor such changes will inevitably lead to dissatisfied customers. Quality, like all other corporate matters, must be continually reviewed in the light of current circumstances.

A traditional approach to many transformation processes is to depend on 'production' to make the product and 'quality control' to inspect it and divert that output which does not meet the requirements. This is a strategy of *detection* and is wasteful, because it allows time and materials to be invested in products which are not always saleable. This post-production inspection is expensive, unreliable and uneconomical.

It is much more effective to avoid waste by not producing unsaleable output in the first place—to adopt a strategy of *prevention*. The prevention strategy sounds sensible and obvious to most people. It is often captured in slogans such as; 'Quality—Right First Time'. This type of campaigning is, however, not enough on its own. What is required is an understanding of the elements of a systematic control system which is designed for the prevention of products or services which do not conform to requirements. Management must be dedicated to the on-going improvement of quality, not simply a one-step improvement to an acceptable plateau.

A *quality policy* then requires top management to:

1. Establish an 'organization' for quality
2. Identify the customer's needs and perception of needs
3. Assess the ability of the organization to meet these needs economically
4. Ensure that bought-out materials and services reliably meet the required standards of performance and efficiency
5. Concentrate on the prevention rather than detection philosophy
6. Educate and train for quality improvement
7. Review the quality management systems to maintain progress

The quality policy must be publicized and understood at all levels of the organization.

Design and conformance

We have defined quality as the degree of fitness for purpose or function, indicating that it is a measure of the satisfaction of customer needs. So the quality of a motor car, or washing machine, or a banking service is the extent to which it meets the requirements of the customer. Before any discussion on quality can take place, therefore, it is necessary to be clear about the purpose of the product, in other words, what those customer requirements are. The customer may be within or without the organization and his/her satisfaction must be the first and most important ingredient in any plan for success.

The quality of a product has two distinct but inter-related aspects:

Quality of design, and
Quality of conformance to design

Quality of design

This is a measure of how well the product is designed to achieve its stated purpose. If the quality of design is low, the product will not satisfy the requirements.

The most important feature of the design, with regard to the achievement of the required product quality, is the *specification*. This describes and defines the product and should be a comprehensive statement of all aspects of it which must be present to meet customer requirements.

The stipulation of the correct specification is vital in the purchase of materials and services for use in the transformation process. All too frequently, the terms 'as previously supplied' or 'as agreed with your representative' are to be found on purchasing orders for bought-out items. The importance of obtaining inputs of the appropriate quality cannot be over-emphasized and this cannot be achieved without adequate specifications.

A specification may be expressed in terms of: the maximum amount of tolerable variation on a measurement, the degree of finish on a surface, the smoothness of movement of a mechanical device, a particular chemical property, the number of times the phone rings before it must be answered, etc. There are a variety of ways in which specifications may be stated and the ingenuity of man must be constrained in order to control the number of forms of specifications present in any organization.

Quality of conformance to design

This is the extent to which the product achieves the quality of design. What the customer actually receives should conform to the design, and direct production or operating costs are tied firmly to the level of conformance achieved. Quality cannot be inspected into a product, the customer satisfaction must be designed into the production system. The conformance check then makes sure that things go according to plan.

A high level of final product inspection or checking of work is often indicative of attempts to inspect in quality, an activity which will achieve nothing but spiralling costs and decreasing viability.

The area of conformance to design is concerned largely with the quality performance of the transformation function. The recording and analysis of data play a significant role in this aspect of quality and it is here that the tools of 'statistical process control' described in Chapters 20 and 21 must be applied effectively.

The costs of quality

Manufacturing a product which has 'fitness for purpose' is not enough.

The cost of achieving quality must be carefully managed so that the long-term effect of quality costs on the business is a desirable one. These costs are a true measure of the quality effort. A competitive product based on a balance between quality and cost factors is the principal goal of responsible POM. This objective is best accomplished with the aid of competent analysis of the costs of quality.

The analysis of quality costs is a significant management tool which provides:

(*a*) A method of assessing the overall effectiveness of the management of quality.

(*b*) A means of determining problem areas and action priorities.

The costs of quality are no different to any other costs in that, like the costs of maintenance, design, sales, production, management information, and other activities, they can be budgeted, measured and analysed.

Design quality

At the design stage, the criteria for establishing the precision of the design of the product or service should be predominantly its in-service performance requirements. The movement by a designer towards tighter and tighter specifications generally requires a change towards processes which are more and more costly. This is represented by the cost curve in Fig. 8.1, which rises more and more steeply as attempts are made to further increase precision. Specification tolerances which are based on

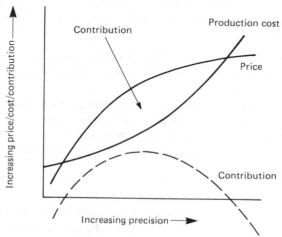

Fig. 8.1 Contribution and precision of design

idealistic design concepts will result in high process operating costs.

As the precision increases, the unit price obtainable increases, but at a decreasing rate so that greater and greater precision brings smaller and smaller increases in price (Fig. 8.1). This does not, of course, take into account the increases in market share which may derive from the increased capability associated with greater precision. The total market value may behave in a completely different way in certain situations.

Contribution—the difference between unit price and cost—is shown as the dotted curve in Fig. 8.1. The precision level at which the contribution per unit is a maximum is the point at which the market dictates production should operate. Designers must share the corporate understanding of the organization's position in the market place. It is not sufficient that marketing establishes what the customer requirements are; there must also be agreement that operations have the capability of meeting those requirements. Should that not be the case, then one of two things must happen. Either the company finds a different position in the market place or substantially changes the production/operations facilities.

Conformance quality

Having specified the quality of design, the POM has the task of achieving a product which matches this quality. This comprises activities which will incur costs that may be separated into the categories of failure costs, appraisal costs and prevention costs. Failure costs can be further split into those resulting from internal and external failure.

Internal failure costs
These costs occur when products fail to reach designed quality standards and are detected before transfer to the consumer takes place. Internal failure includes:

Scrap—defective product which cannot be repaired, used or sold.
Rework or rectification—the correction of defective output to meet the required specifications.
Re-inspection—the re-examination of output which has been rectified.
Downgrading—product which is usable but does not meet specifications and may be sold as 'second quality' at a low price.
Failure analysis—the activity required to establish the causes of internal product failure.

External failure costs
These costs occur when products fail to reach design quality standards and are not detected until after transfer to the consumer. External failure includes:

Repair—either of returned products or those in the field.

Warranty claims—failed products which are replaced under guarantee.

Complaints—all work associated with servicing of customers' complaints.

Returns—the handling and investigation of rejected products and services.

Liability—the result of product liability litigation and other claims.

External and internal failures produce the *costs of getting it wrong*.

Appraisal costs
These costs are associated with the evaluation of purchased materials, processes, intermediates, products and services, to assure conformance with the specifications. Appraisal includes:

Inspection and test—of incoming material, process set-up, first-offs, running processes, intermediates, final products and services, and includes product performance appraisal against agreed specifications.

Quality audits—to check that the quality system is functioning satisfactorily.

Inspection equipment—the calibration and maintenance of any equipment used in appraisal activities.

Vendor rating—the assessment and approval of suppliers of all products and services.

Appraisal activities result in the *costs of checking it is right*.

Prevention costs
These are associated with the design, implementation and maintenance of the quality system. Prevention costs are planned and are incurred prior to production. Prevention includes:

Product requirements—the determination of quality requirements and the setting of corresponding specifications for incoming materials, processes, intermediates, finished products and services.

Quality planning—the creation of quality, reliability, production, supervision, inspection and other special plans (e.g. pre-production trials) required to achieve the quality objective.

Quality assurance—the creation and maintenance of the overall quality system.

Appraisal equipment—the design, development and/or purchase of equipment for use in appraisal.

Training—the development, preparation and maintenance of quality training programmes for operators, supervisors and managers.

Miscellaneous—clerical, travel, supply, shipping, communications and other general office management activities associated with quality.

Resources devoted to prevention give rise to the *costs of making it right the first time*.

The relationship between the so-called direct costs of prevention, appraisal, and failure costs and the ability of the organization to meet the customer requirements is shown in Fig. 8.2. Where the ability to match a quality acceptable to the customer is low, the total direct quality costs are high, the failure costs predominating. As ability is improved by modest investment in prevention and possibly appraisal, the failure costs drop, initially very steeply. There may be an optimum operating level at which the combined costs are at the minimum.

So far little has been said about the often intractable indirect quality costs associated with customer dissatisfaction, and loss of reputation or goodwill. These costs reflect customer attitude towards an organization and may be considerable. Indirect quality costs, like direct costs, may be lowered by relatively small increases in prevention costs which subsequently reduce external failure—the cause of customer dissatisfaction and loss of reputation.

The quality–productivity link

Total direct quality costs, and their division between the categories of

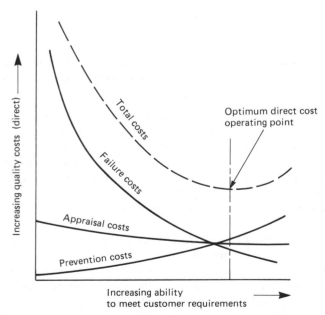

Fig. 8.2 Relationship between direct costs of quality and organization capability

prevention, appraisal, internal failure and external failure, vary considerably from industry to industry and from plant to plant. Juran's work, showing that total quality costs in manufacturing average 10 per cent of sales turnover, means that in the average organization there exists a 'hidden plant', amounting to approximately one-tenth of productive capacity. This is devoted to producing scrap, re-work, correcting errors, replacing defective goods and so on. Thus, a direct link exists between quality and productivity, and there is no better way to improve productivity than to convert this hidden plant to truly productive use. A systematic approach to the control of quality provides an important way to accomplish this.

Responsibility and the quality management system

'Quality is everyone's business' is an often quoted cliche, but 'Everything is everyone's business', and so quality often becomes 'Nobody's business'. The responsibility for quality begins with the determination of the customer's quality requirements and continues until the product or service is accepted by a satisfied customer. The management functions identifiable within this process, together with their duties (some of which are shared activities and, therefore, appear under several functions), are as follows:

Senior management
    (*a*) A clear understanding of quality.
    (*b*) A commitment to a defined quality policy.
    (*c*) Ensure that the correct quality systems and attitudes pervade the organization.
    (*d*) Support and encourage the quality policy.

Marketing
    (*a*) Determination of customer quality requirements.
    (*b*) A knowledge of the competitors' quality levels.
    (*c*) Setting of product specifications.
    (*d*) Analysis of customer complaints, sales staff reports, warranty claims and product liability cases.
    (*e*) Downgrading of products for sale as seconds, etc.

Research and development/design/management services
    (*a*) Setting of appropriate specifications (including bought-out materials, processes and products).
    (*b*) Pre-production and prototype trials.
    (*c*) Design and specification of inspection and checking equipment.
    (*d*) Analysis of some re-work and rectification problems.

(e) Downgrading of products.

(f) Product complaints and warranty claims.

Production (including production engineering) or *operations*

(a) Agreeing specifications.

(b) Pre-production and prototype trials.

(c) Training of operations and associated personnel, including supervisors, foremen, etc.

(d) Special handling and storage during production.

(e) Supervision and control of quality at all stages.

(f) Line or process control.

(g) Finished product control.

(h) Analysis of scrapped, re-worked, rectified, replaced and downgraded products.

Purchasing

(a) Vendor supplier selection rating and approval.

(b) Procuring of materials of the required quality.

After-sales and technical service

(a) Product specification and performance evaluation.

(b) Pre-production and prototype product evaluation.

(c) Analysis of customer complaints and material returned.

Stores, transport and distribution

(a) Special handling and storage.

(b) Receiving and checking of bought-out items.

(c) Checking and despatching of finished or replacement products or services.

(d) Receiving, checking and sorting of returned products for replacement or repair.

Quality assurance

(a) Quality planning.

(b) Quality advice and expertise.

(c) Training of personnel.

(d) Provision of inward goods, process and finished products appraisal methodology.

(e) Analysis of customer complaints, warranty claims and product liability cases.

A quality assurance system, based on the fact that all functions share responsibility for quality, provides an effective method of acquiring and maintaining desired quality standards. The quality assurance department should not assume direct responsibility for quality but should support, advise and audit the work of the other functions, in much the same way as a financial auditor performs his duty without assuming responsibility for the profitability of the company.

The actual control of quality during manufacture must rest squarely on the shoulders of POM, who must ensure that all the appropriate concepts and techniques are applied to this task. Organizationally, this means that staff carrying out work to control quality must be within the POM function.

A good quality management system must be documented, i.e. the procedures and paperwork referred to in Chapter 1. This usually, but need not necessarily, takes the form of a quality manual, the sections of which cover such matters as:

(a) who should be responsible for the functions affecting quality;
(b) once installed, how the system should be reviewed to remain effective;
(c) the planning considerations involved in setting up the quality system;
(d) the documented work instructions required;
(e) the records that will be required;
(f) how defects may be found and corrected;
(g) which design functions need to be controlled;
(h) the sort of system required for the control of documentation and changes;
(i) the control of inspection, measuring and test equipment required;
(j) the control of purchased materials;
(k) the controls required during production or operations;
(l) the requirements at final inspection;
(m) the sampling procedures which should be used;
(n) the control of non-conforming materials or services;
(o) the identification of inspection status of materials in the production process;
(p) the procedures required to protect and preserve product quality;
(q) the need for training.

The control of quality is a managerial function in which the quality of materials, processes, skills and products is controlled for the purpose of preventing defective output. To meet this responsibility, organizations must use every device practicable to prevent, detect and correct errors that occur in the steps of production. This implies that, to achieve the control of quality, the variables which may affect quality and which can result from the actions of people, the nature of materials, and the performance of machines, must all be controlled. Technologies and market conditions vary between different industries and markets, but the basic concept of quality management and the financial implications are of general validity. The objective should be to produce, at an acceptable cost, goods which conform to the requirements of the customer. The way to accomplish this is to use a systematic approach in the operating departments of: marketing, design, production or operations, quality assurance, purchasing, sales and others—nobody should be exempt. The systematic approach to quality is not a separate science or a unique theory, rather a set of valuable tools which becomes an integral part of the 'total' quality approach.

Quality circles

It is claimed that quality circles (QCs) originated in the early 1960s in Japan with the purpose of improving the quality of Japanese products. They have certainly become one of the most publicized aspects of that country's approach to quality.

It is very easy to regard quality circles as the magic ointment to be rubbed on the affected spot, and unfortunately many managers in the West see them as a panacea which will cure all ills. There are no panaceas and to place this concept into perspective, Juran, who has been an important influence in Japan's improvement in quality, has stated that quality circles represent only 5–10 per cent of the canvas of the Japanese success. The rest is concerned with understanding quality, its related costs, and the organization and techniques necessary for achieving customer satisfaction.

Given the right sort of introduction, commitment by top management, and environment in which to operate, quality circles can produce the motivation to achieve quality performance at operator level. Circles should develop out of an understanding and knowledge of quality on the part of senior management. They must not be introduced as a desperate attempt to do something about poor quality.

In essence a quality circle can be easily defined: 'A quality circle is a group of employees who meet voluntarily at frequent and regular intervals to discuss problems encountered in their work with a view to discovering solutions to these problems, these being installed with, where necessary, managerial support.'

Successful installation and continuation of such circles requires that all concerned, *and particularly management*, should examine the QC concept from the three fundamental aspects of production management: the social, the technical and the managerial.

Social aspects of QCs

Quality circles can only operate successfully if there is *commitment* on all sides. Membership is voluntary, and meetings in Japan are usually outside normal working hours, though in the UK they are often within normal time. No interested person from the working group should be excluded, although effective circles seem to contain 7–10 members. Participation in discussions should be free and ideas, however wild, should be encouraged and discussed. The experience of value analysis teams (pages 72–5) is very pertinent here.

The social purpose of quality circles is to provide the powerful motivation of allowing people to take some part in deciding their own actions and futures. A financial budget is a strong motivating force *if those who are held responsible take part in its preparation*, and the quality circle should bring with it a similar motivation. A good well-trained and sympathetic leader will see it as an essential part of his task to develop the abilities of each member of the circle. Since the circle leader is usually the group supervisor, he or she benefits directly by considerable assistance in solving nagging problems.

Technical aspects of QCs

There are available a wide range of invaluable techniques which may be used by circles. These include:

Brainstorming
Data gathering and histograms
Cause and effect analysis
Pareto or ABA analysis
Sampling
Control charts

and before any circle can be set up the leader must have some knowledge of the above so that he may train his circle, usually by example rather than by precept. The techniques listed are not exclusive to quality circles and find application in most fields of management. None of them require a high initial level of education, even control charting and sampling being capable of understanding at all levels if properly explained. Outside assistance in training may, however, be desirable.

Managerial aspects of QCs

Quality circles, like any other technique, will not operate unless there is complete managerial commitment and support. The quickest way to kill a circle is to ignore a proposal arising from it. If the leader has been properly trained, only feasible solutions will be proposed, and these should be implemented as rapidly as possible. This requires an open-mindedness on the part of managers, which some find difficult. It must be realized that the real 'experts' on performing a task are those people who do it day after day.

Recommended reading

British Standards Institution, *Quality Assurance*, BSI Handbook 22, 1983.
>Contains seven standards related to quality assurance; BS4778 *Glossary of Terms*, BS4891 *Guide to QA*, BS5233 *Glossary of Metrology Terms*, BS5750 *Quality Systems*, BS5760 *Reliability of Systems*, etc, BS5781 *Measurement and Calibration*, BS6143 *Quality Related Costs*.

British Standards Institution, *Quality Systems*, BS5750, 1987.
>The new international standard for quality management systems.

Crosby, Philip B., *Quality is Free*, McGraw-Hill, 1979.
>A very readable book in which the author uses real case histories to illustrate points. The style is very American.

Crosby, Philip B., *Quality without Tears*, McGraw-Hill, 1984.
>The follow-up to *Quality is Free*. Using more case histories Crosby sets out his approach to implementing quality management.

Feigenbaum, Armand V., *Total Quality Control*, 3rd edn, McGraw-Hill, 1983.
>The first author to coin the term *total* quality. This provides a comprehensive guide to the language and meaning of quality.

Gitlow, Howard S. and Gitlow, Shelly J., *The Deming Guide to Quality and Competitive Position*, Prentice-Hall, 1987.
>Based on the philosophy of Dr W. Edwards Deming, it gives a clear, concise, understandable approach. Very light on statistics and many examples used to aid learning.

Murphy, John A., *Quality in Practice*, Gill and MacMillan, 1986.
>Written by the Chief Executive of the Irish Quality Control Association for the 'working manager'. It is a practical book covering the organizational, behavioural and managerial aspects of quality.

Townsend, Patrick L., *Commit to Quality*, Wiley, 1986.
>A blend of traditional ideas and techniques offered to the manager to improve competitiveness and employee morale.

9 Reliability

Introduction

Quality is a property which may change with the age of the product or service. Clearly, part of the acceptability of a product will depend on its ability to function satisfactorily *over a period of time*. This aspect of performance has been given the name *reliability*:

> *Reliability* is the ability to continue to be fit for the purpose or function

Reliability ranks with quality in importance, since it is a key factor in many purchasing decisions where alternatives are being compared. Many of the general management issues related to achieving quality, which were discussed in Chapter 8, are also applicable to reliability. It is not proposed that these should be repeated here, but the critical requirements of:

(a) a company policy on reliability,
(b) top management commitment,

cannot be over-emphasized.

Clearly, every product will eventually fail, although in some cases the possibility is small enough for it to be effectively immortal. With the current pressures to reduce cost, and with the need for increasing complexity, the probability of a product or service failing within the user's anticipation of its working life is likely to be finite. As reliability is now an exceedingly important aspect of competitiveness, there is a need to *design reliability into* products. Unfortunately, the testing of a design to assess its reliability is difficult, sometimes impossible, and the designer must therefore invest in any insurance which is practicable. Some methods of attempting to assure reliability are:

(a) use proven designs;
(b) use the simplest possible design—the fewer the components and the simpler their designs, the lower the total probability of failure;
(c) use components of known or likely high probability of survival; it is usually easier to carry out reliability tests by over-stressing components

of a product or service than by over-stressing the complete product or service;

(*d*) employ redundant parts where there is a likelihood of failure. It may be that a component or part of a system must be used which has a finite probability of failure (*F*). Placing two of these parts in parallel will reduce the probability of *both* failing to F^2. Three in parallel will *all* fail with a probability of F^3, and so on. Clearly the costs of redundancy must be weighed against the value of reliability;

(*e*) design to 'fail-safe';

(*f*) specify proven manufacturing methods.

Use proven designs
Use simple designs
Use high-reliability components
Use redundancy
Use 'fail-safe' methods
Use proven manufacturing methods

The designer and reliability

Failure

In the discussion of reliability, it is important to be clear about what is meant by failure. When a product, system or component no longer performs its required function, it is said to have failed. This definition assumes that the required function is known exactly. A motor car could be described as either working perfectly or broken down completely, but there could be something in between. It may, for example, achieve a lower mileage to the gallon than when new. Whether the latter is regarded as failure depends entirely on what is defined as the required function and this in turn may depend on the use of the product or service.

To assist in the definition of failure, it may be useful to consider the various types and causes.

Types of failure

Total failure: this results in a complete lack of ability of the product or service to perform the required function.

Partial failure: the item does not work, or the service is not provided, as well as expected, but it has not completely failed.

Gradual failure: this takes place progressively over a period of time and could possibly be anticipated by some sort of examination.

Sudden failure: occurs very quickly and is not easily predicted by investigation or examination.

Causes of failure

Clearly there are many causes of product and/or service system failure, but two main general ones are common:

Weakness: this is inherent in the product or service itself and, when subject to the normal stresses of use, results in one of the types of failure described above. Weakness is usually introduced by poor or wrong design, materials, processes or operation.

Misuse: this represents the application of stresses which are outside the usual capability of the product or service system.

Failure mode, effect and criticality analysis (FMECA)

It is possible to analyse products and services to determine possible modes of failure and their effects on the performance of the product or operation of the service system. Failure mode and effect analysis (FMEA) is the study of potential failures to determine their effects. If the results of a FMEA are ranked in order of seriousness, then the word *criticality* is added to give FMECA.

The primary objective of a FMECA is to determine the features of product design, production and distribution which are critical to the various modes of failure. It uses all the available experience and expertise from marketing, design, technology, purchasing, production, distribution, service, etc., to identify the importance levels or criticality of potential problems and stimulate action which will reduce these levels. FMECA should be a major consideration at the design stage of a product or service.

The elements of a complete analysis are:

1. *Failure mode*—the anticipated conditions of operation are used as the background to study the most probable failure mode, location and mechanism of the product or system and its components.

2. *Failure effect*—the potential failures are studied to determine their probable effects on the performance of the whole product and the effects of the various components on each other.

3. *Failure criticality*—The potential failures in the various parts of the product or service system are examined to determine the severity of each failure effect in terms of lowering of performance, safety hazard, total loss of function, etc.

FMECA may be applied at any stage of design, development, production or use but, since its main aim is to prevent failure, it is most suitably applied at the design stage to identify and eliminate causes. With more complex product or service systems, it may be appropriate to consider these as smaller units or sub-systems, each one being the subject of a separate FMECA.

Special FMECA pro-formas are available (for example, see Fig. 9.1) which set out the steps of the analysis as follows:

1. Identify the product or system components.
2. List all possible failure modes of each component.
3. Set down the effects that each mode of failure would have on the overall function of the product or system.
4. List all the possible causes of each failure mode.
5. Assess numerically the failure modes on a scale from 1 to 10. Experience and reliability data should be used, together with judgement, to determine the values, on a scale 1–10, for:

P   the probability of each failure mode occurring
     (1 = low, 10 = high)
S   the seriousness or criticality of the failure
     (1 = low, 10 = high)
D   the difficulty of detecting the failure before the product or service is used by the consumer
     (1 = easy, 10 = very difficult)

Value	1	2	3	4	5	6	7	8	9	10
P	low chance of occurrence → almost certain to occur
S	not serious, minor nuisance → total failure, safety hazard
D	easily detected → unlikely to be detected

6. Calculate the product of the ratings, $C = P \times S \times D$, known as the criticality index, for each failure mode. This indicates the relative priority of each mode in the failure prevention activities.
7. Indicate briefly the corrective action required and, if possible, which department is responsible and the expected completion date.

When the criticality index has been calculated, the failures may be ranked accordingly. It is usually advisable, therefore, to determine the value of C for each failure mode before completing the last columns. In this way, the action required against each item can be judged in the light of the ranked severity and the resources available.

Product – Small engine			Sub-system – In line pump	P Probability of occurrence S Severity of failure			D Difficulty of detection C Criticality index = P × S × D	FMECA No. X206 Date
(1) Component	(2) Failure mode	(3) Effect of failure	(4) Cause of failure	(5) P	(5) S	(5) D	(6) C	(7) Corrective action
Cams	Fatigue cracking	Loss of power, complete functional failure	Nozzle blockage Dirty or no oil Poor surface finish	3	2	9	54	Determine failure definition Change operating pressure
Bearings	Cracking across bridge	Cosmetic Oil seepage		2	3	10	60	Re-design die case pumps
Valve holder	Erosion in bore	Blockage, loss of performance	High flow rates Cavitation	4	4	9	144	Samples to be tested and re-design initiated if necessary
Valve	Consistency wear	Engine performance Delivery balance	Assembly Adjustment Poor filter/water	4	9	5	180	Full machine test and examination of system detail
Valve spring	Fatigue, erosion or wear	Loss of engine performance	Hydraulic duty	4	3	3	36	Specification detail to be examined
Peg	Wear – fracture	Loss of engine performance	Hydraulic dirty	3	5	2	30	Adjust injection rates
Plunger	Slot polishing	Seizure leading to functional failure	Erosion of pump body	1	9	10	90	Change procedure for hardening and grinding. To be re-assessed after tests

Fig. 9.1 Failure mode, effect and criticality analysis (FMECA)

Identify components
List failure modes
List failure effects
List causes of failure modes
Assess failure modes → P, S, D
Calculate criticality index, $C = P \times S \times D$
Rank failure modes
Indicate corrective action

FMECA

Measures and analysis of reliability

For the purposes of illustrating some of the more common measures of reliability in current use, a 'life-table' for 150 door locks operated over 30 units of time has been set out in Table 9.1. Note that in practice a much larger number of items would be likely to be tested if valid results were required.

Clearly, all measures of reliability are time dependent.

The reliability $(R(t))$ of a product is the probability that it will be still functioning at time t. This may be calculated as follows:

$$R(t) = \frac{\text{Number surviving at time } t}{\text{Number existing at } t = 0}$$

The other side of this coin is $F(t)$ the so-called *cumulative distribution of failure*:

$$F(t) = 1 - R(t)$$

$$\text{or } F(t) = \frac{\text{Cumulative number of failures by time } t}{\text{Number existing at } t = 0}$$

There are two other similar measures of reliability in use: the *probability density function of failure, f(t)*:

$$f(t) = \frac{\text{Number failing in unit time at time } t}{\text{Number existing at } t = 0}$$

and the *failure or hazard rate, λ(t)*:

$$\lambda(t) = \frac{\text{Number failing in unit time at time } t}{\text{Number surviving at time } t}$$

In Table 9.1 for the time period 10–11, in which 60 units were functioning at the beginning and 57 were functioning at the end of the period:

Table 9.1 'Life-table' for 150 door locks

Operating period in units of time	Number operating at start of period (units)
0– 1	150
1– 2	123
2– 3	109
3– 4	99
4– 5	91
5– 6	84
6– 7	78
7– 8	74
8– 9	69
9–10	65
10–11	60
11–12	57
12–13	54
13–14	51
14–15	49
15–16	47
16–17	44
17–18	42
18–19	40
19–20	38
20–21	35
21–22	32
22–23	29
23–24	26
24–25	24
25–26	22
26–27	20
27–28	17
28–29	15
29–30	13

Number existing at $t = 0$	150
Number surviving at $t = 10$	60
Number surviving at $t = 11$	57
Cumulative number of failures at $t = 11$	93
Number failing in unit time at $t = 11$	3

Hence, at time $t = 11$, the reliability function

$$R(11) = \frac{57}{150} = 0.380$$

the cumulative distribution function of failure

$$F(11) = 1 - 0.380 \quad \text{or} \quad \frac{93}{150} = 0.620$$

the probability density function of failure

$$f(11) = \frac{3}{150} = 0.02$$

the failure or hazard rate

$$\lambda(11) = \frac{3}{57} = 0.053$$

The values for $R(t)$, $F(t)$, $f(t)$ and $\lambda(t)$ for the 30 test periods under consideration are shown in Table 9.2 and represented graphically in Figs. 9.2 and 9.3.

The curve produced by plotting $F(t)$ is clearly an integration of the probability density function of failure $f(t)$. The curve derived from the $R(t)$ plot is a mirror image of the $F(t)$ plot. The last curve from the plot of failure or hazard rate $(\lambda(t))$ is known as the 'bath-tub curve' from its shape, and it is extremely useful in the analysis of product reliability. This shape is characteristic of the failure-rate curve of many well-designed components, including the human body (Fig. 9.4).

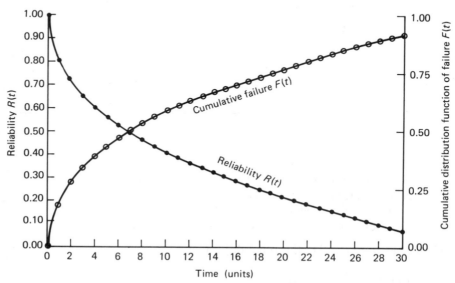

Fig. 9.2 Curves for reliability and cumulative distribution function of failure

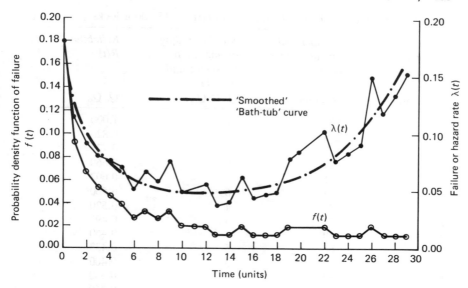

Fig.9.3 Curves for probability density function of failure and failure or hazard rate

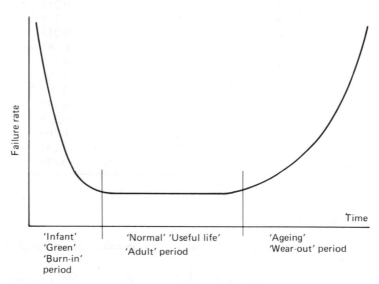

Fig. 9.4 The bath-tub curve

Table 9.2 Calculations of $R(t)$, $F(t)$, $f(t)$ and $\lambda(t)$ for 150 door locks

Time elapsed since start of operations t (time units)	Number still operating at time t Q_t units	Number failing during the period between t and $(t + 1)$ $Q_t - Q_{t+1}$	Reliability $R(t)$ Q_t/Q_0
0	150	27	1.000
1	123	14	0.820
2	109	10	0.727
3	99	8	0.660
4	91	7	0.607
5	84	6	0.560
6	78	4	0.520
7	74	5	0.493
8	69	4	0.460
9	65	5	0.433
10	60	3	0.400
11	57	3	0.380
12	54	3	0.360
13	51	2	0.340
14	49	2	0.327
15	47	3	0.313
16	44	2	0.293
17	42	2	0.280
18	40	2	0.267
19	38	3	0.253
20	35	3	0.233
21	32	3	0.213
22	29	3	0.193
23	26	2	0.173
24	24	2	0.160
25	22	2	0.147
26	20	3	0.133
27	17	2	0.113
28	15	2	0.100
29	13	2	0.087
30	11	—	0.073

The bath-tub curve

The bath-tub curve is usually considered to be made up of three distinct parts:

(*a*) the 'infant' or early failure phase, when the failure rate decreases rapidly;

Cumulative distribution function of failure $F(t)$ $(Q_0-Q_t)/Q_0$	Probability density function of failure $f(t)$ $(Q_t -Q_{t+1})/Q_0$	Failure or hazard rate $\lambda(t)$ $(Q_t - Q_{t+1})/Q_t$
0.000	0.180	0.180
0.180	0.093	0.114
0.273	0.067	0.092
0.340	0.053	0.081
0.393	0.047	0.077
0.440	0.040	0.071
0.480	0.027	0.051
0.507	0.033	0.068
0.640	0.027	0.058
0.567	0.033	0.077
0.600	0.020	0.050
0.620	0.020	0.053
0.640	0.020	0.056
0.660	0.013	0.039
0.673	0.013	0.041
0.687	0.020	0.064
0.707	0.013	0.045
0.720	0.013	0.048
0.733	0.013	0.050
0.747	0.020	0.079
0.767	0.020	0.086
0.787	0.020	0.094
0.807	0.020	0.103
0.827	0.013	0.083
0.840	0.013	0.083
0.853	0.013	0.091
0.867	0.020	0.150
0.887	0.013	0.118
0.900	0.013	0.133
0.913	0.013	0.154
0.927	—	—

(*b*) the 'adult' or 'useful life' phase, when the failure rate is almost constant;

(*c*) the 'wear-out' phase, when the failure rate increases.

Clearly, it is desirable that the initial phase should be as short as possible, and to this end manufacturers may 'load' or 'burn-in' their products before sending them to the user, so that the consumer meets the product at the beginning of its 'adult' or 'useful' life. The constant value of the failure rate, which pertains during most of the useful life of the product, is the value usually implied when reference is made to 'the failure rate of the component'. When the failure rate has increased to a value twice that during the constant failure rate period, the 'wear-out' phase is said to start. Knowledge of when this begins is vital if warranty or guarantee periods are to be determined on the basis of the product reliability.

Significance of the constant failure rate
For a constant failure rate λ:

$$\lambda = \lambda_i = -\frac{1}{Q}\frac{dQ}{dt}$$

i.e. $\dfrac{dQ}{Q} = -\lambda dt$

whence $Q = Q_o e^{-\lambda t}$

where Q_o is the initial quantity functioning at the beginning of the adult life.

The ratio Q/Q_o is the *reliability R(t)* of the product and for the useful life phase:

$$R(t) = e^{-\lambda t}$$

During this period the reciprocal of the constant failure rate $1/\lambda$ is known as the *mean time between failures (MTBF)*:

$$\text{MTBF} = \frac{\text{Evaluation time period}}{\text{Number of failures in the time period}}$$

For example, during the time period 10–20 in Table 9.1:

$$\text{MTBF} = \frac{10 \text{ time units}}{25 \text{ failures}} = 0.4 \text{ time unit}$$

and a component can be expected to fail, on average, every 0.4 time units in this phase, i.e. we can expect 2.5 failures every time unit.

Generalized expression for the reliability function
During the 'useful-life' phase, the reliability function is effectively in the 'exponential form', but this does not hold during the early failure and wear-out stages. A more generalized expression due to Weibull may be used for the whole life of the product, when:

$$R(t) = \exp - \left[\frac{t - \gamma}{\alpha}\right]^{\beta}$$

where α is the 'scaling parameter', β is the 'shaping parameter' and γ is the 'locating parameter'. By choosing appropriate values of α, β and γ the whole bath-tub curve may be regarded as a series of Weibull frequency distribution curves where:

$\beta < 1$ during the early failure period
$\beta = 1$ during the useful-life or constant rate period
$\beta > 1$ during the wear-out period

Estimation of the Weibull parameters

The estimation of the three Weibull parameters, α, β, γ, is carried out easily by means of Weibull probability graph paper (such as Chartwell Graph Data Ref. 6572). In order to use this paper, the age at failure must be plotted against the cumulative percentage of failures at that time. The latter is obtained by multiplying by 100 the cumulative distribution function of failure, $F(t)$. For example, a company was considering using a new design of electronically operated thermostats and a sample batch of 40 was installed in a testrig. One factor investigated was the time-to-failure of the devices with the results quoted in Table 9.3.

Table 9.3

Cumulative failures	1	2	3	4	5	6	7	8	9	10	11	12
Cumulative percentage failures	2.5	5	7.5	10	12.5	15	17.5	20	22.5	25	27.5	30
Operating life (days)	19	29	37	45	52	58	64	71	76	82	86	93

The cumulative percentage of failures is readily calculated: since there were 40 thermostats in the sample, one failure is equivalent to $\frac{1}{40} \times 100$ $= 2.5$ per cent; two failures is $\frac{2}{40} \times 100 = 5$ per cent, etc.

This data is plotted on Weibull probability paper in Fig. 9.5 and is found to be a straight line. Now, from the equation for $F(t)$:

$$F(t) = 1 - R(t)$$
$$100F(t) = 100(1 - R(t))$$

and substituting the Weibull equation for $R(t)$:

$$100F(t) = 100 \left(1 - \exp - \left[\frac{t - \gamma}{\alpha} \right]^{\beta} \right)$$

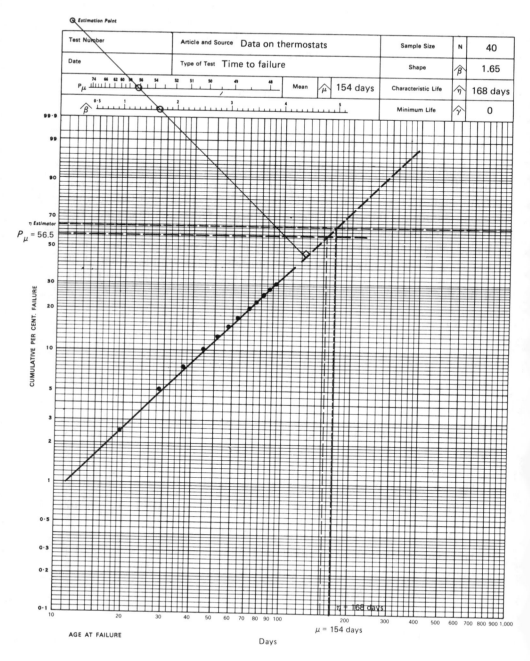

Fig. 9.5 Weibull plot of observed data on thermostats (Table 9.3)

Thus, a plot of $100F(t)$ against $(t - \gamma)$ should give a straight line on the Weibull paper. We have plotted $100F(t)$ against t and, since this gives a straight line,

$$t = t - \gamma, \quad \text{therefore } \gamma = 0$$

Hence, γ, the *locating parameter*, has a value of zero. If γ is not zero, then a straight line will not be obtained.

The *shaping parameter*, β, is found by drawing a perpendicular from the 'estimation point' to the plotted Weibull line. Where this intersects, the β scale gives the estimate of β. In this example, $\beta = 1.65$, indicating that the sample is in the 'wear-out' phase.

In the design of the Chartwell paper, simplification is achieved by replacing the *scaling parameter*, α by the *characteristic life parameter*, η, that is the time at which 63.2 per cent of the units are expected to have failed ($F(t) = 0.632$). This can be shown as follows:

$$\alpha = (\eta - \gamma)$$

Hence, $R(t) = \exp -\left[\dfrac{t - \gamma}{\eta - \gamma} \right]^{\beta}$

When $\gamma = 0$, this reduces to:

$$R(t) = \exp -\left[\frac{t}{\eta} \right]^{\beta}$$

and when $t = \eta$:

$$R(t) = e^{-1} = 0.368 \quad \text{and} \quad F(t) = 0.632$$

The characteristic life parameter, η, is found by reading the age on the horizontal scale at which 63.2 per cent of the items have failed. In this example, the 'η estimator' line gives the characteristic life as 168 days.

A further useful parameter can be obtained from the Weibull plot. The perpendicular from the estimation point to the Weibull plot also intersects a scale labelled P_{μ}. The value of P_{μ} so obtained is the percentage of items which have failed by a time equal to the mean life, μ (or the 'mean time to failure', MTTF). In this example, $P_{\mu} = 56.5$ and from the Weibull plot this indicates that the mean life of the thermostats is 154 days. The MTTF should be the average life of the entire sample, if all units were allowed to go to failure. In the example, the test was terminated after 93 days when only 30 per cent of the units had failed. The excellent straight-line plot allows us to extrapolate to 154 days as the mean life. This will be true only if there is no change in the mode of failure.

Not all failure data is adequately represented by a single Weibull distribution. For example, the data on door locks, given in Table 9.1 and used earlier to illustrate the various reliability curves, can be plotted on Weibull paper. $F(t)$ may be obtained from Table 9.2.

The plot of $100F(t)$, the cumulative percentage failure, against time is shown in Fig. 9.6. The data can be 'fitted' by *two* straight lines, with the 'break' of approximately 19 weeks. The earlier failures have a shape factor, $\beta = 0.65$, indicating that, initially, the units are in a 'burn-in' or infancy stage, with a mean life of 16.0 time units, and a characteristic life of 11.7 time units. The later failures occur when a 'wear-out' failure pattern predominates with $\beta = 1.46$. This portion has a mean life of 13.8 units and characteristic life of 15.5 units. In each case, the scale parameter, γ, or 'minimum life' has a value of zero, since each distribution gives a straight-line plot on the Weibull paper. The interpretation of this data, following the Weibull analysis, is that there is, in fact, no genuine 'useful-life' period. The early failure period is particularly long in this case, continuing until 76 per cent of the population has failed (derived from the intersection of the two straight Weibull lines). This raises the following questions concerning this product:

(*a*) Was it properly designed?
(*b*) Was it produced correctly?
(*c*) Were suitable materials used?
(*d*) Has it been appropriately installed?
(*e*) Is it being used correctly?

The wear-out phase indicates that preventative maintenance may be appropriate in this period (see Chapter 14), but the absence of a useful life suggests a product which will lead to excessive warranty claims and a poor reputation for reliability.

When γ is not zero
As already mentioned, if the locating parameter, γ, is not zero, then a plot of the cumulative percentage failure against the time of failure will not give a straight line. Consider the failure data in Table 9.4 on the performances of standby storage batteries which are used to cover breakdowns in the electrical supply to a unit needing constant power facilities. A batch of 100 were tested at half-hourly intervals.

Table 9.4

Time (hrs)	0.5	1.0	1.5	2.0	2.5	3.0	3.5	4.0	4.5	5.0	5.5	6.0
Number already discharged	22	32	45	59	70	80	88	93	96	98	99	100

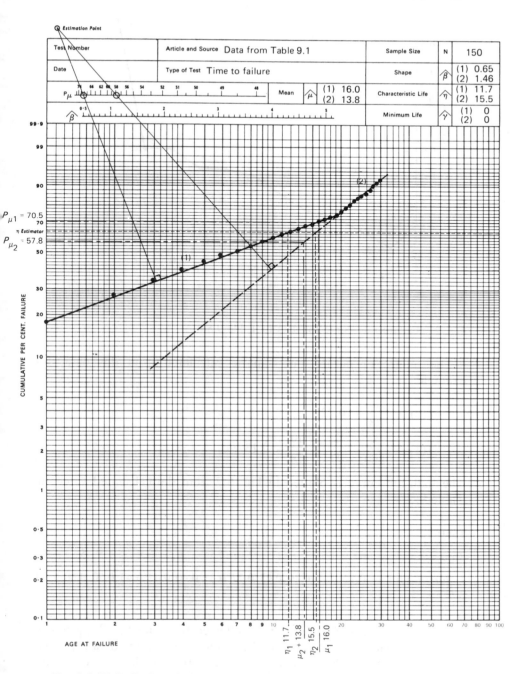

Fig. 9.6 Weibull plot of observed data on door locks (Table 9.2)

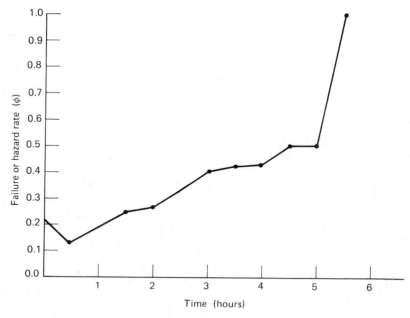

Fig. 9.7 Failure rate curve for data in Table 9.5

The failure or hazard rate can be calculated from this data, for example:

$$\lambda(0) = \frac{22}{100} = 0.22$$

$$\lambda(1) = \frac{32 - 22}{100 - 22} = \frac{10}{78} = 0.13 \text{ etc.}$$

The bath-tub curve is plotted in Fig. 9.7 from the calculated values in Table 9.5.

Table 9.5

Time	0	0.5	1	1.5	2	2.5	3	3.5	4	4.5	5	5.5
Failure/hazard rate λ	0.22	0.13	0.19	0.25	0.27	0.33	0.40	0.42	0.43	0.50	0.50	1.00

It shows an 'early-failure' section followed by a steadily rising 'wear-out' section with no sign of a 'useful-life' phase. When the data is plotted on Weibull probability paper, the line shows a definite curvature (Fig. 9.8). The location parameter, γ, can be estimated as follows:

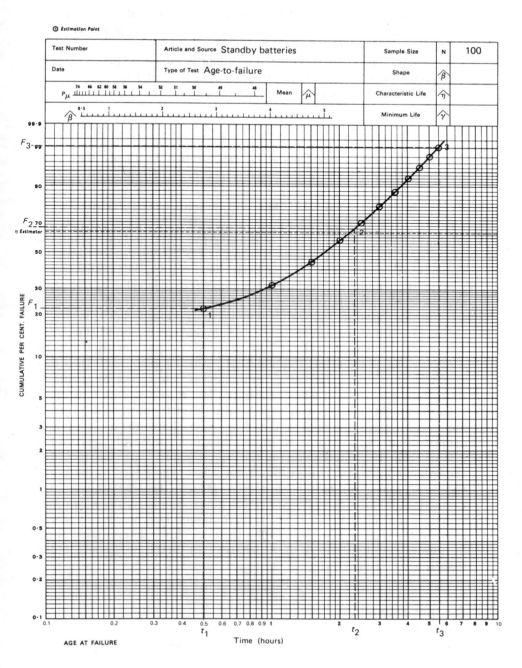

Fig. 9.8 Weibull plot of observed data on storage batteries (Table 9.5)

(*a*) on the initial Weibull plot, draw any three horizontal lines equally spaced on a linear scale, which intercept the data curve at points 1, 2 and 3, such that $(F_3 - F_2) = (F_2 - F_1)$;

(*b*) where these lines cross the Weibull curve, draw perpendiculars to the age-at-failure scale and read the values of t_1, t_2 and t_3;

(*c*) use the following expression to estimate:

$$\gamma = \frac{t_1 t_3 - t_2^2}{t_1 + t_3 - 2t_2}$$

For example, if the three lines are drawn through F_1, F_2, F_3, the corresponding values of t are $t_1 = 0.5$, $t_2 = 2.35$, $t_3 = 5.5$ hours and

$$\gamma = \frac{0.5 \times 5.5 - 2.35^2}{0.5 + 5.5 - 2 \times 2.35} = -2.13 \text{ hours}$$

Due to the inherent inaccuracy of drawing the curve and of reading the t values on the non-linear scale, it is advisable to check the γ value by taking other sets of points. It would thus seem reasonable here to assume a value of c 2 hours for the location parameter γ. The value of γ is negative, indicating an upward or concave curve; a downward or convex curve gives rise to a positive value of γ. The value of γ is now subtracted from the original values of age-at-failure and the data is replotted (Fig. 9.9). The effect of this γ correction is to displace all the parts by (in this case) $+2$ hours, hence the name 'location factor' which is given to γ. The other Weibull parameters may now be estimated as before, not forgetting to restore the γ correction when necessary. The replotted data falls on to a good straight line, showing that a Weibull distributor, with $\gamma = -2$ hours, adequately represents the data. The shape factor β of 2.65 confirms that the batteries are in the 'wear-out' phase of the bath-tub curve. From the intersection of the 'η estimator' with the replotted Weibull curve, $\eta = 4.2$ hours, but 2 hours has been added to the *actual* times to failure, for plotting purposes. Hence, the true value of the characteristic life, η is $(4.2 - 2) = 2.2$ hours. Similarly, the mean time to failure (MTTF, $\hat{\mu}$) is $(3.75 - 2) = 1.75$ hours. One possible interpretation of the data is that the standby batteries suffer deterioration while in storage so that in service they 'behave' as if they were 2 hours 'older' than is actually the case.

System reliability

Systems, *including managerial systems*, can be considered to be of two kinds:

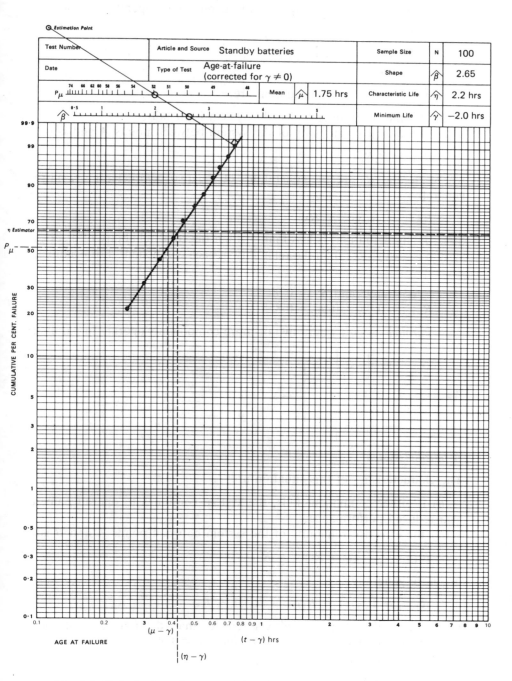

Fig. 9.9 Weibull plot of corrected data in Table 9.5 ($\gamma = -2$)

1. *Series systems* where two or more components operate in series:

A series system

The characteristics of this situation are:

(*a*) if either component fails, the system itself fails;
(*b*) the effective reliability of the system between points *A* and *B* is

$$R_{AB} = R_1 R_2$$

where R_1 and R_2 are the reliabilities of the two components or, more generally:

$$R_{\text{Total}} = R_1 R_2 \ldots R_N$$

Since *R*, by definition, is less than 1, then the total reliability of a series system is always less than the reliability of each component. For example, if:

$$R_1 = 0.95 \text{ and } R_2 = 0.90$$
$$R_{AB} = 0.95 \times 0.90 = 0.855$$

2. *Parallel systems* where two or more components operate in parallel:

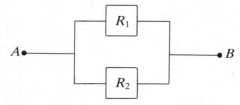

A parallel system

The characteristics of this situation are:

(*a*) if either component fails, the system continues to operate, albeit at a reduced performance;
(*b*) the effective reliability of the system between points *A* and *B* is:

$$R_{AB} = 1 - (1 - R_1)(1 - R_2)$$

or, more generally:

$$R_{\text{Total}} = 1 - (1 - R_1)(1 - R_2)(1 - R_3) \ldots (1 - R_N)$$

Here the total system reliability is *greater* than the reliability of each component. As before, if $R_1 = 0.95$ and $R_2 = 0.90$:

$$R_{AB} = 1 - (1 - 0.95)(1 - 0.90)$$
$$= 0.995$$

In managerial terms, this means that the combined reliability of two control systems acting in parallel is greater than that of either system, and the greater the number of systems, the greater the total reliability. Thus, a cost control and a stock control system acting in parallel will be more effective than either system acting singly.

A final word

Reliability, like all other properties of products and services, will not just happen: it must be designed and built in using systematic methods and techniques. These include establishing a quantified reliability specification, techniques for failure prediction, testing, data collection and analysis. Reliability can be influenced by everyone involved in the producing organization from marketing right through to delivery and after-sales service, and those outside it concerned with the supply of goods and services.

The authors are grateful for the contribution made by J. Geoff Marsland during the writing of this chapter.

Recommended reading

Basu, A. P., *Reliability and Quality Control*, Elsevier, 1986.
  Covers the general principles of quality/reliability, showing the relationship between them and how managerial activity affects both.
Dhillon, Balbir S. and Reiche, Hans, *Reliability and Maintainability Management*, Van Nostrand Reinhold, 1985.
  288 pages of reasonably straightforward advice on the managerial aspects of reliability. Well illustrated.
Lloyd, D. K. and Lipow, M., *Reliability: Management, Methods and Mathmatics*, 2nd edn, American Society of Quality Control, 1985.
  At times a mathematical approach, but it does give a clear indication of the methods required to manage reliability.
Smith, David J., *Reliability and Maintainability in Perspective*, Macmillan, 1985.
  Practical, contractual, commercial and software aspects of reliability covered in detail.

10 Design of the product

Nowhere is there more confusion in terminology than in the field of design, development or research. In order that in this volume some degree of clarification is achieved, the following working definitions are offered and will be used throughout the present text:

1. *Research:* the discovery of novel techniques, ideas, information or systems. Thus, market research is certainly part of research as here defined.

2. *Development:* the improvement of existing techniques, ideas or systems.

3. *Design:* the translation of requirements into a form suitable for production or use. It may include re-design to cater for ease of production or changes in specification.

Accepting the above definitions, it will be seen that design may encompass both research and development. Both of these are creative activities, both, to quote J K Page, '. . . the imaginative jump from present facts to future possibilities', and hence not easy to discuss. The difficulties are so great, and in some cases the personnel concerned so unworldly, that often no attempt is made to control them. This is a policy of despair and, while it must be accepted that tight control is impossible, some attempt must be made to provide guidance—particularly as the size, cost and technological complexity of many of today's new products, whether artefacts, services or systems, are so great that disaster can result if control is lacking. It should be noted that in other creative activities in industry, for example, work study, tool design or management consultancy, close control is accepted as normal.

Responsibility for design

The design function sits between the marketing and the operations functions. Its purpose is essentially to take the needs of the market, as determined by the marketing department, and translate them into such a form that they can be satisfied within the operating unit.

It is clear that the decisions taken during the design stage can have significant and very long-term effects upon the whole organization. A badly designed coat, for example, will never sell however well it is made; a poorly designed questionnaire which asks the wrong questions will never elicit the right information *however well it is presented and distributed*; an 'extravagant' design will involve costs which can never be recovered in the market place. The importance of the design function can hardly be over-estimated, and its organizational location is not easily defined. Three locations are commonly found:

1. *Within the marketing department.* The argument here is that the marketing department is the only source of complete knowledge concerning the needs of a customer. This argument probably holds true for products which involve extremely high technology, for example, electronic equipment, or for products which are dependent on an extremely variable market such as ladies' high-fashion goods. It may also hold good for products designed to a customer's specification since the marketing department should effectively be the customer's representative within the organization.

2. *Within the operations department.* The argument here is that, providing an accurate and comprehensive specification has been laid down by the marketing department, it is essential that it should be executed as rapidly and economically as possible and therefore the organizational links between design and operations should be as tight as possible. Situations where this sort of organization functions satisfactorily are those where the products are standardized, requiring only minimum modification to make them acceptable to the customer. Such products might well be components which are used within larger assemblies.

3. *As an independent unit*, directly responsible to the board. The advantages of independence are clear: the designers are not inhibited either by marketing or operations and can therefore produce the most effective design. This situation probably holds best where products are genuinely in advance of the market. This sort of design function may very well provide the stimulus for the marketing department to 'create a market'.

It is not possible to state which of the above locations is the most satisfactory—as with all organizational problems, the design/structure must be made on the basis of the detailed requirements of each organization. One thing, however, is clear: close liaison must be maintained at all times between the design, marketing and operational functions.

Five stages of a design project

In every project the design programme will pass through the following stages:

1. *Conception*, when a draft specification is laid down incorporating the user requirements.

2. *Acceptance*, where the specification is shown to be achievable by mathematical calculation, preliminary drawings, 'bread-board' or 'mock-up' models or laboratory-scale processes. It is here that the trade-offs between requirements and achievability are made explicit *and resolved*.

3. *Execution*, where a number of models are prepared from the work above, or pilot plants are made up following the laboratory-scale experiments.

4. *Translation*, where the project is put into such a form that it can be made within the organization, and to the specification laid down at stage 2.

5. *Pre-operational*, where quantities are produced sufficient to check the design, equipment and specification. It is not until this stage that drawings or specifications can be 'frozen', that is, considered to be final and not liable to change without authorization.

The above five steps are always present in some form, although in small organizations they may be telescoped, while in very small quantity operation pre-operational models very often coincide with the first, possibly with the only product. In projects where large articles—boilers, power plants—are being designed, the last three stages effectively coalesce with the actual production stage. It must be remembered that the decisions taken at each stage are never taken in isolation: they all affect, in some degree, previous and succeeding stages and the activities of the marketing and operations functions (Fig. 10.1). To adapt Donne: 'No designer is an Island, entire of itself: every designer is a piece of a Continent, a part of the Main.' Once a design is complete, steps must be taken to maintain it, or to amend it *formally*.

Conception

This first stage is most important in providing the basis for control of all subsequent design activity. A specification must be drawn up in as much detail as possible by the marketing department in discussion with the design department. Where highly technical and capital goods are concerned, discussions are often on an 'engineer-to-engineer' basis, as the technical requirements and consequences may be extremely taxing.

Time spent here will not only indicate to the designers exactly what is required, it will enable the marketing department to discuss the project

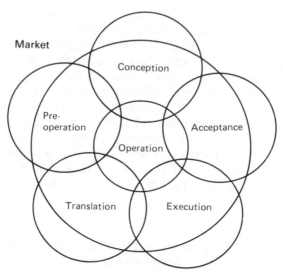

Fig. 10.1 The interaction of the five stages of design with marketing and operations

with actual or potential customers, and it will enable some measure of the cost of changes in requirement upon the design effort to be made and charged to the appropriate source. In effect, this is a translation of a marketing requirement into terms intelligible to the designer.

The following minimum information should be given on a design specification:

1. The technical or performance requirements, including explicit statements on quality and reliability.
2. The appearance or 'styling' requirements.
3. The intended selling price or operational cost. This can often only be in the form: 'Price not to exceed . . .'
4. The date when output, that is 'product' must be available.
5. The probable quantity that will be required. This quantity can substantially affect the design and, as a consequence, the first cost.
6. The maximum cost of designing which can be accepted, since the final product must bear the cost of the design.
7. Information concerning any special safety, legal or quality features required by current legislation.

Acceptance

This is essentially a 'back-room' function carried out in the design department by designers and their associates. It is usually the first stage where costs for the design work will be assigned directly to the project, and is normally initiated by a formal instruction embodying the draft specification laid down at conception. The draft specification is tested, being subjected to calculation, model-making or such other activity as is appropriate, and is then accepted, rejected as impracticable, or modified in conjunction with the marketing department. Sometimes, particularly in simple projects, this stage will coincide with the previous one, and may consist of only a meeting between all interested parties. At this stage it is particularly important for the designer to know the capability of the operating unit which will carry out the final design. Formal and frequent consultation between design and operations here and in all later stages can save much trouble and cost when producing 'the product'.

Execution

A working model (or series of models) is made based on the ideas thrown up at stage 2 and on general design considerations, both theoretical and practical. The models should as far as possible conform to the specification; where this is not possible, the differences should be known and their effects considered. The differences usually arise either from the scale of the problem (for example, an oil refinery) or from the need for special parts whose cost cannot be justified until the design is finalized. While cost considerations must not be overlooked, the technical and appearance requirements are most important at this stage, and the models made should indicate clearly the feasibility of the proposed design meeting the specification at all points. The cost of the final product is a matter which must be accepted by the design department as a factor as important as any other, although subsequent technical development can often produce significant reductions in cost.

Translation

At this stage the appropriate operations and after-sales service departments must be involved in the design work. It is quite common practice for the teams responsible for the original work and for the model to hand over their task to a development team which, while appreciating the originality of the design, can also appreciate the problems involved in its execution. This development team should discuss at all stages the operating problems with the appropriate departments. Detailed estimates will begin to be formed, and it will be possible to assign maximum acceptable costs to the various components. The question 'This part must not cost more than . . . Can it be made for this? If not, how should it be redesigned?' must be asked at all times. Lack of co-operation at this time between designers and the operating department will prove very costly;

the design finally placed upon the operating unit will be difficult to produce, and emergency re-designs carried out 'on the floor' will result in a debasing of the product. Too often a sense of economy on the part of the management, or of aloofness on the part of the designer, has resulted in this stage being omitted or made vestigial; in every case, an inferior product has eventually been sold.

Work will also be proceeding on preparing the final operating information, this information summarizing all the design and development effort. Control of the amount of work put into drawing up this information is both important and difficult, and it must be remembered that the information is intended to aid operation, and not be an end in itself.

Pre-operation

Once all the foregoing has been completed, it is desirable, particularly in high-volume productions, to carry out a pilot run or test marketing under normal operating conditions. In addition, tests to the customer specification should be carried out again under normal operating conditions. Both tasks should be done at some time before the start of delivery in order that any faults or weaknesses which are shown up can be corrected. Such a pre-operation run will check:

(*a*) operational information;
(*b*) operational resources;
(*c*) operational techniques and estimates;
(*d*) specifications;

and only after such a run should the operational information be considered to be final.

The above outline of the processes of designing for satisfying the customer is an attempt to separate out the various stages of a creative act. In small organizations, one person might well carry out two or more of the above tasks and, indeed, it may then be impossible to analyse the work done. Nevertheless, it is suggested that some process similar to the above must be carried out whenever design is necessary.

The control of a design project

As pointed out above, it is not possible to exert the same tight control on design effort as on operational effort, yet the cost involved and the time used are often substantial and both must appear somewhere within the organization's budget. Design must never be a task undertaken 'for its own sake'. The following points are worth considering:

1. No design will ever be 'complete' in the sense that, with effort, some modification (improvement?) can always be made.

2. Few designs are entirely novel. An examination of a 'new' product will almost certainly show that it largely employs existing techniques, components or systems to which have been added a comparatively small novel element. Figures are difficult to obtain here, but the author believes that in most 'new' products the 'novel' design work rarely exceeds 10 per cent of the total design work, the rest being modifications to existing material. The effort which must go into these modifications is likely to be reasonably predictable.

3. There appears to be a 'law of diminishing returns' on design effort. The longer the time which is spent on a design, the less the increase in the value of the design unless a technological breakthrough is achieved.

4. External and/or internal circumstances will impose limitations on design time and cost. It is as difficult to imagine a design project whose completion date is not implicitly fixed, either by a promise to a customer, the opening of a trade show or exhibition, a seasonal 'dead-line', a production schedule or some other constraint, as it is to imagine an organization whose funds are unlimited, or a product whose price has no ceiling.

The use of critical path analysis in design

The most effective tool for the control of design is critical path analysis. This will exert a discipline and enforce a degree of pre-planning upon the design effort which is invaluable. It will ensure that the sequence in which design tasks are undertaken is determined by need rather than by interest, and it will enable the supervisor concerned to compare the progress made with that planned.

A common difficulty in using CPA in design tasks is the belief that it is not possible to assign duration times to design activities. When dealing with this problem, the following steps are useful:

1. Determine the design specification as accurately and in as much detail as possible.

2. Involve the people concerned in the drawing of the network. (It will be found that the logical basis of CPA is appealing to most designers.)

3. Establish any fixed dates. If a fixed completion date is not available, agree a reasonable one.

4. Assign duration times on non-contentious activities.

5. Break contentious activities into smaller parts, on some of which times can be readily agreed since past experience can be a guide.

6. Examine the remaining activities to see whether there are any historical precedents. If not, then assign to them as much time as possible without over-running the fixed completion date. It is then possible to pose the question, 'There are Y units of time in which to design X—is this possible?' which is often found to be more stimulating than the question 'How long will it take to design X?' If at this stage the designer will not, or cannot, accept the available time, then either the logic or the resources must be changed, or a re-negotiation of the completion date must take place.

Once a network has been completed and analysed it must be used as a control device, otherwise much of its potential value will not be realized. This is probably done most simply by holding a regular meeting at which all those concerned report on progress. This meeting should be a progress meeting, not a design meeting to which problems are brought for solutions. Problem-solving is best treated separately. It will be found that the effectiveness of this meeting will depend almost entirely upon the manner in which it is run. A tradition of the accepting of the discipline of time is an invaluable asset to the design department.

Many design offices undertake a number of projects simultaneously, and the problem of sharing limited resources among these projects is an important one. Here it is probably simplest to draw a network for each project, to translate each of these into bar charts and to superimpose the various bar charts upon each other. From this superimposition it will be possible to read off the total resources of any type required at any time and, if this exceeds the resources available, then some float manipulation must take place. It must be remembered that the more float is absorbed by resource allocation, the more critical the project becomes, and the effect of over-running of time becomes more serious. Float represents flexibility.

Project cost control

An estimated cost for design should be one of the figures submitted at the design acceptance stage. It must be recognized, however, that the calculation of this cost is not easy, and no general recommendations can be made since different situations will require entirely different systems. Thus, a design office set up to deal with one special project will need to be controlled more carefully, and in more detail, than a department which undertakes all the design tasks within a consumer-product/service company, and both need different treatment from a design office which exists to produce designs for other organizations to use.

The purpose of the costing system must be clearly established before any system is installed. Essentially the purpose must be to enable the design manager to manage; to extract figures 'because they would be interesting' is expensive and valueless. As with any other situation, detail should be minimized.

In setting up an estimate and subsequently using it for control, it must be remembered that labour costs are derived from labour times, so that if times are controlled, the derived costs are also controlled. This means that using a network to control times will automatically control labour costs—and in design projects it is these labour costs which generally form by far the largest portion of the total costs. Consumable items are best dealt with as burden spread over all projects and included in the on-costs assigned to direct labour costs, leaving the design manager to control these as items appearing on his budgetary control returns. Special items, purchased solely to meet the needs of particular tasks must, of course, be assigned to those tasks, as must the use of expensive equipment.

Reducing design costs

Buying design effort

Design effort is expensive; a qualified designer not only has a high basic pay but may attract considerable support staff and sometimes heavy capital equipment. It is frequently possible to avoid the heavy fixed costs of permanent staff by purchasing design effort. There are a number of sources:

1. *Research associations*: at the moment there are at least 42 of these in the UK covering most industries. Their income is partly derived from government grants and partly from members' subscriptions. They offer information services, bulletins, and research/development facilities.

2. *Government research stations*: these can often undertake development work for companies.

3. *Educational establishments*: within the technical colleges, polytechnics and universities there are substantial resources which can be tapped. Staff will sometimes undertake work at very low cost if it is academically interesting and capable of being published, or they will act as consultants charging a normal consultant's fee. Most academic and learned societies have extensive libraries which can be used at negligible cost.

4. *Private design companies*: there are an increasing number of commercial design research companies which undertake fee-paid assignments. These include 'industrial designers', and though most have specialist training and ability in aesthetics, they will frequently bring to a task a fresh and uninhibited attack on function and cost. It is foolish

to introduce an industrial designer to a product when all the 'real' design is complete and expect him to carry out some painless cosmetic surgery. The industrial designer should be involved in a design project from its inception. Frequently, the fee required by a commercial designer appears high, but it must be remembered that it does not involve the user company in the heavy fixed expense of employing his own staff.

5. *Licences to manufacture*: it is often possible to buy the results of other companies' efforts by negotiating licences to manufacture new products. This is most commonly done with companies in other countries, and it should be remembered that conditions may be different in those countries, and that there will usually be a need to ensure that any drawings, specifications and methods are appropriate to the licensee.

Use of a computer

The tremendous speed and vast storage capacity of a computer aid the designer in a number of ways:

1. Frequently-repeated, and long, tedious calculations can be carried out rapidly. Without a computer a designer will reduce the need for calculations by using tables or graphs of 'established standards' or 'good practice'. These, to become manageable, are the abbreviated results either of a few calculations or of a series of trials, and in either case contain ample 'safety' factors which usually over-compensate for the inadequacies of the calculations. As a result, the design produced may be unnecessarily costly in some way. The computer enables these calculations to be carried out as and when needed, reducing wasted effort.

2. A library of 'ready-made' designs can be easily stored in and retrieved from a computer.

3. Some calculations are so lengthy that they cannot be carried out by hand. A computer may perform these if appropriate software is available.

4. A lengthy calculation by hand will produce an acceptable result, but the effort of examining the effect of changing one or other of the constituent parameters may be so great that no such examination is made. This may result in accepting a result which could be modified. Again, the computer's abilities could be used to check the effect of modification.

5. Quantities of data can be held in the computer's store and withdrawn with such ease that it becomes possible to refer readily to previous designs, experience, data.

6. Computer graphics may well permit a visual display of a design under various conditions, so that the effects of, say, bending can be immediately observed.

7. The computer can store the results of the design process and issue it in a useful form, often obviating the need for the preparation of drawings.

Specialization by designers

Concentration upon a limited field allows a designer to build up a body of knowledge which will permit him to answer questions within that field very much more rapidly than if his interests ranged over a wide area. This again does not produce stagnation, since the concentration brings with it a deepening knowledge and a more fundamental understanding of the problems within that field of limited study. This is generally recognized so that there are now no individual designers responsible for, say, the complete design of an aeroplane; there are design teams, each member of which specializes upon a few aspects.

Families of products

When designing a product, it is frequently possible to do so in such a way that it can be scaled up or down as need arises. A firm which organizes conferences is likely to have a basic conference design which can be enlarged or reduced as required.

Use of sound classification and coding system

The fewer the designs, the greater the productivity of the design office. It is frequently found that something will be designed which could be identical to or is replaceable by an existing item. This wastes not only design effort but all subsequent effort. Often minor modifications to an existing item will render it useful for a number of functions other than that for which it was first designed. At first this might appear to impose restrictions upon the designer which might inhibit his creative ability, yet in fact it will release him from the drudgery of detailed designing. No designer calls for special screws, nuts, wire diameters, sheet metal thicknesses—standardization is accepted here—yet the variety of products which can be made from these items is infinite. While computer search techniques are available, a sound classification and coding system is invaluable (see Chapter 5).

Use of library and technical information service

Considerable savings in time and money can often be effected within a project by reference to published information. This is true of all departments including research or development, but it is usual to house all technical sources, standards and codes of practice within one area which forms part of the design department.

In its simplest form, a library consists merely of a passive collection of books, but it should play a very positive function by being an information department from which information can be requested. A librarian trained in searching and abstracting can rapidly and cheaply produce information from which problems can be solved or new developments advanced. With the present enormous flood of technical information being published each day, no scientist, technologist or manager can hope to be up to date with his subject except in a very narrow field. The librarian, by discriminating and abstracting, can assist by limiting any field of inquiry to that of immediate interest.

Within a small company it is probably more effective to employ an information officer than to start a library. The information officer would rapidly build up the comparatively small volume of essential reference books and would be able, by collaborating with local municipal libraries, national libraries, professional institutions and research associations, and the excellent lending libraries, to provide quickly any reference book needed. He would also be able to abstract appropriate journals and circularize bulletins of information to all who require them. This would enable the engineers and designers to assess their need for the journal and save much wasted time in examining articles of no interest to them. Of course, journals should be available for inspection, as 'browsing' can be a very effective method of cross-fertilization. The various makers' catalogues and data sheets can also be housed in the library rather than in the buyer's office. These will be readily accessible to all, and should be kept up to date as a matter of course. The collection of such catalogues by the librarian or information officer rather than by the more directly interested persons has the practical advantage that designers, for example, are insulated from the enthusiastic representatives of firms who will call upon the request for a catalogue. Requests from librarians are not usually followed up so vigorously by personal calls.

Properly organized, controlled and supported by management, an information department can be a tool as useful to a designer as a calculator. Regrettably, it is found all too infrequently, and expensive effort has often gone to waste carrying out work which has already been published and completed. It has been estimated that up to 30 per cent of the cost of a development project can be saved by an effective information department, and the savings in time can be equally great.

1. Buying-in design effort — getting dev done elsewhere
2. Computer-aided design — CAD
3. Specialization by designers — specialist fields
4. Families of products — large/small version
5. Classification and coding
6. Library

The drawing office

Where information is conveyed to the operating unit by drawings, the drawing office is an essential part of the design department. In some industries, drawings may be replaced by product specifications or by process layouts, but *throughout the following section the word 'drawing' will be used to indicate any device from which operating information is derived.*

The authority for publishing and amending finalized drawings must be vested in one department only, which must also be responsible for ensuring that all drawings held by that department are up to date and represent current practice in that organization. Drawings should contain all the information necessary for the production of the article concerned, either explicitly or by reference to published standards, specifications or codes of practice.

No drawing should be issued which has not been checked by some authorized person, since a drawing error, even though apparently trivial, can have a profound effect upon production. Some organizations require not only that the drawing be checked before issue but that it should be authorized by the designer responsible for the whole project. If this is done, care must be taken to avoid any very great reliance on the value of this 'authorizing' signature, because in a complex project the signature becomes a purely automatic device since the authorizer has no time to check each drawing personally.

Drawings once issued may be found to be required to be modified or changed. It may appear that should any member of the organization wish to change a drawing he should have freedom to demand that the change be made. However, it will be found that this freedom will permit changes to be made either irresponsibly or without a realization of the full implications. For example, a change on one small component may render the complete stock of mating components obsolete, or a change permitting easier assembly may require re-tooling, the cost of which far outweighs the saving in assembly cost.

Change system

To control changes (or modifications) to drawings, a formalized change system is usually necessary. This can take a form similar to the following:

1. A change proposal is raised by any interested person but, to avoid any changes of a frivolous nature, this should be countersigned by the appropriate departmental supervisor. This proposal should state:
   (*a*) drawing concerned;
   (*b*) change required;

(*c*) reason for the change;

(*d*) degree of urgency—that is, whether 'retrospective', 'immediate', 'as convenient' or 'as from . . . date'.

2. Comments on this proposal must be made by departments concerned. Thus, the production control department might comment on the stock situation and the cost of scrapping that stock; the work study department would discuss the changes in method; the buyer, the availability of the new materials, and so on.

3. Acceptance is given by a committee sitting to consider all the changes and the comments arising from them.

4. A change note is originated if the change proposal is accepted, and this note is published generally, being used by the drawing office as an authority to change the drawing concerned. The drawing itself will be changed; a note of the date of the change and a brief description of it made on the drawing; and a new drawing issued, the number of the issue also being recorded. Ideally, all old drawings should be withdrawn and destroyed, but it is found in fact that this is very difficult to do, and in practice new drawings are issued to departments with a request (frequently pious) that all old ones be destroyed.

Once a change system is in effect, it must be clearly understood that no person has the right to change a drawing without recourse to a change proposal. At the design stage this can often be a considerable hindrance, and drawings are often assumed to be free from the change system until they are 'frozen' at the completion of the 'consolidation' stage. Before drawings are so frozen it is unwise to engage in any substantial expenditure or action derived from them, and often drawings are not published until they are frozen. Should preliminary drawings be required, for example for estimating purposes, they are best issued suitably marked across their face FOR ESTIMATE ONLY or some other appropriate wording.

Recommended reading

Anderson, N. G., *From Concept to Production: a Management Approach*, Taylor and Francis Ltd, 1975.

  While this is a little dated in that it cannot deal with modern computer usage, it is a valuable practical book. Contains a wealth of detail. A book for the engineer.

Lorenz, C., *The Design Dimension: Product Strategy and the Challenge of Global Marketing*, Basil Blackwell Ltd, 1986.

  Deals with the impact of good design upon competitiveness. Very well illustrated by case studies. Well worth reading as a stimulant.

Section III **The plant**

11 Location and design of the plant

The supply-distribution system

One of the key features of a transformation system is the efficiency with which the output is transferred to the recipients. Any consideration of this will include the determination of where to place the plant or production facility, and how much transportation of the inputs and outputs will be required. The way in which the inputs are obtained and the outputs distributed has an effect on the:

   (a) total cost of the product or service;
   (b) number of customers that can be reached;
   (c) location of the organization and its units;
   (d) design of the plant.

An efficient supply–distribution system will reduce costs and lead to a more effective service in the form of quicker deliveries and less stock-outs. The type of output involved is clearly a major factor in the determination of the best distribution system. The plant producing artefacts can be located near to the consumer, or such that products must be transported. Services, such as those provided by hotels, golf courses, churches, schools, hospitals and hair salons, are either expensive, difficult or even impossible to transport and these organizations usually perform the service in the recipients' vicinity. There are other examples of services of such rarity, fame or excellence that consumers transport themselves to the location of the facility, e.g. Disneyland, London and New York theatres and the Mayo Clinic in Switzerland.

The supply, receipt, storage and movement of materials, people, equipment and finished goods or services affects not only the number and location of units to be established, but also the design of the transformation facilities. All the potentially available plant must be considered as part of the whole supply–distribution system to devise the best strategy for obtaining the right inputs and desired outputs. Plant flexibility, efficiency, effectiveness, capacity, lead times, and so on, will be determined by plant design, and constantly changing environments may require repeated re-designs if forecasting methods do not allow the establishment of stable plant for the foreseeable future. The advancements in computers and robotics, the shortages of certain materials and energy sources also must be carefully examined by the operations management team engaged in plant location and design.

Choice of location

It is difficult to set down rules whereby the problem of plant location can be programmed but there are a number of factors which should be considered. It is worth differentiating between the problems of *location* and of *site*: the *location* is the general area, and the *site* is the place chosen within the location. The decision on siting thus probably proceeds in two stages: in the first, the general area is chosen; and then a detailed survey of that area is carried out to find possible sites. The final decision is then probably made by taking into account more detailed requirements.

The following are some of the factors which will influence the choice of location:

1. *Proximity to market*
Organizations may choose to locate facilities close to their market, not merely to minimize transportation costs, but to provide a better service. The closer the plant or facilities are to the consumer, the easier it is to provide just-in-time delivery, to respond to changes in demand and to react to field or service problems. The choice of market proximity is clearly restricted for those providing a pure service, which is not easily transported.

2. *Integration with other parts of the organization*
If the new plant or facility is one of a number owned or operated by a single organization or group, it should be so situated that its work can be integrated with that of the associated units. This will require that the group should be considered as an entity, not as a number of independent units.

3. *Availability of labour and skills*
Labour may be more readily available in some cases than in others. Certain geographical areas have traditional skills but it is very rare that a location can be found which has appropriately skilled and unskilled labour, both readily available, in the desired proportions or quantities. The choice often has to be made between a location where skilled people exist but are not readily available, and one where there is a supply of unskilled labour. Of course, new skills can be taught, processes simplified and/or made less exacting, and key personnel moved.

4. *Availability of amenities*
A location which provides good external amenities—housing, shops, community services, communication systems—is often more attractive than one which is more remote. One important amenity in this connection is good *personnel* transport—buses and trains—and some companies find this so vital that they provide special company transport facilities.

5. *Availability of transport*
It is important that good transport facilities are readily available. There are five basic modes of physical transportation: air, road, rail, water and pipeline. Goods intended largely for export may indicate a location near a seaport or a large airport, but the choice of transport method and, therefore, location will clearly depend on relative costs, convenience and suitability.

6. *Availability of inputs*
Good transport facilities will enable goods and services to be obtained and delivered readily, but a location near main suppliers will help to reduce cost and permit staff to easily meet suppliers to discuss quality, technical or delivery problems. Any purchaser who has tried to improve the delivery performance of an inaccessible supplier will bear witness to the considerable difficulties involved. Important supplies that are expensive or difficult to obtain by transport should be readily available in the locality.

7. *Availability of services*
There are five main services which need to be considered:

(*a*) gas;
(*b*) electricity;
(*c*) water;
(*d*) drainage;
(*e*) disposal of waste.

Certain industries use considerable quantities of water, e.g. food preparation, laundries, chemicals, metal plating, etc.; others use a great deal of electricity, e.g. steel and smelting processes. An assessment must be made of the requirements for these, for as far ahead as possible. Underestimating the needs of any of the services can prove to be extremely costly and inconvenient.

8. *Suitability of land and climate*
The geology of the area needs to be considered, together with the climatic conditions (humidity, temperature and atmosphere). Modern building techniques are such that almost all disadvantages of terrain and

climate can be overcome, but the cost of so doing may be high and a different locality could avoid these initial costs.

9. *Regional regulations*
It is important to check at an early stage that the proposed location does not infringe any local regulations. A study must be made of the appropriate by-laws and of any special regulations concerning the disposal of effluents, hiring, etc.

10. *Room for expansion*
It is most unwise to build to the limit of any site unless the long-range forecast indicates very definitely that the initial building will never be required to increase in size. This is a most unlikely circumstance and adequate room for genuine expansion should be allowed.

11. *Safety requirements*
Some production units may present, or may be believed to present, potential dangers to the surrounding neighbourhood; for example, nuclear power stations, chemical and explosives factories are often considered dangerous. Location of such plants in remote areas may be desirable.

12. *Site cost*
As a first charge, the site cost is important, although it is necessary to prevent immediate benefit jeopardizing long-term plans.

13. *Political, cultural and economic situation*
The political situation in potential locations should be considered. Even if other considerations demand a particular site, knowledge of the political, cultural (e.g. restriction of women or foreign workers) and local prejudice or economic difficulties can assist in taking decisions.

14. *Special grants, regional taxes and import/export barriers*
Certain government and local authorities often offer special grants, low-interest loans, low rental or taxes and other inducements in the hope of attracting industry to particular locations. As these are often areas with large reservoirs of labour or natural resources, such offers can be most attractive. Location of factories in foreign countries to avoid exportation difficulties is now well accepted, and certain Japanese companies have used this method successfully throughout the world.

1. Proximity to market
2. Integration with the organization
3. Availability of labour and skills
4. Availability of amenities
5. Availability of transport
6. Availability of inputs
7. Availability of services
8. Suitability of land and climate
9. Regional regulations
10. Room for expansion
11. Safety requirements
12. Site cost
13. Political, cultural and economic situation
14. Special grants, regional taxes and import/export barriers

Factors influencing the choice of location

Plant location evaluation methods

In most location problems there are some 'mandatory' factors which must be fulfilled. Thus, an oil refinery *must* have excellent main services, in particular fresh water. Once these key factors are identified, the location problem ceases to be open and becomes a choice from a number of sites. Here, an *evaluation* technique, based on ranking the various weighted factors, can be helpful. There are a number of methods, but the principles are similar:

1. Examine the various factors and assign to them weights representing their importance to the situation being changed. The least important factor may be given a weighting of 1 and all other factors then expressed as multiples of this, as whole numbers. It may be that a rather coarse scale is produced, but time should not be wasted striving after unnecessary accuracy and precision; a crude indicator is all that is required.
2. Each of the locations is examined and 'ranked' for each factor, this ranking being carried out factor by factor, not location by location.
3. Each ranking is then multiplied by the appropriate weighting factor and the scores totalled for each possible location. These totals indicate the desirability of the possible locations compared with each other.

The results *for a hypothetical case* are shown in Fig. 11.1. The matrix form is convenient: the rank is placed in the left-hand side of the cell, above the diagonal, while the result of multiplying the ranking by the weight is placed in the right-hand side, below the diagonal. The total score is the sum of these right-hand entries.

Factor	Weight	Possible location				
		A	B	C	D	E
Proximity	6	3 / 18	3 / 18	2 / 12	5 / 30	1 / 6
Integration	0	— / 0	— / 0	— / 0	— / 0	0
Labour	9	1 / 9	5 / 45	4 / 36	2 / 18	3 / 27
Amenities	6	1 / 6	2 / 12	4 / 24	5 / 30	3 / 18
Transport	4	5 / 20	4 / 16	3 / 12	2 / 8	1 / 4
Inputs	4	4 / 16	1 / 4	2 / 8	3 / 12	5 / 20
Services	5	1 / 5	2 / 10	2 / 10	5 / 25	4 / 20
Land and climate	2	4 / 8	2 / 4	5 / 10	3 / 6	1 / 2
Regional regulations	8	5 / 40	2 / 16	4 / 32	3 / 24	1 / 8
Expansion	2	3 / 6	4 / 8	2 / 4	5 / 10	1 / 2
Safety	0	— / 0	— / 0	— / 0	— / 0	— / 0
Cost	1	5 / 5	1 / 1	2 / 2	3 / 3	4 / 4
Politics/ culture	0	— / 0	— / 0	— / 0	— / 0	— / 0
Special grants etc.	2	2 / 4	1 / 2	5 / 10	4 / 8	3 / 6
TOTALS		137	136	160	174	117

Fig. 11.1 Assessment of possible plant location

Note: It must be emphasized that this is a hypothetical example: the weights assigned to each factor must not be taken to be recommendations of any kind.

Linear programming in plant location

The problem of selecting a location is characterized by numerous factors with complex interrelationships, which can be evaluated only qualitatively. Moreover, the information required to make the decisions is often incomplete and the prediction of future conditions difficult. Various techniques developed to solve parts of the total problem include linear programming, and heuristic and simulation models based on a particular aim, such as minimizing transport costs.

Linear programming (LP) may be helpful after an initial screening phase has narrowed down the feasible alternative sites to a small number. The remaining candidates are then evaluated, one at a time, to identify the one that provides the best overall system performance. Most frequently, overall transportation cost is the criterion used for performance evaluation. A special type of linear programming called the *transportation method* (see Chapter 32) has been found to be useful in plant location. The most common example of this type of problem is that where a plant or facility 'feeds' a number of units or warehouses—or, inversely, where a producing unit is 'fed' from a number of sources—and the site location must be chosen to give a minimum total transportation cost. If the cost of transportation is directly proportional, both to the distance travelled and the number of units, then mathematical equations can be produced relating the total cost to the number of 'units' transported to/from each source and to the distance between the 'feeder' and the 'fed'. The equations may then be solved to give the location which will minimize total transport costs, and this location is then accepted as the recommended site for the plant. In any but the most trivial of examples, the manipulations are tedious to perform manually and a computer is generally used for this purpose. Many standard programs are available and readily adaptable to specific situations.

Computerized planning of location and distribution

Plant location and transport or distribution decisions are obviously very interdependent, and for large companies, supplying many products from multi-site locations to thousands of customers, the problems are staggering in their complexity. The most effective planning systems are those that tackle the complete location and distribution problem. Owing to recent technological advances, the use of micro-processors, computers and containerization, comprehensive computerized planning and distribution systems are available to aid production/operations managers determine the following factors related to distribution centres:

(a) number;
(b) location;
(c) size;
(d) allocation by customers;
(e) allocation by manufacturing or supply centres;
(f) quantities involved;
(g) modes of transport.

Other questions (e.g. what savings will be derived from improving the system?) should also be answered. To determine these answers and factors, large quantities of data are required to be obtained and manipulated and this will require considerable effort. The benefits of a good system are, however, so great that the effort is worth while.

One of the most powerful applications of computerized location and distribution planning systems is the simulation of the potential changes in the environment and policies, controllable or otherwise, and the study of their effects. This provides information for the decision-maker about the combinatorial effects of changes in such fundamental matters as the:

(a) market and demand structure;
(b) plant capacity (expansion and contraction);
(c) products and product mix;
(d) prices;
(e) material costs;
(f) fuel or energy availability and costs;
(g) resource availability, including labour;
(h) modes and organization of transportation;
(i) number of distribution centres;
(j) weather.

Factors affecting the design of the plant/premises

The detailed design of plant should be undertaken by an operations management team, including an architect, working within a brief which indicates:

1. Accommodation required, both immediate and potential.
2. Latest possible completion date.
3. Life of the plant.
4. Proposed site.
5. Maximum cost.

All the above should derive explicitly from the long-term plans for the organization; if they are not so derived, then it could well follow that the 'immediately useful' plant could, in the long term, be a useless embarrassment to the company. It should be noted that it is unlikely that the brief will be finalized at the first attempt: management is unlikely to be able to estimate for the cost of new plant unless very recent and comparable experience is to hand. The factors which should be considered include:

1. *Size*
Identification with, and commitment to, a place of work are powerful productivity-increasing forces. The larger the unit the more difficult it is to rally these forces . . . everybody, at some time, has experienced with distress the 'small cog in a large machine' feeling. Generally, the smaller the unit the better, and it is often better, considering the *total situation*, to create a number of small discrete units than one large one. Economies of scale here are often illusory.

2. *Number of floors*
A problem requiring very early resolution is that concerning the number of floors. The choice between a single- and a multiple-storey building is one which, unless it is resolved by the circumstances of the site, is difficult to make.

3. *Access*
Free movement of goods in and out of the unit is as important as free movement within the plant. It will, therefore, be necessary to know the anticipated frequency and weight of all goods moving between the unit and its environment, and it is most important to try to forecast these for as long ahead as possible.

4. *Services*
An essential estimate required before detailed design begins is the type and quantity of power and other supplies to be used. Gas, water, electricity and compressed air need to be freely available, and ample provision made for computer terminal points, telephones, public address, burglar- and fire-alarm systems. Fire prevention and control systems—fireproof doors, sprinkler systems, hoses, fire escapes—are invariably best 'built-in' rather than applied as afterthoughts.

5. *Headroom required*
Many modern production techniques require the use of overhead movement, suspended plant and above-head-height storage; in fact, a plant can often be considered to be formed in two layers, one from the floor upwards and one from the ceiling downwards. Inadequate headroom cannot easily be remedied after the building is complete and it is unwise to curtail the distance between floor and ceiling too severely.

6. *Loads to be carried*

The loads developed in a work area arise not only from the immediate production equipment itself, but also from the storage of materials. If the floor is the ceiling of the lower storey it may also be required to carry the weight of any suspended conveyors, tools, trunking or similar fixtures.

7. *Lighting*

There may be special requirements on lighting which must be considered; for example, colour-matching processes are most easily carried out in daylight, while some photographic processes require a complete absence of light. Wherever possible, it seems desirable to provide natural lighting with a sight of the outside world.

8. *Heating and ventilation*

These require to be treated at the start of the design: costs of heating often form a substantial part of total running costs, and every effort should be made to conserve, and usefully distribute, heat and fresh air. Insulation, draught screens, warm air blankets and heating ducts are best installed during construction, and not later when their installation can be costly, unsightly and disruptive. This is particularly true if it is necessary to incorporate air-cleaning, humidifying or drying plant within the ventilation system, and location of noxious processes should be determined early in order that outlet flues may be well clear of any fresh-air intake points, and of any locations where the effluent itself might be harmful.

9. *Disposal of waste*

The social consequences of uncontrolled waste disposal are rapidly and sadly becoming apparent, and all waste products and effluents must be readily dispersed without damage or inconvenience. Reference must be made to local regulations here, since there may be restrictions on emissions, the use of rivers as receivers of waste water, or other special regulations. Specialist advice on these matters is usually available from government sources.

10. *Special process requirements*

If possible, any special process requirements should be known at the outset. Typical examples of such requirements are:

(*a*) Need for particularly close temperature control, for example in calibration or measuring departments.

(*b*) Need for stable floors, for example in laboratories, where transferred vibrations can upset accurate readings and cause considerable waste of time and effort.

(*c*) Need for special, security measures—in noisy, dangerous or secret processes, or when dealing with large sums of cash.

(*d*) Need for special lighting requirements.

(*e*) Need for any special amenities.

1. Size
2. Number of floors
3. Access
4. Services
5. Headroom required
6. Loads to be carried
7. Lighting
8. Heating and ventilation
9. Disposal of waste
10. Special process requirements

Factors affecting the design of plant or premises

Recommended reading

Domschke, W. and Drexl, A., *Location and Layout Planning*, Springer-Verlag, 1985.

   Lecture Notes in Economics and Mathematical Systems series—for those who wish to become involved in the detailed modelling approach to planning the location and layout of the plant.

Greenhut, Melvin L., *Plant Location in Theory and in Practice: The Economics of Space*, Greenwood Press, 1982.

Love, R. F. *et al.*, *Facilities Location: Models and Methods*, Elsevier, 1986.

   The above two books are comprehensive works dealing specifically with location decisions. They should be consulted by those with such decisions to make.

Konz, Stephen, *Facility Design*, Wiley, 1985.

   The title misleads, as the text deals with aspects of plant location, layout and design.

Peters, Max S. and Timmerhans, Klaus, *Plant Design and Economics for Chemical Engineers*, 3rd edn (Chem. Eng. Ser), McGraw-Hill, 1980.

   Clearly a specialist's book, which is useful for all production management personnel in the process industries.

12 Layout of the plant

The meaning and type of layout

The word 'layout' is here used to indicate the physical disposition of the plant and of the various parts of the plant. Thus the *layout* will encompass both the location of equipment within a small department, and the disposition of departments upon a site.

Layout will affect the organization of the plant, the technology whereby the task is carried out, and the flow of work through the unit. The velocity with which work flows through a unit is one of the determinants of survival of that unit, and the plant layout problem is thus one of fundamental importance to the organization. It is necessary, therefore, to ensure that the policy decisions concerning organization, method and work flow are made *before* the plant is laid out rather than to lay the plant out first and then try to fit organization, method and work flow to it. This is a particularly important area of POM responsibility since here we are dealing with the capital equipment of the organization which, in general, is difficult to relocate once it has been put into position. Every practising manager must know of situations where a piece of equipment is in an extremely inconvenient position but, because of the difficulty in moving it, the organization has to tolerate gross inefficiency. Plant layout must express policy and not determine it.

Product and process layout

Broadly, a plant can be laid out in two ways, either to try to serve the needs of the product (product layout) or to serve the needs of the process (process layout). Often organizations start, when very small, with a product layout and as it increases in size, they will tend to move towards a process layout in the belief that such a layout will make better use of the physical resources. The choice of a product or process layout is so bound up with organizational decisions that discussion of them is left to a later chapter (Chapter 15, 'Types of production').

Criteria for a good layout

While the techniques employed in making a layout are normal work-study techniques, the process is a creative one which cannot be set down with any finality, and one in which experience plays a very great part. Furthermore, it is not possible to define a good layout with any precision. However, there are certain criteria which may be satisfied by a good layout, and these are discussed below.

1. *Maximum flexibility*

A good layout will be one which can be rapidly modified to meet changing circumstances. In this context, particular attention should be paid to the supply of services (electricity, gas, water, etc.), which should be ample and of easy access. These can usually be provided much more simply and cheaply at the outset of a layout, and failure to do so can often prevent very necessary modifications to unsatisfactory, outdated or inadequate layouts.

2. *Maximum co-ordination*

Entry into, and disposal from, any department or functional area should be in such a manner that it is most convenient to the issuing or receiving departments. Layout requires to be considered as a whole and not parochially.

3. *Maximum use of volume*

A plant must be considered as a cubic device and maximum use made of the volume available: pipelines and conveyors can be run above head height and used as moving work-in-progress stores, or tools and equipment can be suspended from the ceiling. This principle is particularly true in stores, where goods can be stacked at considerable heights without inconvenience, especially if modern lifting devices are used. In some cases, material can be moved by conveyors or pipework slung outside the building. In offices, racking and ducting can be installed to minimize floor space.

4. *Maximum visibility*

All the people and materials should be readily observable at all times: there should be no 'hiding-places' into which goods or information can get mislaid. This criterion is sometimes difficult to fulfil, particularly when an existing plant is taken over. It is also a principle which is strongly resisted, and special offices, stores, cupboards and enclosures are often requested, not because of their utility but because they form a symbol of office or status. Every piece of partitioning or screening should be scrutinized most carefully, as it introduces undesirable segregation and reduces effective floor space. Definite lines of travel should be provided and, if necessary, clearly marked. No gangways, passages or corridors should ever be used for storage purposes, even temporarily.

5. *Maximum accessibility*
All servicing and maintenance points should be readily accessible. For example, equipment should not be placed against a wall in such a manner that necessary maintenance cannot easily be carried out. The maintenance under these circumstances is likely to be skimped—at best it will occupy an excessive time. Similarly, equipment or storage units placed in front of a fuse box will impede the work of the electricians and may cause an unnecessary stoppage of operations when the fuse box is opened. If it is impossible to avoid obscuring a service point, then the equipment concerned should be capable of being moved—it should not be a permanent installation.

6. *Minimum distance*
All movements should be both necessary and direct. Handling work adds to its cost but does not increase its value, consequently any unnecessary or circuitous movements should be avoided. It is a common failing for material to be moved from a work station to a temporary storage place while waiting finally to pass to the next storage point. This intermediate rest-place is often unnecessary and unplanned, being used only because an empty space appears convenient. The providing of 'extra' shelves, benches and tables should be questioned very thoroughly and avoided if possible.

7. *Minimum handling*
The best handling is no handling, but where it is unavoidable it should be reduced to a minimum by the use of conveyors, lifts, chutes, pipework, hoists and trucks (see Chapter 29). Material being worked on should be kept at working height, and never have to be placed on the floor if it is to be lifted later.

8. *Minimum discomfort*
Draughts, poor lighting, excessive sunlight, heat, noise, vibrations and smells should be minimized and if possible counteracted. Apparently trivial discomforts often generate troubles greatly out of proportion to the discomfort itself. Attention paid to the lighting and general decoration and furniture can be rewarding without being costly. Professional advice on the recommended intensity of lighting for various tasks can be obtained, and most manufacturers of lighting equipment will provide useful suggestions on this subject. The Health and Safety at Work Act (1974), and the various regulations associated with it, are relevant here and specific requirements are often laid down (see Chapter 36).

9. *Inherent safety*
All layouts should be inherently safe, and no person should be exposed to danger. Care must be taken not only of the persons operating the

equipment but also of the passers-by, who may be required to go behind equipment, the back of which may be unsafe. This is both a statutory and a moral requirement, and great attention should be paid to it. Adequate medical facilities and services must be provided, and these must satisfy the Inspectors of the Health and Safety Executive. Experience shows that the Inspectors are not only competent to advise on these matters, they are always most anxious to be of assistance. Fire is an ever-present hazard and much useful advice can be obtained from the local fire service and from the company's insurers.

10. *Maximum security*
Safeguards against fire, moisture, theft and general deterioration should be provided, as far as possible, in the original layout rather than in later accretions of cages, doors and barriers.

11. *Efficient material flow*
Work lanes and transport lanes should not cross. Every effort must be made to ensure that material flows in one direction only, and a layout which does not conform to this will result in considerable difficulties, if not downright chaos. The use of gravitational force, in certain types of processing, can lead to great savings in energy and time. The inefficient pumping of materials round chemical plants often results from insufficient attention paid to the alignment of certain equipment at the layout stage.

12. *Identification*
Wherever possible, working groups should be provided with their 'own' working space. The need for a defined 'territory' seems basic to many animals including the human being, and provision of a space, with which a person can identify, can often enhance morale and provide a very real feeling of cohesion.

1. Maximum flexibility
2. Maximum co-ordination
3. Maximum use of volume
4. Maximum visibility
5. Maximum accessibility
6. Minimum distance
7. Minimum handling
8. Minimum discomfort
9. Inherent safety
10. Maximum security
11. Efficient material flow
12. Identification

Some criteria for a good layout

Advantages of a good layout

A layout satisfying the above conditions will have the following advantages over one which does not:

1. The overall process time and cost will be minimized by reducing unnecessary handling and movement, and by generally increasing the effectiveness of all work.

2. Supervision and production control will be simplified by the elimination of 'hidden corners' in which both information and material can be misplaced.

3. Changes in programme will be most readily accommodated.

4. Total output from a given plant will be as high as possible by making the maximum effective use of available space.

5. A feeling of unity among employees will be encouraged by avoiding unnecessary segregation.

6. Quality of the products or service will be sustained by safer and better methods of production.

Preparing for a layout

The following information should be available before a layout can be planned:

(a) The company organizational structure.

(b) The type of production system to be employed.

(c) Type and quantity of people involved.

(d) Dimensional plan of the space to be laid out. While it is not essential to have accurate scale drawings of the plant, it is usually essential to have an accurate knowledge of dimensions. Thickness of buttresses and skirting boards, and dimensions of protrusions on walls (switchboxes, fuseboards) are sometimes overlooked yet may be significant. The availability of existing supplies (gas, water, electricity, compressed air, telephones and drainage) and the locations of existing offices, toilets and permanent structures must also be indicated.

(e) The volume of work to be produced from the space, both immediately and in the foreseeable future.

(f) The operations to be undertaken, their descriptions, sequence and standard times. Note must be taken of any dangerous, noisy, dust- or smoke-producing, or otherwise special, operations.

(g) The equipment needed to carry out the operations and any special requirements it imposes, such as particularly strong floors, maintenance facilities and safety devices.

(h) The number of movements of material from one work centre to another during a representative working period. This may either be expressed in absolute terms or as a ratio of the number of moves between centres to the minimum number of moves between the 'least used' work centres. This information is conveniently represented on a 'travel chart' (see Fig. 12.1).

(*i*) Any 'dead', 'ageing'. 'stabilizing' or other process storage time.

(*j*) The volume of material, sub-stores or buffer stocks required at each work station.

(*k*) The volume of main stores and finished goods stores required. This depends not only on the type of product and output but also upon the supply and dispersal situations. Any special storage facilities should also be noted.

(*l*) What lines of communication and fire exits are required.

(*m*) What special requirements—burglar alarming, for example—are imposed by the local authority or by the company's insurer.

(*n*) What special inspection requirements exist.

(*o*) What special geographical requirements must be met, e.g. the specific location of a despatch department.

(*p*) If any spare plant will need to be stored in the space under consideration.

Process layout methods

There are probably two levels at which layouts are required. In one, the various *departments* have to be sited, and in the other the items of *plant* within a department need to be located.

Departmental location—operations sequence analysis

It has been pointed out earlier that there are a number of different, and sometimes conflicting, requirements which should be satisfied when preparing a good layout. Since it is usually impossible to resolve the conflicts between these different requirements, it is often convenient when planning process layout to accept a single criterion—that of minimum travel costs—as the starting point for planning:

$$\text{Minimize cost} = \sum_{i=1}^{n} \sum_{j=1}^{n} x_{ij} \, C_{ij}$$

where n = total number of work centres or departments

i, j = individual departments

x_{ij} = number of units, loads, or people moved between departments i and j

TO

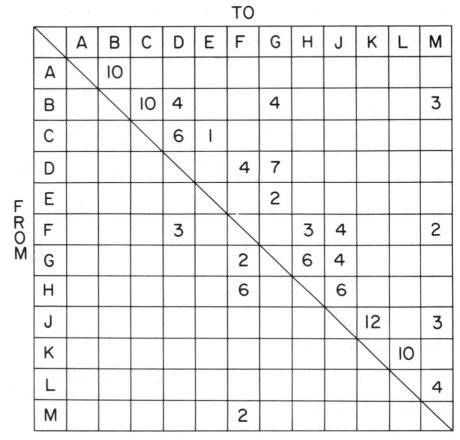

Fig. 12.1 Travel chart

C_{ij} = cost to make one movement between departments i and j (this may be conveniently represented as a distance rather than a worked out cost)

If the movements between departments are known or estimated, the method of *sequence analysis* may be employed to produce a 'proximity' statement which may then be imposed on the plan of the physical structure. This is probably best illustrated by a simple example.

Twelve 'organization units' A, B, C . . . M have been identified, and the number of movements between units discovered, either by direct observation or by analysing the appropriate documents. If no data exists, then estimates of such movements must be made, and it is convenient to express these as a proportion of the movements on the least used route. Thus, in the example, it is estimated that the least number of movements in unit time is from department C to department E. Movements to and from the other departments are given as proportions of the 'from C to E' movement (Fig. 12.1).

Examination of this chart shows that on some routes (for example D–F) traffic is required to flow each way (3 units from F to D, 4 units from D to F). Such two-way traffic inevitably causes difficulties; the existing organization and technology should be examined to see if such traffic can be removed. This will mean inspecting the emptier half of the travel chart—in this case, the half lying beneath the diagonal—to see if any re-routeing can take place which will empty the cells and give a one-way flow.

For the purpose of reducing traffic between departments, a movement *from* department X *to* department Y is effectively the same as a move-

JOURNEYS BETWEEN

	A	B	C	D	E	F	G	H	J	K	L	M
A		10										
B			10	4			4					3
C				6	1							
D						7	7					
E							2					
F							2	9	4			4
G								6	4			
H									6			
J										12		3
K											10	
L												4
M												

Fig. 12.2 'Journeys between' chart

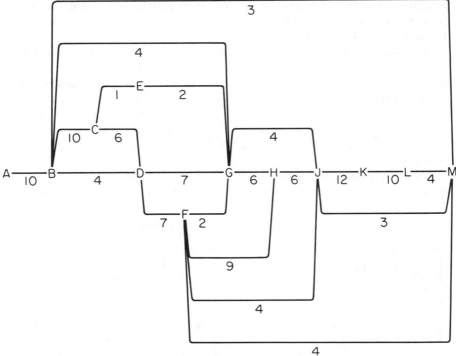

Fig. 12.3 'Journeys between' network

ment *to* department X *from* department Y. The travel chart is therefore converted to a 'journeys between' chart: Fig. 12.2.

This can now be transformed into a 'journeys between' *network*, which has the form of a conventional critical path analysis (CPA) network (see Chapter 30) (Fig. 12.3) with the duration time subscript being replaced by a statement of number of journeys. A forward and backward pass will then identify the most heavily loaded path or paths (in CPA terms, *the critical path*). Clearly, departments on this path should be placed as close to each other as physically possible, a 'head' department on the 'critical path' being adjacent to its 'tail' department, so that in the example, departments A–B–C–D–F–H–J–K–L–M–N should be as close together as possible in the sequence stated.

The area required for, and if necessary, the shape of each department is determined and templates representing these areas are prepared, a square shape being initially used if no other shape is mandatory. These templates are then placed upon an appropriately scaled representation of the total area being planned, and moved in accordance with the results of the 'journeys between' network. As with any other layout technique, no unique solution will emerge, and considerable attention must be given to the physical 'on the floor' conditions.

Layout of work stations

The departments having been located, the equipment within the departments must be laid out. Such a layout is not a task for which a general technique is available. If the technological routes are reasonably constant and the 'journeys between' fairly predictable, then the operations sequence analysis method may be applied.

However, the process tends to be largely one of trial and error, of laying out, modifying and re-laying out. It is desirable therefore that a layout should first be planned not on the space itself but upon models. These models can take one of two forms:

(*a*) Two-dimensional models which consist, in the simplest form, of a plan upon which is laid cut-out representations of the space required by the various items of equipment. It is convenient to make these cut-outs of stiff card or a colour different from that of the plan itself. Similar types of equipment in the same colour are often found helpful, and gangways can also be represented by coloured strips of card.

(*b*) Three-dimensional models, which are built up from scale models of the equipment to be used, and of the operators using them. These models can either be represented by simple blocks of wood, or they can be castings purchased from a company specializing in making such models. Three-dimensional layouts tend to be expensive, and are therefore not used in simple layouts. On the other hand, in a complex or large layout the three-dimensional model has such substantial advantages that it is wise to consider its use. Among the advantages are clarity, vividness, demonstration of the need or use of headroom, and an ability to photograph and transmit elsewhere (e.g. to customers, suppliers and trainees) the proposed new layout. Like any other work-study solution, the idea must be 'sold' to the user, and a three-dimensional model is useful here.

Having decided on the type of model to be used, the operation sequence should be re-examined. It is usually found that there are one or two 'key' operations whose positions are fixed by external requirements. For example:

Packing should be near the point of despatch, that is, a convenient outside door.

Inspection may require daylight and should therefore be near windows.

Painting may require fume extraction, and a location near an outside wall is indicated.

First operations may need to be near a stores whose position is fixed.

Customer service stations will need to be at the 'front' of the operations, nearest to the entrance.

The planning sequence can then be as follows:

1. Locate the 'key' operations on the plan.
2. Locate main passageways or corridors: it is usually better if these are parallel to the main walls rather than running diagonally across a floor space. It is also usually more convenient if these start and finish at outside or connecting doorways, and they must be adequate for the collection and delivery of material.
3. Locate the remaining work areas to allow work to flow naturally between key operations. At this stage it is not necessary to locate equipment in detail but to fix areas occupied by various types of equipment, that is, departmental or sectional areas.
4. Locate minor passageways.
5. Locate equipment in detail within departments or sections.
6. Complete the layout by locating all subsidiary equipment—rubbish bins, telephones, etc.
7. Test the layout against the principles stated above. A string diagram (i.e. the representation of the route of material by a piece of string or cotton—see Chapter 17) is often helpful in establishing the distance of travel.
8. When satisfied with the layout itself, view the actual space, if possible. Visualize the installed proposed layout, walk over the proposed passageways and check the installation. It is often found that time spent here can often be handsomely repaid by discovering features not apparent on drawings and models.
9. Check the final layout against the organization's general policies and specifications.

---

1. Prepare model(s)
2. Study operation sequence
3. Choose 'key' operations
4. Locate 'key' operations
5. Locate main passageways
6. Locate remaining work areas
7. Locate minor passageways
8. Plan individual areas in detail
9. Locate subsidiary equipment
10. Test completed layout against principles of good layout
11. View area to verify layout
12. Check against policy

Layout of work stations

Product layout: line balancing

The design of flow lines to produce specific products is a complex subject which requires the collaboration of technologists, engineers, designers, managers and social scientists. Consideration will be given in Chapter 15 to the factors which should be considered before selecting flow production, and the discussion here concerns line balancing—the attempt to balance the various work stations on a line in time.

There are three basic types of flow lines:

(a) *single model* on which only one product or model is produced;
(b) *mixed model* on which more than one model is produced simultaneously;
(c) *multi-model* involves flow production in batches of different models, which are produced on the same line.

Before introducing the techniques of line balancing, it is necessary to define some terms:

The *demand* is the required production rate, in units (Q) per unit time (T).

A *work element* is a distinct part of a production process, often identified for convenience of observation and measurement. E_i is the work content associated with element i.

A *work station* is a position on a flow line at which certain work elements are performed. N is the number of work stations.

Total work content is the sum of the standard times for all the work elements, i.e. $\Sigma_{i=1}^{k} E_i$, where k is the number of elements.

The *cycle time* (C) is the time available at each station for the performance of the work allocated to it. C is obtained from the demand: $C = T/Q$.

The *service time* (S_j) is the time required to complete the work assigned to the station, j. C must be greater than S_j, otherwise the demand will not be met. $\Sigma\ S_j = \Sigma\ E_i$.

The *balance delay* (D_j) at a particular station j is the difference between the cycle time (C) and service time (S_j). $D_j = C - S_j$. For a whole line, $D = \Sigma\ D_j = NC - \Sigma\ S_j$.

The *balancing loss* (L_j) at a particular station j is the balance delay (D_j) represented as a percentage of the cycle time (C):

$$L_j = \frac{D_j}{C} \times 100\% = \frac{C - S_j}{C} \times 100\%.$$

For a whole line, the average balance loss,

$$L = \frac{D}{NC} \times 100\%$$

$$= \frac{NC - \Sigma S_j}{NC} \times 100\%$$

Precedence constraints are derived from technological relationships between the work elements and affect the order in which they can be carried out. They are usually represented in a precedence diagram.

Zoning constraints either preclude the grouping of certain work elements at the same station (negative) or necessitate the allocation of certain elements to the same work station (positive).

Given the desired output rate of a product, the work elements and their work contents, and other constraints, the objective of line balancing is to allocate work elements to work stations to:

(a) minimize the number of work stations;
(b) conform to the constraints;
(c) minimize the balancing loss;
(d) spread the loss evenly between stations.

Line balancing method

The method is best explained using an example. The forecasts for the likely demand of the AMBLER product indicate that annual sales will be 10,000 units. The product is made up from 16 work elements:

Element	Work content (min)	Precedes
A	3.6	E
B	2.5	F
C	2.7	G
D	2.6	H,J
E	1.6	K
F	1.4	K
G	2.4	L
H	3.3	M
J	1.7	N
K	3.4	S
L	2.8	P
M	1.9	R
N	2.4	R
P	3.6	S
R	2.8	S
S	1.3	—

The technical considerations dictate that elements E and F must not be processed together, neither must elements H and L. If the normal working week is 35 hours and 44 weeks constitute the normal year, the design of work stations may be achieved by the following stepwise process.

Step 1 Draw the precedence diagram
The technological relationships in the production of this product may be as represented in Fig. 12.4, which is similar to an activity-on-node network.

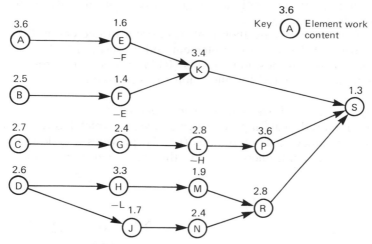

Fig. 12.4 Precedence diagram for the AMBLER product

Step 2 Calculate the cycle time and the minimum number of work stations

Demand = 10,000 per year
T = 1 minute
1 year = 44 × 35 × 60 = 92,400 minutes

Therefore, Q = 10,000/92,400 per minute
Cycle time, $C = T/Q$ = 92,400/10,000 minutes
  = 9.2 minutes
Total work content = $\Sigma E_i = E_A + E_B + E_C \ldots E_S$
  = 3.6 + 2.5 + 2.7 ... 1.3
  = 40 minutes

Minimum number of work stations required,

$$N_{min} = \frac{\text{Total work content}}{\text{Cycle time}} = \frac{\Sigma E_i}{9.2}$$
  = 4.3, i.e. 5 (to higher integer)

Step 3 Calculate and rank positional weights (RPW)
The RPW technique is a rapid heuristic method which provides acceptable solutions to the line balancing problem. The positional weight (PW)
of an element x may be calculated, using the precedence diagram, by
summing the work content values of all elements along all connected
paths from the product to the element x. For example, the PW of element
D in Fig. 12.4 may be calculated:

$$PW(D) = E_D + E_H + E_M + E_J + E_N + E_R + E_S$$
$$= 2.6 + 3.3 + 1.9 + 1.7 + 2.4 + 2.8 + 1.3 = 16.0$$

The remainder of the positional weights have been calculated in this way,
and are shown on Fig. 12.5.

The work elements are then ranked in order of decreasing PW, which
is a measure of the 'size' of an element and its position in the production
sequence. The rank position weights (RPW) provide the order in which
elements are considered for allocation to work stations.

Step 4 Allocate work elements to work stations
You are required to attempt to design a flow line which has the calculated
minimum number of work stations (i.e. 5), provides a cycle time of 9.2
minutes, and contradicts neither the precedence nor the zoning

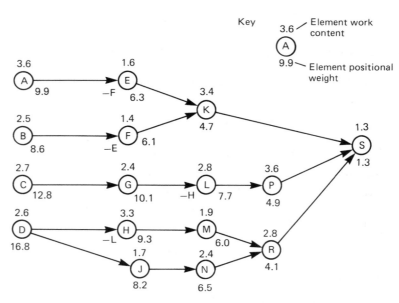

Fig. 12.5 Positional weights (PW) for the AMBLER product

Table 12.1 Allocation of work elements for cycle time of 9.2 min

Work station (WS)	Element i (zone constraint)	PW	Preceded by	Element work content, E_i	Cumulative service time, S_j	Available time, $C-S_j$
1	D	16.0	—	2.6	2.6	6.6
	C	12.8	—	2.7	5.3	3.9
	G	10.1	C	2.4	7.7	1.5
2	A	9.9	—	3.6	3.6	5.6
	H(−L)	9.3	D	3.3	6.9	2.3
	J	8.2	D	1.7	8.6	0.6
3	B	8.6	—	2.5	2.5	6.7
	L(−H)	7.7	G	2.8	5.3	3.9
	N	6.5	J	2.4	7.7	1.5
	F(−E)	6.1	B	1.4	9.1	0.1
4	E(−F)	6.3	A	1.6	1.6	7.6
	M	6.0	H	1.9	3.5	5.7
	P	4.9	L	3.6	7.1	2.1
5	K	4.7	E,F	3.4	3.4	5.8
	R	4.1	M,N	2.8	6.2	3.0
	S	1.3	K,P,R	1.3	7.5	1.7

constraints. The elements are allocated to work stations in order of decreasing RPW as follows.

Element D, with highest PW, is allocated first to station 1. This is acceptable since D is not preceded by any other element, there is spare time available in station 1, and there are no zoning constraints (see Table 12.1). Element C is the next to be allocated, with the second highest PW, no precedence or zoning constraints violated, and sufficient unassigned cycle time to accommodate it. Work station 1 is completed by the allocation of element G, the third highest PW. The same procedure is repeated for the remaining work stations, elements being allocated by RPW, unless cycle time, precedence or zoning constraints prevent this.

Step 5 Calculate balance delay and balancing loss for the line
It is very rare that a perfect balance can be achieved in the design of flow lines: the cycle time (C) will not equal service time (S_j) in all work stations. In the example of the AMBLER product, the allocation has produced the situation shown in Fig. 12.6, in which neither the work station times are balanced nor is the maximum work station time equal to the desired cycle time. The balance delay for this line may be calculated:

$$D = NC - \Sigma S_j = (5 \times 9.2) - 40 = 6.0 \text{ minutes}$$

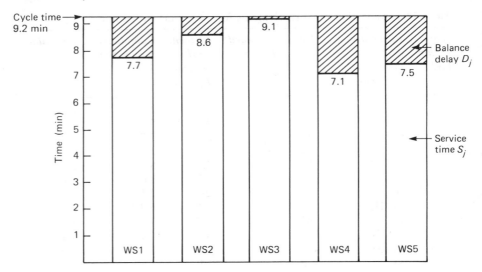

Fig. 12.6 Flow line balance for the AMBLER product

and the balancing loss is:

$$L = \frac{NC - \Sigma\,S_j}{NC} \times 100\% = \frac{6.0}{5 \times 9.2} \times 100 = 13.0\%$$

This represents a significant under-utilization of resources, which may not be apparent to the casual observer because a worker may well perform the allocated work operations in the available time, in other words, the work will expand to fill the cycle time. The cycle time could be reduced to 9.1 minutes (highest S_j) with a corresponding increase in output to:

$$\frac{44 \times 35 \times 60}{9.1} = 10{,}154 \text{ units}$$

and a reduction of balancing loss to:

$$L = \left(\frac{(5 \times 9.1) - 40}{5 \times 9.1}\right) \times 100 = 12.1\%$$

It may, then, be desirable to increase output to minimize balancing loss, and the procedure becomes one of seeking a balance for the initial cycle time (C), followed by achieving the best balance and minimizing the cycle time for the same number of work stations.

1. Draw precedence diagram
2. Calculate cycle time (C) and minimum number of work stations (N_{min})
3. Calculate rank positional weights (RPW)
4. Allocate work elements to work stations
5. Calculate balance delay (D) and balancing loss (L)

Steps in line balancing method

Installation of a layout

Once a new layout has been finalized, it must be put into practice. This involves two separate and distinct steps:

(*a*)   planning the way in which the new installation is to be carried out;
(*b*)   supervising while the plan is carried out.

The planning technique known as critical path analysis (see Chapter 30) is ideally suited for both these tasks, and its use will avoid the common 'Here's the machine—where's its plinth?' type of situation. Every manager will have seen (in other people's organization!) the newly constructed wall which has had to be demolished to allow entry of a new piece of equipment. Time spent in planning is invariably time well spent.

The use of the computer in preparing a layout

The co-existence of a large number of criteria makes the definition of an 'optimum' layout virtually impossible. Furthermore, the writing of a computer program for plant layout becomes a task of some considerable difficulty *unless some very drastic simplifications are made*.

At the time of writing there are four well-known computer programs available to assist in the preparation of a layout. The oldest and most widely discussed is CRAFT (Computerized Relative Allocation of Facilities Technique) which was written in 1963/4 by Armour, Buffa and Vollman: it adopts as the criterion to be minimized that of total handling cost. CORELAP (Computerized Relationship Layout Planning), ALDEP (Automated Layout Design Program) and RMA Comp 1 (Richard Mather and Associates) all adopt some form of proximity criterion, attempting to assemble the resources being planned in such a way as to ensure that those items which need to be near each other are in fact so placed.

The choice of program depends upon the user's objectives and the particular layout problem being studied. It is important for the user to understand the features of the program under consideration, and its limitations. Some experienced plant designers argue that a computer cannot really understand the complexities of the task. One manager, however, experienced a different sort of use for the ALDEP routine. He found that his computer-printed proposals for re-layout were seldom corrected or amended by his superior, but when he presented hand sketches or drawings, his boss had a tendency to change and alter things regularly. The computer can clearly offer a powerful psychic influence! It is clear that the plant layout specialist understands the problem better than a computer assistant, but it makes sense to use the data handling facilities of the microprocessor to aid the decision-making process.

Another aspect which has been observed is the computer's ability to frequently propose unusual or creative solutions, which would normally be rejected at an early stage by manual methods. It is wise for the operations manager, charged with a layout problem, to allow the computer to offer help, but not to be led blindly to an unwise decision or be mesmerised by computer technology.

Recommended reading

Apple, James M., *Plant Layout and Materials Handling* 3rd edn, Wiley, 1977.
A very comprehensive, practical book, well illustrated—particularly in the materials handling/warehousing area.

Domschke, W. and Drexl, A., *Location and Layout Planning*, Springer-Verlag, 1985.
See comments at the end of Chapter 11

Tompkins, J. A. and Moore, J. M., *Computer Aided Layout—A User's Guide*, American Institution of Industrial Engineers, 1980.
This text pulls together a comparison of five of the leading computer programs or routines available for the development and selection of layouts. Still extremely useful for those who need to study this subject in depth.

White, John A. and Francis, Richard L., *Facility Layout and Location*, Prentice-Hall, 1974.
This is a very comprehensive work on the subject. Its subtitle 'An analytical approach' well describes the contents.

13 Equipment selection

Operations managers often initiate proposals for the purchase of equipment, such as production and office machinery, computers, software, cars and trucks. The reasons for its purchase include:

1. New equipment is required for the production of new products or services.
2. Increased sales volumes demand an expansion of the available capacity.
3. Existing equipment has become obsolete and/or changes in technology are required to maintain competitiveness.
4. Existing equipment has entered the wear-out phase of its life and must be replaced.

When it has been decided to purchase equipment, a survey should be carried out. This is conveniently done in two stages, firstly a *use*, or technological sifting will reduce the range of possible equipment to manageable proportions and, secondly, a *cost* or economic analysis will determine, if necessary, which of a number of equally acceptable technical alternatives is the most economical.

The purchase of any piece of equipment must eventually be justified on economic grounds, and its cost recovered from the selling price of the goods made or the services offered. Other criteria may be taken into consideration—for example, prestige—but in general these will be of marginal importance, and of significance principally when deciding between a number of possible pieces of equipment all of similar cost.

A forecast of potential use must be made. If this forecast is *robust*, that is, likely to be achieved, then a predisposition to purchase will follow. If the forecast is weak, and unlikely to be achieved, then a more cautious (risk-averse) decision might be to sub-contract the work.

Technological survey and specification

The following concern the technical specification of equipment:

1. *Capacity*. The capacity of the equipment needs to be ample for the purpose envisaged during the foreseeable future, and in this context

reference must be made to the long-term forecast, particularly when the cost is heavy. While it is foolish to purchase a piece of equipment which will soon be overloaded, it is almost certainly unnecessarily expensive to purchase one of a very much higher capacity than will ever be required unless there are other determining factors.

2. *Compatibility*. Whenever possible, new equipment should be of a type similar to or identical with the existing plant. The resultant simplification in the provisioning of spare parts, in maintenance, in operator training, in setting and preparation, and in loading, are enormous. In the purchase of computer software, for example, compatibility with the existing hardware, operating system and other software is vital.

3. *Availability of associated equipment*. Much of the new, highly complex equipment now available can only be fully utilized if a wide range of associated equipment is employed, and the availability of this can often dictate the choice of plant. This is particularly true of computers and computer-controlled equipment which is of minimal value without its associated 'software'.

4. *Reliability and after-service*. Equipment breakdown can be costly and can also jeopardize service or delivery dates, hence its reliability is very important. Reference to other users, if possible, is often very helpful here. The availability of a good after-sales service should be investigated.

5. *Ease of maintenance*. Maintenance costs need always to be as low as practicable, and equipment which is difficult to service will not only have a high maintenance cost, it will also be an inducement to carry out maintenance inadequately.

6. *Ease of learning to use*. The speed with which new equipment can be utilized depends on how easy it is to learn how to use it. This applies particularly to computers and software, where the quality of the supporting documentation and training will greatly influence the learning period.

7. *Ease of preparation*. Ancillary time (setting up, stripping down, cleaning) is expensive and reduces the running time of the equipment, so its ease of preparation should be considered.

8. *Safety*. Plant needs to be safe and, though it is very rare to find unsafe equipment on the market today, this aspect repays study. Accidents are costly in a lowering of output, in deterioration of morale and in bad labour relations. The onus of preventing them is firmly on the employer and management, both in law and in common humanity.

9. *Ease of installation*. This point can be easily overlooked, when it may then be found that access doors are too low, or permissible floor loading exceeded by the new equipment on installation.

10. *Delivery*. The delivery situation needs to be investigated to see that the needs of the organization can be matched by the delivery promised.

An investigation into the reliability of the supplier in this respect is worth making.

11 *State of development.* Newly designed equipment is sometimes marketed before the design has been entirely finalized or stabilized. Guarantees on this are highly desirable, although it must be recognized that no guarantee can compensate for the loss of goodwill attendant upon broken delivery or service promises.

12. *Effect on existing organization.* Some new equipment, when installed, will demand changes in the existing organization. Thus, a numerically-controlled machine tool, for example, will require that considerable managerial re-thinking takes place. Pre-planning is vital and this is often centralized in the PCD and the production planning department. NC equipment concentrates the planning into action *before* the work commences. If the need for this planning is not accepted, then the benefits of the NC machine will not be realized. Equally, the effects of computers and computer-operated systems being installed without consideration of their impact upon the existing organization can be disastrous.

From an examination of suppliers' catalogues, visits to showrooms and other plant, discussion with colleagues and other interested people, a short-list of equipment will be drawn up using considerations similar to the above. A useful device for carrying out further sifting is a matrix, similar to that which was described in Chapter 11, where the choice of location was discussed. The resulting list must then be subjected to a cost analysis to choose between the various items listed.

Purchasing equipment is similar to buying a car; we would like it to be big and fast enough for our needs, handle well, be tried and tested, well equipped, particularly with safety features, reliable and easy to service, and within our price bracket. It also helps to judge its suitability if we can take it for a test drive.

---

1. Capacity
2. Compatibility
3. Availability of associated equipment
4. Reliability and after-service
5. Ease of maintenance
6. Ease of learning to use
7. Ease of preparation
8. Safety
9. Ease of installation
10. Delivery
11. State of development
12. Effect on existing organization

Use factors affecting choice of equipment

Economic appraisal concepts

There are a number of ways of carrying out an economic analysis, and it must be understood that whatever technique is used it must be consistently applied to all equipment. An economic analysis is more useful in differentiating between different items of equipment than in setting an accurate figure on its absolute cost.

The aim of an economic analysis is to appraise the *cost of producing* from a given piece of equipment, not just the cost of the plant itself. This can be considered to be made up of two parts: (*a*) the standing cost, which is the cost incurred by the equipment installed and ready for use but not being operated; and (*b*) the running cost, which sets down the cost of running the equipment in order to generate the required products or service.

The standing cost

In the calculation of standing cost, executive decisions have to be made: notably, what depreciation should be considered, what is the expected return on invested capital, what allowance should be made for taxes, insurance and rates, and what rent is charged to the floor space occupied. These, together with the purchase price, are summed to give an average annual standing cost. The above discussion implies that the equipment is being *purchased outright*. There are, of course, other ways of obtaining equipment, for example:

1. *Hire purchase.* Contracts can be negotiated for long periods (up to 10 years) with the interest tied to the bank rate. In some cases, payments can fluctuate with a known seasonal variation in output.

2. *Leasing.* Here the user never actually *owns* the equipment leased, it being argued that the *use* of the equipment is more important than its *ownership*.

3. *Hiring.* Effectively, this is leasing, but usually a maintenance contract is implied or required.

All these methods should be considered as they may well have substantial tax and cash advantages over outright purchase. In these cases, of course, the annual charges are the standing charges discussed above.

The running cost

To calculate the average running cost, a knowledge of the average annual total output is required. For equipment producing for stock, this is a comparatively simple piece of information derivable from the sales forecast. For equipment used to produce entirely to customer's order, the details of output cannot be forecast in such detail. The most satisfactory approximation is obtained by forecasting the anticipated average output and using this forecast as the basis of the calculations. From the figure of expected output, the cost of power and supplies, the direct cost of production, the cost of ancillary labour and the cost of upkeep and maintenance are calculated, and then added together to give the average annual running cost. It must be remembered that the material cost may vary with the type of equipment, since different models may require material to be presented in different ways, and so may generate different waste.

The annual cost is the sum of the standing and running costs, and it is calculated for each piece of equipment in the short-list. The life cycle cost (LCC) is then the sum of the annual costs over the whole life of the equipment. Obviously, the final decision will depend on the results of both the use and the economic analyses.

Depreciation and obsolescence

Once a piece of equipment has been installed it will, in general, immediately start to lose value. This arises from two main causes, namely: *depreciation*, which may be defined as the diminution in the intrinsic value of an asset due to use and/or the lapse of time, and is a result of normal usage, bad handling, bad maintenance, accidents, or wear due to disease or chemical action; and *obsolescence*, which is the loss in the intrinsic value of an asset due to its supercession, and is a result of a reduction in market for the product or service for which the equipment is intended, a change in design of the type of equipment or a change in legislation.

The purchase of a piece of equipment involves an expense which must, if the organization is to continue in being independently, be recovered from the proceeds of running the organization. The usual way of recovering this expense is by a charge in the profit and loss account against the profits before arriving at the net profit, and of showing the loss of value of the equipment by reducing the value of the asset in the balance sheet. This reduction in value is known as the *depreciation* suffered by the equipment.

Recovery can be effected in a number of different ways. Ideally, of course, the total cost of the equipment should be recovered when its 'life' has been spent. Since it is extremely difficult to predict the life of some equipment, arbitrary methods of writing down depreciation are adopted as policy. These may vary from organization to organization but should always remain constant within an organization. The Institute of Cost and Management Accountants lists nine different methods of calculating depreciation, and many others can be found. The choice of depreciation method depends largely upon convenience, and the effects of the prevailing tax laws. Two of the most common methods are as follows.

Straight line or linear depreciation
In this method the same absolute value is deducted each year from the value; for example, if equipment is depreciated over five years, its value each year will be (as a percentage): 100; 80; 60; 40; 20; and from the sixth year onwards it will have no book value.
   Algebraically this is represented by:

$$\text{Value} = P - \frac{P(n-1)}{N}$$

where P is the initial price, N the number of years over which it is being depreciated and n the number of years at which the value is being calculated.

Reducing balance method of depreciation
In this a constant percentage of the book value is deducted each year from the book value. For example, if the depreciation each year were 50 per cent *of the remaining book value* then the value each year would be (stated as a percentage of the initial value): 100; 50; 25; 12.5; 6.25; and in fact would never become zero, although when its value became negligible (say 1 per cent of initial cost) its value would be 'written off'. Algebraically this is represented by:

$$\text{Value} = P(1 - R)^{n-1}$$

where P and n have the same significance as previously and R represents the depreciation rate.
   This method is simple to calculate, and provides heavier charges at the beginning of the equipment's life—when maintenance costs can reasonably be expected to be lighter—and lighter charges at the end of the equipment's life, when maintenance costs are likely to be heavier. Against these two advantages can be set the apparent disadvantage that, unless the sum of the depreciation and maintenance charge is constant each year, the apparent cost of producing from a piece of plant will change from one accounting period to the next.

The 'life' of equipment

It is helpful to recognize that equipment may have several different 'life-spans':

1. *The physical life.* This is the length of time over which the equipment can be usefully and *economically* used. It depends upon a number of factors including the maintenance carried out and the use to which the plant is put, and it is usually determined by the maintenance and breakdown costs which become excessive at the end of physical life.

2. *The technological life.* This is the length of time elapsing before new equipment becomes available which makes the existing plant obsolete.

3. *The product (or market) life.* This is set by the product which is made or the service offered, by the equipment no longer being required. This may be very much shorter than the physical life, and the plant may be in excellent physical condition. While normal market conditions will force recognition of the product life, there is a danger of equipment in large groups of companies being worked beyond the product life, since the products are perforce being sold to captive purchasers within the group.

4. *The 'book' life.* This is the time during which the equipment is depreciated to a nominal value. This is often calculated on the basis of minimizing tax, rather than any other consideration.

5. *The economic life.* This is the shortest of the first three lives. If it can coincide with the book life, then there may be some agreement between the book-keeping and the financial considerations.

1. Physical
2. Technological
3. Product
4. Book
5. Economic

The 'lives' of plant

Methods of economic appraisal

A 'use' or technological survey may reveal that for a project there are a number of equally acceptable pieces of equipment: the choice between them must then be resolved on cost or economic grounds. There are a number of methods used to carry out this resolution, and to illustrate these the following example will be used:

A forecast for a photocopying service suggests that 100,000 copies a year will be required at a selling price of 5p. There are two alternative pieces of equipment, A and B, with the following characteristics:

	A	B
Installed price	£6,000	£8,000
Direct labour costs/copy	0.833p	0.625p
Direct material costs/copy	2.50p	2.605p
Indirect labour/year	£400	£330
Services charges/year	£180	£150
Maintenance charges/year	£80	£150
Economic life	7 years	10 years

Defining 'profit' as the difference between income and necessary out-of-pocket expenses, the annual 'profit' achievable from A and B can be derived:

	A (£)	B (£)
Annual direct labour cost	833	625
Annual direct material cost	2,500	2,605
Annual indirect labour cost	400	330
Annual service charges	180	150
Annual maintenance charges	80	150
Total out-of-pocket expenses:	3,993	3,860
Annual income	5,000	5,000
∴ Annual 'profit'	1,007	1,140

The payback period

In this technique of capital appraisal, the time taken to recover the initial investment from the 'profit' is calculated:

	A	B
Payback period	$\dfrac{6,000}{1,007}$ = 6 years	$\dfrac{8,000}{1,140}$ = 7 years

Return on investment (ROI)

Here, the 'profit' is considered as a return upon the investment. There are a number of different definitions possible, for example the investment can be considered as the total initial investment (£6,000 in the case of A, £8,000 in the case of B) or the average investment, assuming the value of the plant is depreciated to zero (that is £3,000 for A, £4,000 for B). Taking this latter definition, we have:

	A (£)	B (£)
Annual depreciation charge	6,000	8,000
(depreciating to zero by the end	÷7	÷10
of economic life)	= 857	= 800
'Profit' as defined above	1,007	1,140
∴ Return	150	340

	A	B
	$\dfrac{150}{150}$	$\dfrac{340}{340}$
∴ Return on investment (ROI)	$3,000 \times 100$	$4,000 \times 100$
	= 5%	= 8½%

The above results thus conflict: by the 'payback period' techniques, equipment A is the more desirable since it is 'bought' quicker, while the 'return on investment' system suggests that equipment B should be chosen since it has a higher rate of return. Both methods, however, suffer from the same weakness, that is, that no account is taken of the *time* at which earnings are made. A more precise technique, known as discounted cash flow, enables this, and other pertinent aspects of the movements of funds, to be considered.

Discounted cash flow (DCF)

The appraisal technique known as the discounted cash flow (DCF) method takes cognizance not only of the earnings made, but also of the *time* at which they are made. Thus, the method recognizes that £1 now and £1 in a year's time have today quite different values, and that a profit of £1,000 obtained in a stream of £200 a year for 5 years has a different value from a stream of £100 a year for 10 years.

The concept of present value
£1 available now, and invested to produce an income of 10 per cent a year (this income being immediately reinvested) would grow as follows:

	£	£
Now, beginning of year 1	1	
end of year 1	1 + 0.1	= 1.1
end of year 2	1.1 + 0.11	= 1.21
end of year 3	1.21 + 0.121	= 1.331
end of year 4	1.331 + 0.1331	= 1.464

and so on. It is thus possible to say that £1.464 in 4 years' time, at an earning rate of 10 per cent, has a *present value* of £1. The figure of £1,464 in 4 years' time is an inconvenient one, and it is usually reduced to £1, which thus has a present value of £1/1.464 = £0.683, and the table above could be rewritten:

Present value of £1, at earning rate of 10 per cent

obtained one year hence $= £1/1.1$ $= £0.909$
obtained two years hence $= £1/1.21$ $= £0.826$
obtained three years hence $= £1/1.331$ $= £0.751$
obtained four years hence $= £1/1.464$ $= £0.683$

and so on. The validity of the above table can be checked, and the meaning of present value underlined by taking the present value of £1 obtained 4 years hence and calculating backwards, that is, calculating the value to which £0.683 would increase in four years if invested in an enterprise continuously producing a 10 per cent return on income:

£0.683 at the beginning of year 1 would become by year end
$£0.683 + £0.0683 = £0.751$

£0.751 at the beginning of year 2 would become by year end
$£0.751 + £0.0751 = £0.826$

£0.826 at the beginning of year 3 would become by year end
$£0.826 + £0.0826 = £0.9086$

£0.909 at the beginning of year 4 would become by year end
$£0.909 + £0.0909 = £0.9999$

which is effectively £1.

Had there been a steady stream of £1's received at the end of each year, then the following table could have been constructed:

Present value of £1 received annually at earning rate of 10 per cent

for one year $= 0.909$
for two years $= 0.909 + 0.826 = 1.735$
for three years $= 1.735 + 0.751 = 2.486$
for four years $= 2.486 + 0.683 = 3.169$

and so on. Thus £1 a year received annually for four years is equivalent to £3.169 available now, which is *invested in a project which produces a return of 10 per cent*. Note: it is assumed that the project earns at a rate of 10 per cent and that the earnings are immediately reinvested to earn at the same rate, the original capital investment remaining unchanged. If the capital had been invested in material at the rate of £1 each year, and the material had lain idle but still useful, then this would have had an earning rate of 0 per cent and a present value of £4.

If the annual £1 had been received in amounts of $£\frac{1}{12}$ at the end of each month, or continuously throughout the year, different tables of present value would have been constructed. Such tables are readily available commercially and, of course, programming a computer to carry out DCF calculations is quite simple.

Discounting

The act of taking a sum in the future and calculating its present value, assuming some particular rate of return, is called *discounting*, and it can be considered the inverse of compounding. To return to the original table, a single sum of £1 in 4 years' time is said to be discounted at a rate of 10 per cent to a value of £0.683. If there is a stream of £1's in cash, or a cash flow of £1 at the end of each year, then it can be said to form a *discounted cash flow* with a present value of £3.169 if the earning rate is 10 per cent. Clearly, different earning rates will produce different present values.

Present value of £1 received annually at earning rates of:

	1%	2%	4%	6%	10%	20%	50%
for one year	0.990	0.980	0.962	0.943	0.909	0.833	0.667
for two years	1.970	1.942	1.886	1.833	1.735	1.528	1.111
for three years	2.941	2.884	2.775	2.673	2.486	2.106	1.407
for four years	3.902	3.808	3.630	3.465	3.169	2.589	1.605

If we now return to equipment A, which involved an initial investment of £6,000 and produced an annual 'profit' of £1,000, it can be said that for the equipment to be justified, a cash flow of £1,000 a year, if discounted backwards to produce a present value of £6,000, must have an earning rate and a duration which will produce a factor of 6,000/1,000 = 6. There are a number of different combinations of rate and duration which will produce this result.

Present value of £1 received annually at earning rates of

	1%	2%	4%	6%	10%
for 1 year					
2					
3					
4					
5					
6	5.795	5.601	5.242		
7	6.728	6.472	6.002	5.582	
8				6.210	
9					5.759
10					6.145

or interpolating simply:

if the duration is $6\frac{3}{12}$ years the earning rate is   1%
$6\frac{6}{12}$ years the earning rate is   2%
7   years the earning rate is   4%
$7\frac{8}{12}$ years the earning rate is   6%
$9\frac{9}{12}$ years the earning rate is 10%

As the economic life is stated to be 7 years, the equipment can be said to have an earning rate of 4 per cent. Taking equipment B, this has a present value factor of 8,000/1,140 = 7, which can be produced as follows:

if the duration is $7\frac{6}{12}$ years the earning rate is 1%
$\qquad\qquad\qquad\quad 7\frac{7}{12}$ years the earning rate is 2%
$\qquad\qquad\qquad\quad 8\frac{5}{12}$ years the earning rate is 4%
$\qquad\qquad\qquad\quad 9\frac{4}{12}$ years the earning rate is 6%
$\qquad\qquad\qquad\quad 12\frac{7}{12}$ years the earning rate is 10%
$\qquad\qquad\qquad\quad 16\frac{1}{12}$ years the earning rate is 12%

and as the economic life is stated to be 10 years, the equipment can be said to have an earning rate of about 6 per cent over the economic life of the equipment. If the desirability of purchasing only B were being considered, then this earning rate would be a representation of the earning capacity of equipment B. However, since B is being compared with A, the time periods must be the same: thus, either we have to assume A has a life of 10 years, or B has a life of 7. To compare A at 7 years with B at 10 years is to ignore that the capital for A is continuously reinvested, and that when A is exhausted, the available funds are immediately reinvested, again producing a return which must be taken into account. In this case, assume that B has an effective life of 7 years: the earning rate is then less than 1 per cent, and it is this which is compared with the earning rate of 4 per cent derived from A. Under these circumstances, A is clearly the more desirable purchase.

The internal rate of return (IRR)

Any single project will, as discussed above, generate a series of in- and outflows of cash. It is possible to discover the earnings rate which allows the present value of the inflows and the outflows to balance. This rate is the *internal rate of return* (IRR), the *time adjusted return* or the *project rate of return* (PRR). Discovering this rate allows competing projects to be compared, the most desirable having the highest rate of return. This technique is probably best illustrated by an example which, for the purpose of clarity, is greatly simplified.

A project has the following characteristics: annual costs are committed at the beginning of each year, and these are the only costs during the year.

Cost at the beginning of year	Value (£)
1	2,500
2	3,000
3	6,500
4	4,500
5	4,000
Total	20,500

It is anticipated that when the project is complete at the end of year 5 it will be worth £32,000. The project rate of return is calculated by a trial and error procedure:

Earnings rate 15%

	Cash flow (£)	PV factor	PV (£)
Beginning of year 1	2,500	1	2,500
Beginning of year 2 (after 1 year)	3,000	0.870	2,610
Beginning of year 3 (after 2 years)	6,500	0.756	4,914
Beginning of year 4 (after 3 years)	4,500	0.658	2,961
Beginning of year 5 (after 4 years)	4,000	0.572	2,288
		Net present value (NPV) =	15,273

A cash inflow of £32,000 after 5 years has an
NPV value of £32,000 × 0.497   = 15,904

Earnings rate 20%

	Cash flow (£)	PV factor	PV (£)
Beginning of year 1	2,500	1	2,500
Beginning of year 2 (after 1 year)	3,000	0.833	2,499
Beginning of year 3 (after 2 years)	6,500	0.694	4,511
Beginning of year 4 (after 3 years)	4,500	0.579	2,605
Beginning of year 5 (after 4 years)	4,000	0.482	1,928
		NPV =	14,043

A cash inflow of £32,000 after 5 years has a
NPV value of £32,000 × 0.402   = 12,864

Earnings rate 25%

	Cash flow (£)	PV factor	PV (£)
Beginning of year 1	2,500	1	2,500
Beginning of year 2	3,000	0.800	2,400
Beginning of year 3	6,500	0.640	4,160
Beginning of year 4	4,500	0.512	2,304
Beginning of year 5	4,000	0.410	1,640
		NPV =	13,004

A cash inflow of £32,000 after 5 years has a
NPV value of £32,000 × 0.328   = 10,496

Given these three sets of figures it is possible to sketch (Fig. 13.1) the NPVs of the in- and outflows at various discount factors, the intersection of the two curves indicating the balancing point and hence the PRR of, effectively, 17%. Alternatively, a series of 'homing-in' calculations can

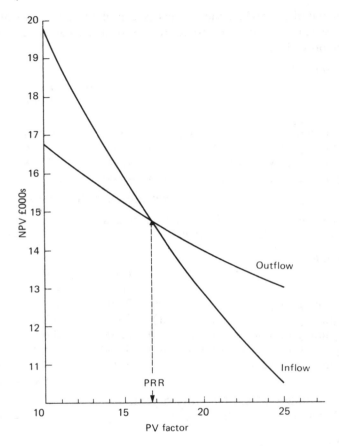

Fig. 13.1 NPVs of cash in- and outflows at various PV factors

be carried out. Clearly, attempts at high accuracy are time-consuming and unnecessary. The PRR value is then used to compare this project with any competing projects.

The above discussion takes into account only the 'profit' and lumps together all outgoing cash as 'annual costs'. In practice, there may be effective movements of funds due to factors such as:

wages,
payment for materials,
taxation,
allowances for depreciation,
various government grants,
maintenance effect,
training effort,

and so on. Further, these, and the income, may not be constant over the various periods of time: taxation allowances and grants tend to be substantial in the early periods, and output may increase as demand increases. In addition, the 'profit' may not appear in the year in which goods are made—it is not uncommon to find that goods made in one year are paid for in the next, so that the 'profit' accrues in the year after manufacture. All these points must be taken into account in order to produce as accurate an assessment of the flow of *cash* as possible, and it is *this* cash flow which is discounted back. The DCF technique is thus one which takes account not only of the effect of time upon earnings ('£1 *now* is worth more than £1 *later*'), but also of the other factors which affect profitability and which are not easily dealt with by other techniques.

Appraisal not costing

It must be emphasized that the above techniques and their variants are methods of judging the desirability of alternative capital expenditure decisions—they permit comparison of one project with another, or one project with a standard set for use in the company. They do not readily form the basis of costing systems, and they should not be used as such.

It is invaluable to check the actual results from an investment against the forecast results. This will test the assumptions upon which the forecasts have been made and help in the preparation of future plans.

Recommended reading

Clark, John, *et al., Capital Budgeting*, Prentice-Hall, 1984.
    A well-illustrated exposition on the planning and control of capital expenditures.
Holt, Robert N., *Capital Budgeting*, Ivy Soft, 1986.
    A short but excellent discussion of the salient features of the subject.
Kaufman, Mike, *Capital Budgeting Handbook*, Down Jones-Irwin, 1985.
    A fairly comprehensive statement of the subject with an international perspective.
Mott, G., *Investment Appraisal*, Pan Books, 1987.
    Short, inexpensive, simple to read. Includes discussions on DCF and Life Cycle Costing. Very useful.
White, John A., *Production Handbook*, 4th edn, Wiley, 1986.
    Provides some information which may help in the technical assessment of equipment.

14 Maintenance of the plant

Maintenance policies

Maintenance of plant and equipment in good working order is essential to achieve specified levels of quality and reliability, and efficient working—the best equipment will not work satisfactorily unless it is cared for, and the cost of a breakdown in the system can be very high, not only in financial terms but also in poor staff morale and bad relations with customers. The workforce and the materials must also be 'maintained', through training, motivation, health care and even entertainment for the people, and proper storage and handling of materials.

The objectives of maintenance are to:

1. Enable product quality and customer satisfaction to be achieved through correctly adjusted, serviced and operated equipment.
2. Maximize the useful life of the equipment.
3. Keep equipment safe and prevent the development of safety hazards.
4. Minimize the total production costs directly attributable to equipment service and repair.
5. Minimize the frequency and severity of interruptions to operating processes.
6. Maximize production capacity from the given equipment resources.

Within the context of maintenance, failure is defined as an inability to produce work in the appropriate manner rather than an inability to produce any work (see Chapter 9). Thus a piece of plant which deteriorates and consequently produces work of too low a quality or at too high a cost is said to fail. Work carried out before failure is said to be overhaul, or preventive maintenance work, while that carried out after failure is emergency, breakdown or recovery work (Fig. 14.1). It is worth noting that work can sometimes actually proceed while a plant has 'failed' but continues to produce: for example, some types of overhauls may be carried out at a power station while electricity is still being generated, albeit at an enhanced cost.

It has been pointed out by Chase and Aquilano that the maintenance

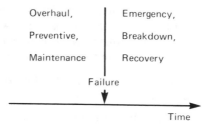

Fig. 14.1 The time of failure

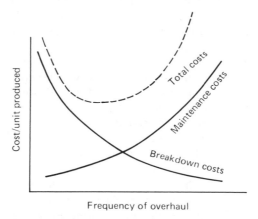

Frequency of overhaul

Fig. 14.2 Derivation of total cost of maintenance policy (*Note:* the *total* cost
curve is the sum of the other two)

system exists within and as a part of the operating system as a whole.
Inevitably the needs of the sub-system may appear to conflict with the
needs of the system itself. For example, frequent overhauls may reduce
costs by avoiding expensive breakdowns or replacements. Unfortunately,
the more frequently the overhaul the lower the availability of the plant,
so that direct production costs will increase (Fig. 14.2). Clearly it is the
total cost which must be examined in order to discover the most satisfactory maintenance policy. As in other areas of management, this 'most
satisfactory' policy is unlikely to occur by chance. Data must be systematically gathered and analysed. The costs associated with equipment
failure and the costs of overhaul work are compared and a maintenance
plan prepared, which offers a satisfactory match of costs and equipment
availability. In this sense, *all* maintenance work should be *planned*.
Historically, the term 'planned maintenance' has been misguidedly
restricted solely to the overhaul work; this is better described as *preven-*

tive. There are many cases where the best policy is to allow the equipment to fail before carrying out maintenance work. Such work is undoubtedly 'planned' even though the timing of the work is uncertain.

There are then broadly two types of maintenance policy:

1. Repair or replacement due to equipment failure.
2. Preventive maintenance.

The first type is an emergency-based policy, in which the plant or equipment is operated until it fails and then it is maintained. Formal preventive maintenance may take four different forms:

(*a*) Time-based, which means doing maintenance at regular intervals, e.g. every 2 months. It is easy to monitor time and this form is used when deterioration is likely to be time rather than usage dependent, or when usage cannot easily be measured.

(*b*) Work-based, i.e. maintenance after a set number of operating hours of volume of work produced, e.g. every 40,000 photocopies. Usage can be more difficult than time to monitor and some form of 'auto-counting' of output should be used, if possible.

(*c*) Opportunity-based, where repair or replacement takes place when the equipment or system is available, e.g. during a holiday closure. This can extend the interval between maintenance to an unacceptable level, but it may be suitable for equipment which has intermittently heavy use.

(*d*) Condition-based, which often relies on planned inspection to reveal when maintenance is prudent, e.g. replace a brake pad when it has worn to 2 mm thickness. This is dependent on monitoring equipment condition which can be difficult, and out of the question if a time-consuming strip-down proceeds any examination or inspection.

These various types of policy often operate together, overlap or coincide. For example, time-based and work-based maintenance will coincide if the rate of work is constant; condition-based replacement may occur during a time, work or opportunity-based maintenance activity.

The need for data

Choice between the various policies needs to be made on objective grounds if possible and this underlines the need for good data collection and analysis.

It is not easy to try to discover the actual time taken and the work involved when carrying out a maintenance task, particularly when the plant is large and/or complex and the maintenance work carried out far from simple. Rational policies, however, need to be based on data, and the need for the collection and analysis of reliability and maintenance information cannot be over-emphasized. Furthermore, it is invaluable to feed particular problems and difficulties back to the designer or supplier of equipment since it may be possible to reduce overhaul times on new equipment.

The collection of costs over the life of a piece of equipment, and the use of these costs to project costs over the life of new equipment, is known as life-cycle costing. Basically, the question to be asked is: *How does the cost of maintaining compare with the cost of not maintaining?* This is not always an easy question to answer, and some policies, particularly preventive maintenance policies, are often taken 'on trust'.

Preventive maintenance

Well-designed, preventive maintenance plans can reduce the incidence of emergency maintenance. In the production of standardized product design along flow lines, where there is little if any work-in-progress between adjacent operations, an equipment breakdown at one operation will quickly cause all other down-stream operations to come to a standstill. This situation can arise just as easily in the supply of cheeseburgers in a 'burger-bar' and the preparation of letters of credit in a bank as in the assembly of motor cars. An extensive preventive maintenance programme is essential to reduce the frequency and severity of work flow interruption in these situations.

In automated production environments, again not restricted to manufacturing, preventive maintenance programmes must be part of the POM policy. Where automated equipment operates continuously, without the need for operatives, human intervention will be required in the form of a maintenance unit to keep the equipment lubricated, adjusted and generally operating in good condition. As automation increases throughout various types of operation, there will be a need to move to smaller production workforces and larger maintenance crews. Hence, some of the production operatives replaced by robotics and computer-aided production systems will require retraining to provide the necessary increase in maintenance staff.

Because of the increasing introduction of just-in-time (JIT) methods, in which in-process stocks and batch sizes are reduced to very low levels, the near absence of work-in-progress will focus attention on equipment and system failure. JIT demands perfect equipment maintenance, since breakdowns cannot be tolerated. It is not sufficient to speed up repairs to minimize down-time: breakdowns must be eliminated through an effective prevention strategy.

Where operatives are employed in production, this strategy requires their total involvement. They must be given the responsibility for preventing equipment failure by conducting checks, inspecting, lubricating and adjusting their own equipment with meticulous attention to detail. Just as in the achievement of quality of conformance, operators must be given the tools to do this, and this means providing the appropriate training to be able to detect, find and eliminate potential causes of trouble before they manifest themselves in a system failure.

The maintenance unit

Duties

Many of the activities associated with effective preventive maintenance require particular knowledge and training, meaning that maintenance is a specialized service to production. In order to take advantage of the benefits of specialization, all direct maintenance should be carried out by one unit under a maintenance manager, who may be responsible for duties other than the maintenance of equipment. Since the production unit employs the bulk of the physical assets of an organization, it will be found to be most satisfactory if the maintenance department is part of the production/operations manager's responsibility. Separation between production and maintenance inevitably leads to frustration and dysfunction.

The duties of the maintenance unit include the care of plant, buildings and equipment, the installation of new equipment, and the supervision of new building. Typical sections of the maintenance department are:

1. *The millwrights and fitters*, who install, maintain and repair all mechanical equipment.

2. *The electricians*, who install, maintain and repair all electrical equipment including power plants and all communications equipment. A vital subsection is the group of electronic specialists who look after the increasingly important control systems so prevalent in today's automated plants. Although the actual maintenance of some of these may be in the hands of the owners of the equipment—for example, the telephone company or the local suppliers of electricity—all dealings with the owners should be through the maintenance department, so that individual complaints or comments should be made first to the appropriate maintenance supervisor(s)

3. *The builders*, which include any carpenters, bricklayers, plumbers or painters. Included in the responsibility of this section may be the provision and upkeep of all fire-fighting equipment (hoses, extinguishers, sprays, sprinklers), unless a separate department exists only for this purpose, and the care and control of the heating and ventilating plant.

4. *General labourers*, who will carry out the moving of material and equipment. These will usually include a 'heavy gang' equipped for and capable of manhandling bulky and heavy loads.

5. *Cleaners*, who will be responsible for all cleaning and sweeping, including the care of toilets and wash-places.

6. *Sub-contractors*, who are necessary to maintain specialist equipment, for example, telephones, computers and office equipment.

Rules governing maintenance work

In order that there should be some control over the work of maintenance, three rules should be enforced:

1. All requests for formal maintenance work must be made (preferably in writing) to one central control point. No work should be carried out without the knowledge and approval of the maintenance supervision at that point. Lack of strict adherence to this rule will result in a wasteful use of skilled staff and an inability to keep to any schedule of essential work.

2. Maintenance stores must be as carefully controlled as any other of the company's stores, as the absence of a vital part can lead to an expensive plant shut-down. On the other hand, excessive stocks can tie up valuable capital.

3. Records of all work carried out, including a statement of materials required, should be kept as these may assist in setting rational maintenance, replacement and depreciation policies. They are part of the essential database referred to earlier.

Planned maintenance programme

A routine maintenance programme can be set up as follows:

1. List all work which is required to be carried out by external authorities:

(*a*) The washing and/or the painting of all inside walls, partitions, ceilings and staircases.

(*b*) The thorough examination, followed if necessary by an overhaul and accompanied by a written report issued by a competent person, of all lifts, lifting equipment, cranes, hoists, boilers, weighing machines, weighbridges, postal and insurance franking machines, etc.

2. List, with the frequency required, all work deemed desirable by the appropriate manager. This will include the overhaul and servicing of all machines and items of plant, including office equipment, computers and any company cars or other transport. The frequency of maintenance may need to be set initially by the 'best guess' or manufacturer's recommendations but thereafter it should be verified against records kept of performance and breakdown.

3. Prepare standard documentation and instructions covering the maintenance required on each item listed. These instructions should be *in detail* and should avoid the 'overhaul as necessary' type of instruction.

The purpose to which the equipment is put should be considered when deciding the scale of the maintenance required, as identical pieces of plant being used for different purposes may well need entirely different levels of maintenance. In setting up these standard instructions, CPA can be invaluable in examining and determining the methods and in instructing the staff on all types of maintenance, from short-duration overhauls, with individual activities of only a few minutes, to very lengthy plant shut-downs.

4. Prepare a plan of work covering at least 12 months, in such a way that no maintenance section is in any way overloaded. This is very conveniently done on a Gantt chart, or one of the equivalent computerized planning programs for the control of maintenance work which are commercially available.

5. From the plan, issue instructions to the appropriate staff when necessary, requiring them to carry out work, and record on the plan when the work has been done.

6. Carry out post-maintenance audits to verify the times allowed for various tasks and to provide information for future policy-making.

To ensure that all items of equipment are included, it is desirable to number them and then to make a plant register. At the outset, this must be prepared from a physical inventory which is then checked against the organization's asset register. Thereafter it should be kept up to date by an information system that reports every piece of equipment purchased, replaced or removed.

The effectiveness of a maintenance policy and programme should be judged not by the vigour with which emergency repairs are carried out but on the freedom from such emergencies.

Reliability statistics and maintenance decisions

Maintenance staff will need to make decisions about whether to repair or replace items, components or parts of equipment and when to carry out scheduled maintenance. Reliability data can be useful to aid these, and many clues will come from the bath-tub curve (Fig. 14.3—see Chapter 9) which will be of use to the maintenance manager for:

(a) *diagnosis* of the causes of equipment failure problems;
(b) *prescription* of solutions to these problems.

As mentioned in Chapter 9, Weibull analysis of the reliability data enables maintenance staff to glean even more information. In particular, the slope of the Weibull plot (β) is of great assistance in selecting an appropriate maintenance policy.

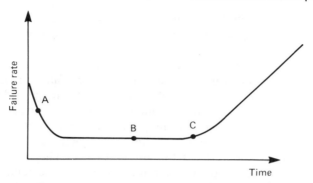

Fig. 14.3 Failure rate or bath-tub curve—typical of many products and systems

In Fig. 14.3:

Point A. Early failures (β <1). These are associated with a running-in period and may be due to sub-standard components of the product or service, or excessive stresses induced by incorrect installation or adjustment. As the weak parts are replaced by non-defective parts, the trouble should die away. Total system replacement at point A is not recommended since this will return the bath-tub curve to its start point and the early failure period will recommence. Improvements in failure rate can be made by better design and careful running-in and adjustments during commissioning. Should the hazard rate curve have the appearance of Fig. 14.4, a high initial failure rate, followed by a low and very long constant failure rate period—a characteristic typical of many electronic components—then scheduled replacement every 1,000 hours of service may result in 30 per cent failures in the first 24 hours! Replacement here, after the initial 'burn-in' period, is pointless.

Point B. Constant failure probability ($\beta \approx 1$). Random failures occur due to various possible combinations of circumstances. To reduce the level of failure rate in this period, it is necessary to examine the design and

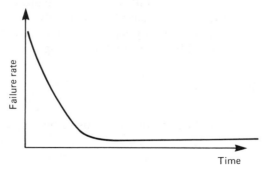

Fig. 14.4 Failure rate curve with extended random failure period

operation of the equipment. Emergency maintenance is required for the remaining random breakdowns since system replacement will re-introduce early failures.

Point C. Wear-out failures ($\beta>1$). The equipment, having survived the chance failure period, will encounter an increased failure rate associated with wear out. At this stage, the relationship between age and failure rate can be predicted, should be well-defined, and the preventive maintenance may be quantified. One important parameter to be determined is the interval between the preventive maintenance actions. If a time-based system is being considered, let this interval be T. The fraction of items which may be expected to survive until this time is the reliability, $R(T)$. This should be available from maintenance records. The fraction which fails, and hence requires emergency or breakdown maintenance before preventive maintenance is due, will be $1-R(T)$. From Chapter 9, the average or expected life of the items *if all are allowed to operate until breakdown* is

$$E(t) = \int_0^\infty tf(t)\mathrm{d}t$$

where $f(t)$ is the p.d.f. of failure. However, when a preventive maintenance policy (PMP) is operated, all surviving items are overhauled and, ideally, restored to an 'as good as new' condition. The expected life of the equipment can now never exceed the maintenance interval, T, and will in fact be less than T if any items fail during the period. The expected time for which the equipment is now functional is given by

$$E(T) = \int_0^T tf(t)\ \mathrm{d}t + T.R(T)$$

This can be rearranged to give

$$E(T) = \int_0^T R(t)\ \mathrm{d}t.$$

In the great majority of cases, $R(t)$ will be available as a table of values and not as a mathematical function. Even when such a function exists, it may well be difficult, if not impossible, to integrate by methods of calculus. It can always be evaluated numerically, e.g. by computer package, by graphing and counting squares to measure the area under the curve, or by a 'finite difference' method, using

$$E(T) = \sum_{t=0}^T R(t)\triangle t$$

Three examples should illustrate the methods to be employed.

Example 14.1

Ten identical pieces of equipment were installed during an annual shut-down. Their performance had been monitored over the previous 50 weeks and the times noted at which failure of the items necessitated their replacement. One item was still functioning at the end of the year.

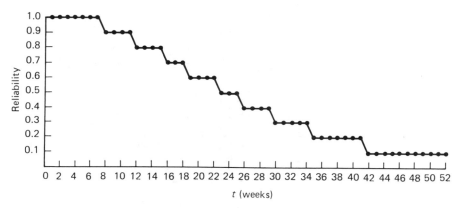

Fig. 14.5 Reliability data from Example 14.1

The reliability vs time data is plotted in Fig. 14.5. The average or expected life to failure of the ten items cannot be obtained directly as one is still functioning. If the company were considering a PMP for the items, involving maintenance every T weeks, then $E(T)$ can be calculated by measuring the area under the curve for the period $0-T$. (Table 14.2).

Table 14.1

Time (weeks)	8	12	16	19	23	26	30	35	42
Cumulative failures	1	2	3	4	5	6	7	8	9
$\therefore$ Realiability $R(t)$	0.9	0.8	0.7	0.6	0.5	0.4	0.3	0.2	0.1

Table 14.2

T weeks	4	8	12	16	20	24	28	32	36	40	44	48
$E(T)$	4	7.95	11.50	14.65	17.30	19.55	21.30	22.65	23.70	24.50	25.05	25.45

However, a PMP should only be considered if the equipment is in the wear-out phase of the bath-tub curve, i.e. has a Weibull parameter $\beta > 1$. The Weibull plot of the data is shown in Fig. 14.6. This shows that $\beta = 1.8$ and hence a PMP should be considered. The average life to

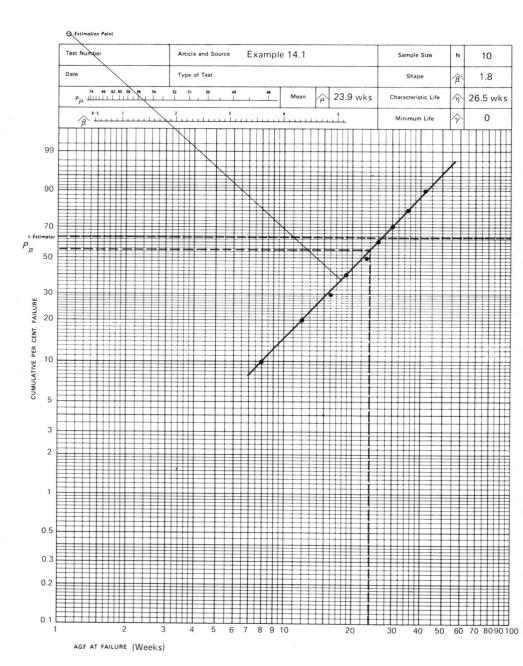

Fig. 14.6 Weibull plot of data from Example 14.1

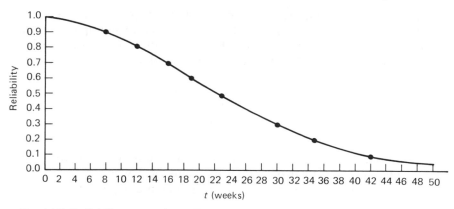

Fig. 14.7 Reliability curve from Example 14.1

failure of all ten items may be obtained, as described in Chapter 9 and is 23.9 weeks. Why is this less than the expected life if the items are replaced at, say, 40 or 44 weeks? The explanation lies in the overall sample size of only ten items and the random nature of the failures. A more accurate estimate of $E(T)$ would be obtained if a smooth curve were drawn through the points (Fig. 14.7) or observed reliability values were replaced by values from the Weibull curve. (Table 14.3).

Table 14.3

T weeks	4	8	12	16	20	24	28	32	36	40	44	48
$E(T)$	3.96	7.75	11.15	14.15	16.69	18.77	20.39	21.60	22.47	23.06	23.44	23.68

These values are now consistent with the Weibull value for expected life. A rather less tedious method of calculation uses the equation $E(T) = \Sigma R(t)\triangle t$.

So far, analysis of the reliability data has yielded an expected life, $E(T)$, the fraction of items to be repaired due to breakdown, $1 - R(T)$, and the fraction to be overhauled due to the PMP, $R(T)$. In unit time, $1/E(T)$ items would be expected to receive attention, e.g. if $E(T)$ is 6 months then, on average, $1/6$ of the items would be maintained each month; $R(T)/E(T)$ of those would be preventive maintenances and $(1 - R(T)/E(T))$ would be due to breakdown. It is now necessary to look at the costs involved in order to choose the optimum value of the maintenance interval, T.

If the item survives until the planned time, let the cost of the preventive maintenance action be C_M. Any item failing in service will almost certainly incur a greater expense, e.g. loss of production, programme interruption, damage to work in progress, cost of assembling an emergency repair team etc. Let this cost be C_F. In the simplest case, both C_F

and C_M will be constant. The cost per unit time incurred by items failing will be $C_F [1 - R(T)]/E(T)$, i.e. the cost per failure multiplied by the number of such failures. Similarly, the cost of the preventive maintenances will be $C_M R(T)/E(T)$ and the average cost of all maintenance action per unit time $K(T)$ is therefore:

$$K(T) = \{C_F[1 - R(T)] + C_M R(T)\}/E(T)$$
$$= \frac{C_F}{E(T)}\left[1 - R(T)\left(1 - \frac{C_M}{C_F}\right)\right]$$

The optimum policy is that which gives the lowest value of $K(T)$ and the problem posed is that of finding the value of T which achieves this. Usually, K_T is plotted against T to find the minimum value.

Example 14.2

Suppose that the items in the above example are submerged bearings in a fermentation vessel. Since they operate in a mildly abrasive environment, they are liable to failure and the maintenance work is to replace them. The fermentation takes 5 days and the vessels are then available for 2 days for cleaning, maintenance, sterilization and re-charging. If the bearing is replaced during this turn-round period, the cost is £400. If, however, it breaks down in service, an additional cost of £600 is incurred for items such as additional cleaning and preparatory work. A further £5,000 is attributed to loss of profits, etc.

Thus $C_F = £6,000$ $C_M = £400$ $C_M/C_F = 1/15$

$$K(T) = \frac{6,000}{E(T)}\left[1 - R(T)\left(1 - \frac{1}{15}\right)\right] = \frac{6,000}{E(T)}\left[1 - \frac{14R(T)}{15}\right]$$

Values of $R(T)$ are obtained from the Weibull plot, Fig. 14.6, and $E(T)$ from Table 14.3.

T	$R(T)$	$\frac{14}{15}R(T)$	$1 - \frac{14}{15}R(T)$	$E(T)$	$\frac{6,000}{E(T)}$	$K(T)$
4	0.97	0.905	0.095	3.96	1,515.2	143.9
8	0.91	0.849	0.151	7.75	774.2	116.9
12	0.81	0.756	0.244	11.15	538.1	131.2
16	0.69	0.644	0.356	14.15	424.0	150.9

Further calculations of $T = 6$ and $T = 10$ confirm that the minimum cost occurs after 8 weeks and the average cost is £116.9 per week per bearing.

By comparison, if the bearings are replaced only on failure, then the average life is 23.9 weeks, cost is £6,000 and average weekly cost is £251.

The ratio C_M/C_F clearly has a considerable influence on the optimum interval.

Example 14.3

Given the same data as in the previous example, with $C_F = £6,000$ but cost of a preventive maintenance now increased to £3,000:

$$K(T) = \frac{6,000}{E(T)}\left[1 - \frac{R(T)}{2}\right]$$

T	$0.5R(T)$	$1 - 0.5R(T)$	$6,000/E(T)$	$K(T)$
8	0.455	0.545	774.2	421.9
16	0.345	0.655	424.0	277.2
24	0.225	0.775	318.0	246.5
32	0.130	0.870	277.8	241.7
36	0.095	0.905	267.0	241.6
40	0.065	0.935	260.2	243.3

The optimum interval is now 36 weeks and the saving over breakdown maintenance alone is £9.4 per week. This may well be greater than the cost of running the scheme! In general, the smaller the value of C_M/C_F, the more likely is a PMP to be a viable proposition.

The above model contains limiting assumptions such as: repair restores equipment to 'as new' condition, costs are constant etc. These restrictions may be relaxed and more complex models developed.

When equipment or systems are designed, produced and assembled so that they run trouble-free, and can be easily rectified when necessary, they are said to have high *maintainability*. This can be quantified by the mean time to repair (MTTR). The measure of reliability introduced in Chapter 9, the mean time before failure (MTBF), can be combined with MTTR to give an overall measure of an equipment's *availability*:

$$\text{Availability} = \frac{\text{MTBF}}{\text{MTBF} + \text{MTTR}} \times 100$$

For example, a word-processor work station which has a mean time between failures of 800 hours and a mean time to repair of 3 work days ($3 \times 8 = 24$ hrs) has an availability of:

$$\frac{800}{800 + 24} \times 100 = 97.1\%$$

If the reliability can be improved and/or the repair time reduced, the availability will increase.

Repair and replacement

The repair limit

Repair—the replacement of defective, damaged or worn parts—is clearly part of preventive maintenance. However, when the costs of repairing are substantial and unforeseen, it is necessary to consider whether it is more economical to replace the equipment rather than to repair it. One simple method whereby this problem is not overlooked—or resolved by default—is to set a repair limit. If the estimated cost of the repair exceeds the repair limit, the piece of plant is considered for replacement. This emphasizes the need for adequate records to be kept for items such as cost of repair. Without these it is difficult to use the repair limit theorem. Easily obtainable, low-cost items are probably replaced automatically, while high-cost or difficult to obtain items are referred to a replacement committee. The value set upon the repair limit is likely to be a complex function, depending upon age, availability of replacement, possible loss of output and resale value. Repair limits should not be set 'once-for-all'—they need to be regularly reviewed.

Replacement due to failure

Group replacement
When it is necessary to maintain a group of items in working order, it is sometimes more economical to replace the group as a whole, even if some of the items are still functioning satisfactorily, than to replace each item as it fails. Such a situation may arise when the cost of replacement of an item as an individual is greater than the cost of replacement when it is replaced as one of a group. This is so well exemplified by the problem of replacing electric light bulbs that it is frequently referred to in the literature as *the light bulb problem*. The method of treating this problem is best demonstrated by an example.

The light bulb problem
Assume that past records reveal that, out of 100 new light bulbs, on average:

    80 survive for at least 1 month
    40 survive for at least 2 months
    10 survive for at least 3 months
     0 survive for more than 4 months

Furthermore, it is found that the cost of replacing a light bulb is made up of two parts:

(*a*) the cost of bringing the electrician, his mate and his equipment to the site, and this cost is £50;

(*b*) the cost of replacing a light bulb once the electrician is available, and this cost is 40p.

Thus the replacement cost:

for a group of n bulbs is   £(50 + 0.4n)
for an individual bulb is   £50.4
and for n bulbs replaced individually is £(50.4 × n)

The problem can now be stated as follows: Should each bulb be replaced as an individual when it fails, or should the whole group of bulbs be replaced after some interval of time?

For the sake of arithmetical simplicity, it will be assumed that there is a total of 100 bulbs at the site, although this restriction is not necessary.

Average bulb life
From the available data it can be seen that, on average, out of 100 bulbs initially good:

by the end of month 1 20 lamps will have failed
by the end of month 2 a further 40 lamps will have failed
by the end of month 3 a further 30 lamps will have failed
by the end of month 4 a further 10 lamps will have failed

Hence, there are, on average:

 10 lamps with a life of 4 months, that is a life of 40 lamp months
+30 lamps with a life of 3 months, that is a life of 90 lamp months
+40 lamps with a life of 2 months, that is a life of 80 lamp months
+20 lamps with a life of 1 month, that is a life of 20 lamp months

 100 lamps thus have a total life of   230 lamp months
that is, the average bulb life is 2.3 months.

Individual replacement
Replacing each bulb singly as it fails would entail replacing 100 bulbs in 2.3 months at a cost of:

    £(100 × 50.4)

that is, an average monthly cost of:

$$£ \frac{100 \times 50.4}{2.3} = £2.191 \text{ per month}$$

Group replacement
As it is necessary to keep the total quantity of working bulbs constant

at 100, group replacement will involve (*a*) replacing defectives as they occur, and (*b*) replacing 100 bulbs at fixed intervals of time. To examine this situation it is therefore necessary to calculate the rate at which individual replacements are necessary. This can be done analytically, but the underlying processes are probably most clearly shown by a failure tree.

At the beginning of month 1, there are 100 bulbs working satisfactorily, but by the end of that month, only 80 of the original bulbs are functioning; this is shown by the horizontal branch:

$$100^{0.8} \longrightarrow S \longrightarrow 80$$

where the transfixed S indicates survival, and the elevated 0.8 indicates the survival rate. In order to keep the number of bulbs constant, the 'dead' 20 bulbs must have been replaced, and this is shown by a diagonal line:

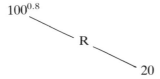

so that at the beginning of the next month the 100 bulbs are made up from 80 'originals' and 20 'replacements'. By the end of the month, the 80 originals will have dropped to 40 originals (a survival rate of 0.5) and 40 replacements. Of the 20 bulbs replaced at the end of month 1, 0.8×20, that is 16, will have survived, and 4 will have needed to be replaced. At the end of month 3, 10 'originals' will have survived, and

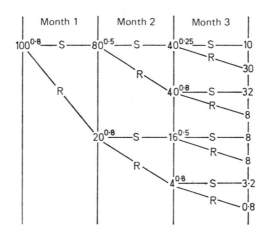

Fig. 14.8

30 will have been replaced; of the 40 replaced during month 2, 32 will have survived and 8 will have been replaced, and so on (see Fig. 14.8). In drawing a replacement tree of this sort, it must be remembered that replacements initially represent 'original' bulbs, and hence survive on average at the rate shown in the initial data, namely:

Out of 100 bulbs:
    80 survive for at least 1 month
    40 survive for at least 2 months
    10 survive for at least 3 months
     0 survive for more than 4 months

A complete survival tree for 5 months is shown in Fig. 14.9. From this it is possible to calculate the number of bulbs replaced on average from an original group of 100 new bulbs:

20 replaced in month 1
44 replaced in month 2
46.8 replaced in month 3
42.96 replaced in month 4
42.512 replaced in month 5

It is now possible to deduce the total cost of replacing the group each month, every two, three, four . . . months, etc.

Group replacement at end of month 1. There will be 20 bulbs replaced as individuals at a cost of:

$$£(20 \times 50.4) = £1,008$$

+ 100 bulbs replaced as a group at the end of the month at a cost of:

$$£(50 + 0.4 \times 100) = £90$$

Group replacement at end of month 2. There will be (20 + 44) bulbs replaced as individuals at a cost of:

$$£(64 \times 50.4) = £3,225.6$$
$$\text{say} \quad £3,226$$

+ 100 bulbs replaced as a group at the end of the period at a cost of £90;

∴ total replacement cost = £3,316

$$∴ \text{average monthly replacement cost} = £\frac{3,316}{2}$$
$$= £1,658$$

Similarly, the average monthly costs of group replacement at the ends of 3, 4, 5 months can be calculated:

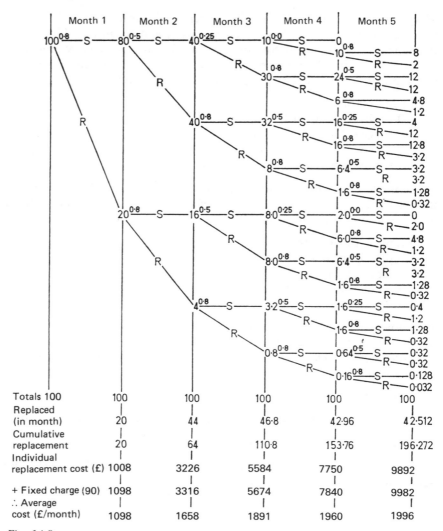

Fig. 14.9

Group replacement at end of month	1	2	3	4	5
Average monthly cost (£/month)	1,098	1,658	1,891	1,960	1,996

and comparing this with the average monthly cost of individual replacement—£2,191 per month—it will be seen that the most economic policy will be to group replace at the end of each month.

Failure which can be tolerated

The above situation implies that failure brings with it penalties so large that replacement must be carried out upon or before failure. In some situations the costs incurred by failure are such that inactivity, both of equipment and of the maintenance department, can be tolerated until some convenient time has elapsed, for example, until a specific number of items are not working, or until a shift has ended.

In this case, it is necessary to balance the costs due to inaction against the costs of replacement. Here again, it is necessary that information concerning failure frequency rates and replacement costs are available, as well as the costs due to inactivity. The necessary criterion then is that: the cost attributable to inactivity during time T must be less than the cost of replacement at time T.

Knowing the various failure parameters, the above conditions enable the optimum replacement time to be calculated.

Replacement due to deterioration

Inevitably, all equipment deteriorates with time, although in some cases the time span may be extremely long. To decide whether equipment should be replaced is a problem identical with that which was considered under the heading 'Equipment selection—methods of economic appraisal' (page 167). Here one of the pieces of plant being considered is the existing plant, and it is this which is compared with the alternative plant available. Clearly the various factors ('installed price', 'indirect charges', 'maintenance charge' . . .) refer to the values applicable at the time when the appraisal is being made, not the initial values which were usable when the plant was first installed.

Aspects of modern maintenance

Technology is increasingly more complex with electronics, robotics and computer control now influencing every walk of life. These have clearly led to many changes in maintenance activities. Special and continuous training programmes are required to provide the necessary knowledge, understanding and skills to service the increasingly specialized equipment, and to keep up with the developments in the field. Specialist organizations have developed to provide maintenance services on a sub-contract basis, and transport vehicles, computers, office equipment and medical support systems are often serviced by outside companies. The specialized technical knowledge and skills are frequently more economical to acquire on a call-in fee basis than an in-house team.

The advances in technology have enabled the development of systems which reduce the cost of maintenance while improving operational performance. These are usually computer-based devices which enable the detection of faults before severe difficulties, and even damage, occur. For example, sensing devices may be installed to monitor factors such as vibration, local temperatures, pressures, consumption of lubricants, changes in electrical resistance, composition of products from a chemical plant, etc. Changes in such factors often indicate changes in the condition of equipment and can give timely warning of approaching failure. This approach has been called *predictive maintenance* and can usefully be coupled to a preventive maintenance policy. Computers can, of course, be used in the actual maintenance for:

(*a*) planning maintenance;
(*b*) financial control of maintenance;
(*c*) spare part inventory control;
(*d*) reliability and failure data collection and analysis;
(*e*) operational research models applied to maintenance, e.g. queuing theory and simulation.

Modern maintenance management is far more than repairing and servicing equipment. The perspectives of maintenance must be broadened to the long-range performance aspects of the complete customer service system. Failure of any component in that system can cause total disaster, and the viability of the whole organization is dependent on effective maintenance policies and operations.

The authors are grateful for the contribution made by J. Geoff Marsland during the writing of this chapter.

Recommended reading

Borsenik, Frank D., *Management of Maintenance and Engineering Systems in Hospitality Industries*, 2nd edn, Wiley, 1987.

A specialist but none the less useful work, recently updated to reflect current thinking and approaches in the area.

Corder, G. G., *Maintenance: Techniques and Outlook*, 3rd edn, British Council of Productivity Associations, 1980.

Its title describes the text admirably. It remains a practical and useful book.

Cordero, S. T., *Maintenance Management Handbook*, Fairmont Press, 1987.

A new and comprehensive work covering the subject fully.

Kelly, A. and Harris, M. J., *Management of Industrial Maintenance*, Butterworth, 1983.

Answers the needs of industry in defining the maintenance management function and making sense of failure statistics and fault diagnosis. Well illustrated with practical examples.

Section IV **The processes**

15 Types of production I: job, batch, flow

It is usually accepted that there are traditionally three main types of production, namely job, batch and flow production, to which may now be added a fourth type, group technology, with its sub-type, the flexible manufacturing system, the subject of Chapter 16. It is important to realize at the outset that these types of production are not necessarily associated with any particular *volume* of production, and that depending upon the circumstances the same task can be undertaken by any of the above methods. It is also equally important to realize that the choice of production *type* dictates the organizational *system* and, to a large extent, the *layout* of the equipment. These three factors—*type* of production, *system* of production, *layout* of equipment—are inextricably mixed. The purpose of the present chapter is to try to indicate the main features of the different types of production.

Each type of production exhibits distinct characteristics and requires different conditions for its effective inception and working. The particular circumstances at any time must be carefully considered before a decision is taken as to the method of production to be used. Frequently the decision reached depends on the development of the company concerned. Many organizations start on a job production basis; proceed, as volume increases, to batch production methods in part at least; and finally manage to flow-produce all or some of the products concerned.

It must be said that it is rare to find in any unit that only one type of production is carried on, so that, in a radio factory for example, the final assembly of the receiver might well be carried out under flow production conditions, while the manufacture of the raw chassis was carried out under batch production conditions, the manufacture of the jigs, tools and fixtures proceeding under job production conditions.

Job production

Job, 'one-off', 'project' or 'make complete' production is the manufacture of a single complete unit by an operator or group of operators. Bridge building, installing capital plant in factories, dam construction and shipbuilding are common examples of this type of production, although even in these batch production techniques are being used.

Low-technology job production

When the technology for the job is low, the organization of job production is extremely simple as skills and processing equipment are readily obtainable. Thus a bespoke tailor with a small clientele will:

   (a) measure the client;
   (b) cut the cloth;
   (c) cut the lining;
   (d) tack the cloth together for a 'fitting';
   (e) try the tacked garment on the customer;
   (f) alter the garment as required;
   (g) make button holes;
   (h) fit all closures;
   (i) press the finished garment;
   (j) parcel up the garment.

The organization required for the above is simple. The tailor will need to have multiple skills, and the equipment needed will be available whenever required—utilization of equipment is unimportant.

Consider a low-technology job producer with, say, 5 orders (I . . . V) to fulfil, each job needing to go through stages A–D. The flow of material and work will effectively be linear:

As each job is finished, the process is repeated. Clearly, the producer must be capable of operating at each stage, and as work proceeds at one stage, say C, the other stages will stay unused. Value is added to the task rapidly and continuously as in Fig. 15.1.

It is conceivable that five producers could be set to produce the five jobs simultaneously so that each producer would have all the requisite equipment. In this situation the value added to each unit will increase continuously and in parallel as in Fig. 15.2.

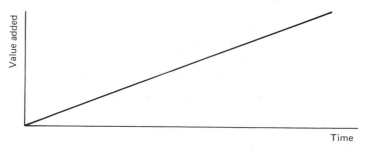

Fig. 15.1 Increase in value added for a single order under job production

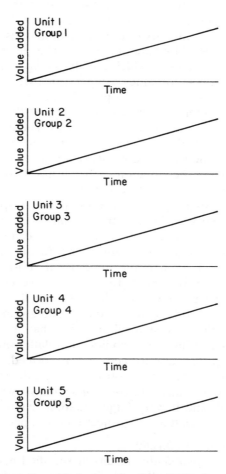

Fig. 15.2 Increase in value added when five identical units are produced by job
       production

Organization simple
Multiple operator skills
Low equipment utilization
Value added rapidly

Characteristics of low-technology job production

High-technology job production

As technology increases, managerial problems also increase, unless the labour force and other resources are dispersed at the end of each job, something which happens, for example, when a film is made by an independent producer. If continuity of employment and resources is required, transfer between jobs will create difficulties. This gives rise to a 'matrix' organization, the problems of which are still being actively explored.

Consider a job (job 1) for which a supervisor (M1) is responsible. The technology of the job calls for it to pass through stages A, B, C and D and technological complexity and cost require that the working group be made up of a number of different skill groups (sub-groups A1, B1, C1, . . .). To allow skills and other costly resources to be employed continuously, the organization as a whole deals with a number of jobs and at the time of examining the situation each job has its own supervisor and its complement of skill groups (see Fig. 15.3).

A member of sub-group A1 has thus a dual responsibility—*to job supervisor* M1 for work on job M1 and to *skill supervisor* SA for his skill performance. However, once sub-group A1 has completed its work on job 1 it will be available for work elsewhere. Assuming that job 10, say, requires the 'A' skill, then if the unoccupied sub-group A1 is of the correct size it may be transferred to job 10. However, if the group size is incorrect, sub-group A1 will be changed, and if several jobs require skill 'A', then there will be competition for sub-group A.

An individual with an 'A' skill will thus find that he not only has a dual responsibility, but that his responsibility and relationships are continually changing as sub-groups are formed and re-formed. Equally, physical resources may pass from job to job and from sub-group to sub-group. These shifting responsibility and communication networks are extremely difficult to control, and in very large situations control disappears altogether. The essential features of project control appear to be:

1. Clear definition of *objectives*.
2. Agreement on *quantifiable* results at specified periods of time.
3. A management committee which is *empowered* to take decisions concerning the needs of jobs, labour and other resources.

	Job		
	1	2	3
Skill / Skill supervisor / Job supervisor →	M1	M2	M3
A SA	A1	A2	A3
B SB	B1	B2	B3
C SC	C1	C2	C3
D SD	D1	D2	D3

Fig. 15.3

Batch production

As quantities increase beyond the few made during the earliest history of many companies, work may be carried out under batch production methods. Such methods require that the work on any product is divided into parts or operations, and that each operation is completed throughout the whole batch before the next operation is undertaken. This technique is probably the most common type of production, typical examples being the production of electronic instruments, transformers and so on. By its use, some degree of specialization of labour is possible, and capital investment is kept low, although the organization and planning required to ensure freedom from idle and waste time is considerable. It is in batch production that the production control department can produce most benefits, and these can often be spectacular, but it is also in batch production that it will be found most difficult to organize the effective working of a production control department.

> Concentrate skills
> Obtain high plant utilization

Aims of batch production

In order to clarify the difference between job and batch production, consider a small quantity of units, say five, being made by a number of operators. Under job production conditions, the operators would be divided into five groups, and each group would be responsible for the complete manufacture of one unit. Under batch production conditions, however, the work content of each unit would be broken into a number of operations not necessarily of equal work content, and the operators would again divide into groups. The first group would then complete the first operation on all five units, passing the batch as a whole on to the next group and so on until the manufacture was complete. In general, the batch is not passed on from one operator or group to the next until all work is completed on that operation: transferring part batches can often lead to considerable organizational difficulties.

It should be noted that, during the batch manufacture of the five units mentioned above, four units are always at rest, no work being carried out on them. Referring to Fig. 15.4, if material is issued at time 0, work will

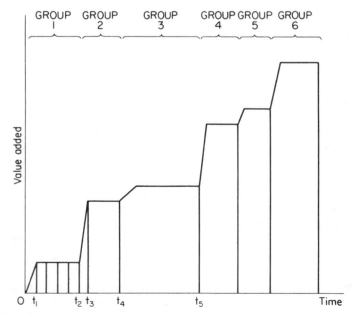

Fig. 15.4 Batch production of five units with no organizational delays between operations

be carried out on one unit during time t_1. This unit will remain stationary until time t_2 while work is being carried out on the other four units. Work will then restart on this unit during time t_2–t_3 when it will again rest until t_4, and so on. In fact, the rest periods of any one unit from a batch of n units totals $(n - 1)$ $n \times 100$ per cent of the total batch production time.

In addition to the rest period indicated above, the organizational difficulties of batch production may well generate other rest times. Where numbers of batches are passing through the same production stages, and competing for resources, it is usual to move a batch from an operator or machine into a 'buffer' or 'work-in-progress' store, to wait (queue) there for the next operator or machine to become available. This is characteristic of batch production, where the work content of the material increases irregularly and results in a substantial work-in-progress. The sequencing of batches from different jobs to reduce this source of 'rest' or queueing time is one of the most difficult problems encountered in the management of a production unit, and however successfully it is solved, there will inevitably be some element of rest time brought about by this competition for resources. Thus, in batch production, there is a rest period for each unit in the batch, while work is proceeding on other members of the batch, and another rest period while the whole batch is in buffer store. This results in the time between the origination of work on a batch and its eventual completion being much greater than the simple manufacturing time for the batch, sometimes startlingly so.

The effect of the considerable time lag between an initial investment in material and its subsequent translation into cash upon the sale of the finished product can be very serious in terms of the investment in capital which is tied up in the work-in-progress. On the other hand, the presence of the buffer stores permits the production unit to absorb shocks and changes, thus building in some element of flexibility, and it assists in making more effective use of the various limited manufacturing resources. This balancing of investment in material against investment in resources is a continually recurring task, and one to which there is rarely a simple, unique answer.

Batch production and functional layout

The statement above, concerning the irregularity of increase in work content, is highly simplified. Another, and much more serious, delay period is created by the layout of equipment in a so-called functional or process layout system. In this system, which is by far the most common within UK and US industry, equipment is grouped together according to the function which it carries out. Thus all drills will be together, as will all mills, presses, lathes and so on. This is most commonly met with in jobbing production, and again may be found in non-manufacturing activities. Provision of typing from a typing pool is a form of process layout, while in design departments it is often found necessary to divide the designers into specialist teams, each team dealing with all the problems of a similar type.

To examine the functional layout problem more thoroughly, consider a six-operation job where work must pass from processor A to processor B, then return ('back-pass') to processor A, thence to processor C, followed by processor D, being eventually completed by a final operation on processor B. This is represented by a 'technological route':

Operation	Processor
1	A
2	B
3	A
4	C
5	D
6	B

In a functional layout, all the A-type processors are grouped together, as are the B-type, C-type, and so on. For the job being considered, material is issued from stores and passes to the first of any unoccupied A-processor, say A2. When this first operation is complete, the material should pass directly to any B-processor. Due to the presence of other jobs, however, no B-processor is available, so that the material queues in a store. This may be a formally constituted and controlled store, or a pile of material next to a processor. For convenience, however, it will here be referred to as S1.

When a B-processor becomes available, say B2, material passes from S1 to B2. Being completed here, it should pass directly back to an A-processor, but again the presence of other jobs forces queuing in, say, S1. Eventually A5 becomes free, and the material passes to it for the third operation. Again storing is necessary before, say, C4 is available, and this 'processing—storing—processing' sequence repeats until eventually the finished job enters the receiving store.

The effect of this complex material flow:

(*a*) Causes material to be in the production unit, though not being worked on, for a time *very considerably larger* than the time represented by the work content. A throughput time less than five times the work content is rarely achieved.

(*b*) Creates an organizational problem of very high complexity. The single job discussed is but one of a number of jobs, each following similar, but not identical, routes. An attempt to display the total material flow situation in a small unit of 6 jobs, 4 processor units, and 24 processors is given in Fig. 15.5. This itself is a gross over-simplification:

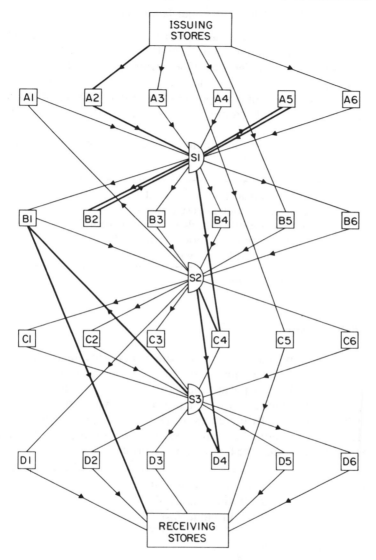

Fig. 15.5 A total material flow situation in functional layout

in reality, 100 jobs and 500 processors would not be unusual.

(*c*) Presents very difficult control problems, since each job must be tracked through each processor. This will often present data collection and processing problems which are so great that the control task is abandoned and all action is taken on an 'emergency' or 'fire-fighting' basis.

The advantages claimed for functional layout are:

1. Flexibility: job sequences and priorities can be readily changed.
2. Utilization of equipment can be high.
3. Since operators will tend to concentrate on a single process, their skills in this process can be considerable.
4. Supervision of a group of processors all carrying out the same, or a similar function, will create a considerable depth of knowledge concerning those processors.
5. The breakdown of a single processor does not immobilize production.

---

1. Organizationally difficult
2. Use of specialized skills
3. Possibility of high plant utilization
4. Probability of poor material flow
5. Value added slowly

Characteristics of batch production

Flow production

Batch production is characterized by the irregularity in the increase of work added to the basic material. Batch production turns into flow production when the rest period mentioned above vanishes, and so flow production can be defined as production during which the work content of the product continually increases or, as Woollard put it, 'the processing of material is continuous and progressive' (*The Principles of Mass and Flow Production*, Iliffe, 1954; now out of print).

---

1 Improve material flow
2. Reduce skills
3. Add value fast

Aims of flow production

Flow production then, means that as the work on each operation is complete the unit is passed to the next work stage without waiting for the work to be complete on the total batch. In order that this can flow smoothly, the times for each operation must be of equal length, and there must be no movement off the production line. For example, inspection must be physically located within the flow production line and the inspection function must not occupy more than the unit operation time. Furthermore, since the whole system is balanced, any fault affects not only the stage at which the fault occurs, but also all the stages in the production line. Thus a fault, occurring at one stage of a flow production line which cannot be cleared within the time cycle of the line, will result in that stage being held up. This in turn causes all the previous stages to be held up and all the subsequent stages to run out of work. So the line as a whole must be considered as a single entity and not allowed to break down at any point.

In order that flow production can function satisfactorily, the following requirements must be met:

1. *There must be substantially constant demand.* Should demand be spasmodic there will be a build-up of finished work which can give rise to storage difficulties. Alternatively, if production is caused to fluctuate along with demand, then the setting-up and balancing of the flow line will need to be carried out frequently, giving an excessively high total cost. In industries with widely varying demands, a levelling-out is achieved by making for stock during the 'flat' periods, the stock supplementing the current production during 'peak' periods. The price paid for this organizational simplification is, of course, the cost of holding the completed products.

2. *The product must be standardized.* A flow line is inherently inflexible and cannot accommodate variations in the product. A quasi-variety is achieved by varying finishes, decorations and other small items.

3. *Material must be to specification and delivered to time.* Due to the inflexibility mentioned above, the flow line cannot accept the variations in material which can be incorporated in a batch or job production process. Furthermore, if material is not available when it is required, the effect is very serious, since the whole line will be frozen.

4. *All stages must be balanced.* If the requirement that the material does not 'rest' is to be fulfilled, then the time taken at each stage must be the same, that is the line must be 'balanced'. This can lead to an inefficiency due to an inability to balance stages. For example, assume that a product with a work content of 8 man hours has to be made at a rate of 300 a week, with a normal working week of 35 hours.

$$\text{The total weekly work content} = 300 \times 8 \text{ man hours}$$

$$\text{Hence the number of operators required} = \frac{300 \times 8}{35} = 68.6 \text{ men}$$

$$\text{And the time for each operation} = \frac{8}{68.6} \times 60 \text{ minutes}$$

$$= 7 \text{ minutes}$$

Clearly it is not possible to obtain 68.6 operators—69 must be used. To meet the required production then, a flow line with at least 69 stages needs to be set up, the work content of each stage being 7 minutes. At best, therefore, there will be a loss due to the employment of the extra 0.4 operator needed to make up a whole number. In addition, it may be found that one stage has a work content of only 4 minutes and that it cannot be compounded with any other stage. Under these circumstances, this stage and another congruent stage will have idle times of 3 and 4 minutes respectively. These losses are 'synchronizing' losses, and the only way of avoiding them would be to increase the rate of production— something which presumably would not be acceptable to the marketing department. In the situation when an element cannot be reduced to the required stage time—for example, a machine-controlled operation is 10 minutes—then resources must be increased so that the effective operation time becomes less than the stage time. This can lead to an under-utilization of resources.

5. *All operations must be defined.* In order that the line will maintain its balance, all operations must remain constant. This can only be done if the operations are recorded in detail.

6. *Work must conform to quality standards.* In job or batch production, variations in quality at one stage can be compensated for by extra work elsewhere: in flow production this cannot happen, since each stage has a defined operation.

7. *The correct plant and equipment must be provided at each stage.* Lack of correct apparatus will unbalance a line, causing weaknesses throughout the whole sequence. This can result in a severe under-utilization of plant: should a work station require a piece of equipment for only a part of the operation time, this equipment must be provided *and its under-utilization accepted.* Attempts to share equipment between stages will, in general, destroy the material flow. In circumstances where the equipment required is extremely costly and its under-utilization cannot be tolerated, the flow line may have to be 'broken' at this point and batch production substituted.

8. *Maintenance must be by anticipation not default.* If equipment breaks down at any one stage, the whole line is halted. To avoid this a programme of preventive maintenance must be in force.

9. *Inspection must be 'in line' with production.* Unless the inspection stage is balanced with the rest of the production, a dislocation of the flow will inevitably take place.

The achievement of the above requires considerable pre-production planning, particularly in assuring that the correct material is delivered on time, and that the operations are of equal length of time. Common examples of flow production are the manufacture of motor cars, watches, domestic radio receivers, etc.

It must be noted that flow production is not necessarily large-scale production. For example, one firm found it profitable to flow-produce three equipments a day, a task which they had previously undertaken by batch production methods. The following advantages can be derived from the effective institution of flow production techniques:

(*a*) The direct labour content will be reduced, since the comprehensive pre-production planning which is necessary will often produce economies in time.

(*b*) Assuming the product is initially designed correctly, the reproducibility, and hence the accuracy and precision, are high.

(*c*) Since inspection is 'in line', deviations from standard are rapidly picked up.

(*d*) Since there is no rest period between operations, work-in-progress is at a minimum.

(*e*) Again, since there is no waiting period, the provision of work-in-progress stores is unnecessary, and the total storage space required is minimized.

(*f*) Handling is reduced.

(*g*) Control (including production, budgetary, quality and supervisory control) is simplified, the flow line being virtually self-controlling.

(*h*) Any weakness in materials or methods is immediately highlighted.

(*i*) Material requirements can be planned more accurately.

(*j*) Investment in material can be more rapidly translated into income from sales.

1. Substantially constant demand
2. Standardized product
3. Material to specification and to time
4. Stages must be balanced
5. Operations must be defined
6. Work must be to quality standards
7. Correct plant and equipment must be provided
8. Maintenance by anticipation not default
9. Inspection 'in line' with production

Requirements for flow production

One possible problem which may arise, particularly in high-volume flow production, is that the constant repetition of a short time-cycle task may induce boredom and frustration and consequent low morale. In turn, this may give rise to lateness, absenteeism, poor quality and, in extreme cases, positive disruption of the flow line to break the monotony.

Line balancing in flow production

In practice, the setting up of a flow production line involves two associated problems:

(*a*) the minimizing of synchronizing loss;

(*b*) the maximizing of resource utilization.

Where a product is complex, there are certainly a large number of possible sequences in which the operations can be carried out, and the choice
of sequence will affect both the above. The choosing of a sequence gives
rise to the class of problems known as *line balancing*, and a wholly logical
solution to these has yet to be found, although several heuristic methods
are available. This is further discussed in Chapter 12.

Continuous production

This term usually refers to production which continues for 24 hours a day,
7 days a week, throughout the year. Clearly this must be a flow
production process, and it usually implies a very high-volume, very
capital-intensive situation—for example, oil refining, sheet glass making.

Jobbing production

The term *jobbing production* is usually used to imply production carried
out only against customers' orders, and not for stock. It does not indicate
any particular type or method of manufacture.

Mass production

There is in common use the term *mass production*, which is often loosely
used to imply a particular type of production. In fact, mass production
is nothing more than production on a large scale, and as such can be
manufactured under either job, batch or flow production methods. The
greater volume of mass production will usually result in a reduced unit
direct labour cost, since a greater total expenditure on production aids
and service functions will produce increases in productivity without an
increase in unit indirect costs. Thus, if a number of small factories all
producing identical articles coalesce into one large unit producing the
same total quantity of the same articles, it is possible to increase considerably the effort on *work study, tooling, plant, inspection* and *production
control* beyond that in any of the individual factories. The total cost could
then be lower than the sum of the costs in all the individual factories—
although flexibility may be lost, inertia may be increased and morale may
suffer.

It is sometimes assumed also that during mass production quality
will of necessity suffer. This is not so: it is not correct to equate mass

production with *low* quality but generally with *uniform* quality, and this quality level depends on managerial policy and not on the scale of production.

Another equally invalid assumption is that increased production *necessarily* leads to increased profits. This is not always so: increased production may lead to reduced *manufacturing* costs, but the total net return to the enterprise may be diminished by the need to reduce selling prices or increase promotional expenses in order to sustain the volume of production.

16 Types of production II: group technology

Value-less costs

In batch production, four sources of value-less cost are important:

(a) costs due to difficulties in scheduling;
(b) set-up costs where preparation for production takes place;
(c) handling costs, where work is transferred to or from work stations;
(d) opportunity costs arising from the delays caused by the complexity of the material flow system.

Unit cost increases as batch size decreases, but it is seldom appreciated how frequently small quantities are produced. Representative figures are difficult to obtain, but Nishizaka and Endo remark 'at present in machining production in USA, lot sizes smaller than 50 pieces occupy 75 per cent of all production'; they continue 'in the factory we are concerned with . . . the batch size is a maximum of 30 pieces' with 'an average batch size of 3–10'. Work by G. Baguley, while in his final year at Loughborough University, showed that on one type of machine in his sponsoring company 80 per cent of the set-ups were for batches of less than 30 parts.

Activity	Percentage of machine time available		
	Centre lathes	Turret lathes	Capstan lathes
Loading and unloading	7.4	7.3	7.7
Idle, loaded, operator absent	17.9	16.0	16.7
Idle, loaded, operator under instruction	2.1	1.2	1.3
Miscellaneous	0.3	1.1	1.2
Setting and handling	25.4	27.8	32.0
Gauging	6.0	4.2	3.6
Cutting	40.9	42.4	37.5
Totals	100.0	100.0	100.0
Proportion of time employed	76.8	82.9	79.8

(*Machinery and Production Engineering*, 9 February 1966)

An exercise showing the effects of large numbers of batches was carried out by the Machine Tool Industry Research Association in 'four selected shops', with the result shown in the table on the opposite page.

Note: the difference between the totals of 100 per cent and the 'proportion of time employed represents . . . the time that the machines were out of use due to breakdowns, lack of operators and similar causes'.

Thus, of the total time the machines were nominally available, metal was actually being cut for only about 40 per cent of the time, while for over 25 per cent of the time 'setting and handling' was carried out.

The student's survey previously referred to obtained similar results in a rather different way. The process layouts for six months for all jobs of 15 components or less for three types of component were surveyed and the standard times both for 'set-up' and for machining were calculated with the following results:

Family	Total machining time (hours)	Total set-up time (hours)
A	402	479
B	460	473
C	541	398
Totals	1,403	1,350

The effect of these observations is to illustrate that, at least in jobbing machine-shops, the time spent on setting up is comparable with the time spent on adding value. In general the technology of production is well known and high: substantial increases in productivity are therefore likely to derive from other causes—for example, better scheduling, lower set-up times, improved material flow, better social relationships—and it is with these areas that group technology (GT) is concerned.

The technical approach

At the First International Seminar on Group Technology, Professor V. B. Solaja of Belgrade is reported by Drurie as saying:

> Group technology is the realization that many problems are similar and that by grouping similar problems, a single solution can be found to a set of problems, thus saving time and effort.

In essence, group technology seeks first for similarities, not differences. Similar parts are then collected into 'families', and these families manufactured on groups of associated machines. A typical family is shown in Fig. 16.1.

Once a family has been identified, a *composite component* may be envisaged, such a component being one which contains all the features

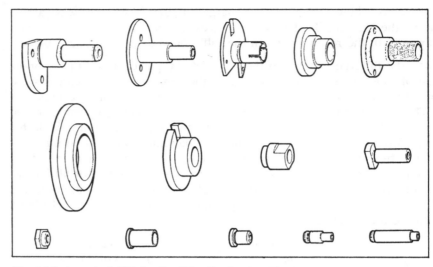

Fig. 16.1 A typical GT family (*The Production Engineer*, February 1970)

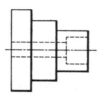

Fig. 16.2 The composite component derived from the family

of all members of the family (see Fig. 16.2). Although this component may have neither physical form nor physical expression, the concept itself is found to be an extremely useful one in later work. The available machines are then surveyed to find which group can best be put together to produce the family, and this group of machines then physically moved together to form a 'cell' or 'group'. The group is set up to make the family and the actual parts then produced by leaving out those operations not appropriate to the particular part being made, the effect of this grouping being to reduce total set-up time.

The social approach

While engineers were considering the problems of reducing set-up time, sociologists were suggesting that many of the current problems of industry were attributable to the 'de-humanization' of work. This resulted from working in highly structured environments, such as the batch production functional layout shop, where it is essential to attempt to plan and control the total working day of each individual, or working on long flow production lines with short cycle times where operators repeat the same simple task very many times during the working day. It was suggested, and experimental evidence was adduced to support the suggestion, that a 'humanization' of work should take place, where jobs were 'enriched', and operators given much more freedom to choose their own methods and tempo of working. Such suggestions clearly require alteration in the magnitude of the working group. Small-group working with considerable operator autonomy, therefore, seemed the next necessary advance in industrial effectiveness.

This 'sociological' suggestion coincides with the needs of group technology and the two streams of thought complement each other. The needs of group technology from a technical sense coincide with the needs for small-group working in a 'sociological' sense.

The managerial approach

Despite the advent of the computer, with its ability to handle vast quantities of data, the production function can require more information than can be handled if the organization is to proceed in a conventional manner. Many managements have attempted to create large 'control' systems whereby detailed reports on the day-to-day, and sometimes hour-to-hour, working of each operator, and location of each job, are recorded. These systems invariably have collapsed, not merely under the mass of information but also because of the difficulty of obtaining up-to-date information from the operating point.

Provided that a sensible balance has been struck between load and capacity in a planning period, group technology reduces this problem in two ways:

1. Planning the work flow requires only that work be planned into and out of a cell. *It is not necessary to plan the work through each processor within the cell.*

2. Monitoring the behaviour of the cell will effectively monitor the behaviour of all the people within the cell.

This delegation of authority 'to the coal face' is a difficult, sometimes traumatic, step for some managements to take. It requires that authority for detailed working be placed at the work point itself and many managers find this unacceptable. However, if an attempt is made to operate a GT system while at the same time planning work in detail on to each machine within each cell, organizational conflicts will arise which will destroy the effectiveness of the cell and of the production effort itself.

Characteristics of a group or cell

John Burbidge, who has extensive experience in the field of group technology, suggests that an effective group has seven characteristics. These are:

1. *The team*. Groups contain a specified team of workers who work solely or generally in the group.

2. *Products*. Groups produce a specified 'family' or set of products. In an assembly department these products will be assemblies. In a machine shop the products will be machined parts. In a foundry the product will be castings.

3. *Facilities*. Groups are equipped with a specified set of machines and/or other production equipment, which is used solely or generally in the group.

4. *Group layout*. The facilities are laid out together in one area reserved for the group.

5. *Target*. The workers in the group share a common product output target. This target output or 'list order' is given to the group at the beginning of each production period for completion by the end of the period.

6. *Independence*. The groups should, as far as possible, be independent of each other. They should be able to vary their work pace if they so wish during a period. Once they have received materials, their achievement should not depend on the services of other production groups.

7. *Size*. The groups should be limited to restrict the numbers of workers per group. Groups of 6–15 workers have been widely recommended. Larger groups to 35 workers may be necessary for technological reasons in some cases. Such larger groups have been found to work efficiently in practice.

Organization into a 'family' and 'group' will not only offer the ability to reduce ancillary time, it will also simplify material flow, increasing the velocity of the material through the system when compared with batch production under functional layout. In Chapter 15 it has been suggested that functional layout is likely to create queues of work as jobs compete for resources, and control problems as is necessary to monitor each job through each processor. In GT, queuing is reduced since cells are balanced to handle the foreseeable market demand, and control is provided by monitoring the *entry to* and *exit from* the cell.

For example, a product has six operations and a technical route as follows:

Operation	Processor
1	A
2	B

3	A
4	C
5	D
6	B

If this is a member of a family, the other members will have very similar technical routes. Demand for the whole family may justify the group comprising the following processors:

Processors	Number
A	2
B	2
C	1
D	1

The cell could then be set out *according to the technical needs of the family* (Fig. 16.3).

The material for the product then enters the cell, flows through it, the members of the family not necessarily taking the same route, and leaves. The only monitoring necessary *from outside the cell* is to observe the times of entry and exit. The control of flow *within* the cell is provided internally by the group leader or the group itself.

Families of parts

From what has been said, it is clear that the key to using group technology successfully is the ability to identify readily items within the same family. In an extremely small organization it is possible that this may be done 'by eye', but this is both haphazard and difficult, and it is desirable that a more systematic technique should be used.

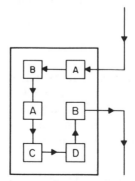

Fig. 16.3 Route for one component of a family

Coding systems

A 'coding' or 'classification' system may be used to group items together and some possible coding systems are discussed in Chapter 10.

Production flow analysis

While coding systems use the physical characteristics of the products to form families, PFA uses *the method of manufacture* as the point of departure for classification. The route cards are examined and progressively sorted into sets, the common factor in each set being the processor on which successive operations are carried out. Thus, the complete set of route cards is first sorted into *first operation sets* (sets A, B, C . . .) one of which (set A) will be the set of routes on which the first operation will be carried out on processor A. Set A is then sorted again into sets, these being determined by the second operation (sets AB, AC, AD . . .). Set A, B, the set which has its first operation on processor A and its second operation on processor B, is again sorted by the *third operation* (sets ABC, ABD, ABE . . .) then by the fourth operation (sets ABCD, ABCE . . . ABDE, ABDF . . . ABEF, ABEG . . .) and so on.

From this sorting, groups will emerge with common processing characteristics. Very small sets are examined to see if routes can be changed in order to move these small-set jobs into other larger sets. The larger sets are examined to see if they present adequate loads to the processors within the set, and again modifications are made to routes to balance loads where necessary. It may also be desirable to combine or to split sets to provide appropriate loading.

This system may appear tedious, but it will be found to be simpler in practice than in precept. Where very large numbers of route cards are involved, a sample can be taken to form the families, and Burbidge suggests that a manual analysis is readily possible with 2,000 route cards, so that a sample of 2,000 from 10,000 would be quite feasible. Clearly, of course, the sample must be a random one.

Choice of family

The composition of the family of parts which are 'housed' in a group is largely determined by the equipment available within the organization: too large a family will require a large number of machines in the machining group; too small a family may result in duplication of plant. Four aspects of the group likely to result from a family should be examined:

1. What load will the family generate?
2. What capacities and capabilities would be needed?

3. Is it possible to set up the group for the family?
4. Are the necessary machines available or obtainable?

It should be noted that:

(*a*) a group may in fact comprise only one machine (for example, a capstan lathe). This was generally the case with the Mitrofanov groupings described in Chapter 10; and
(*b*) it is unlikely that all the machines in a group are equally loaded—some degree of under-utilization is probably inevitable.

Ideally the family should be so chosen that it is economical to set up the group once and then leave it thus set up indefinitely. This is not always practicable, and a group may accommodate two or more related families whose set-ups differ from each other. In these cases it may be considered desirable to code the set-ups themselves, so that the production order not only directs the material to a group, but also indicates which set-up should be used. Note that the group should carry out the *complete* machining of a family in order to achieve the benefits of reduced handling and reduced synchronization loss.

Summary of benefits usually claimed for group technology

1. Reduced unit set-up time.
2. Improved learning, resulting in lower machining times.
3. Improved labour efficiency resulting from standardization and simplification.
4. Improvement in the effective use of machines.
5. Lower handling times due to reduction in transport distances.
6. Simplification in planning procedures.
7. Need for buffer (inter-stage) storage reduced with consequent reductions in:
   (*a*) stocks,
   (*b*) WIP,
   (*c*) storage space.
8. Throughout times reduced.
9. Simpler management.
10. Improved social relationships.

Application of GT to non-machining activities

All the above discussion has been around machining activities. Clearly, GT can be used elsewhere: plastic moulds with removable inserts are a form of GT. The literature describes a number of non-machining applications: see, for example, Ivanov, or an article in *Metalworking Production*, 11 June 1969.

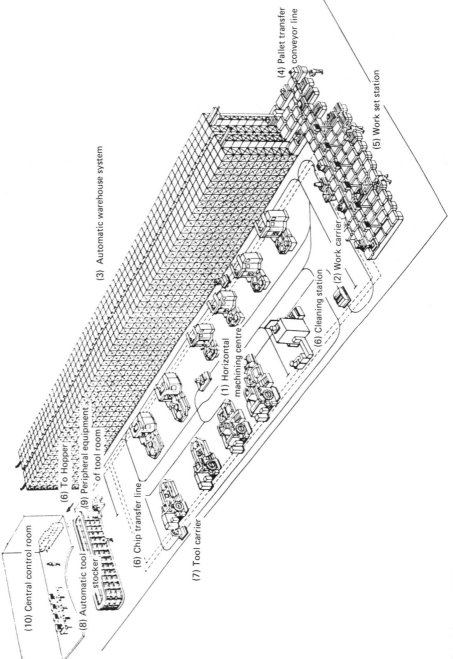

(3) Automatic warehouse system

(4) Pallet transfer conveyor line

(5) Work set station

(2) Work carrier

(6) Cleaning station

(1) Horizontal machining centre

(9) Peripheral equipment of tool room

(6) To Hopper

(6) Chip transfer line

(7) Tool carrier

(8) Automatic tool stocker

(10) Central control room

Fig. 16.4 An FMS—reproduced from *Management Guide to Flexible Manufacturing*. (*Permission:* Institution of Production Engineers)

Flexible manufacturing systems (FMS)

A flexible manufacturing system (FMS) can be considered to be a GT cell with the following facilities:

1. Machines which have the ability to carry out *their own set-ups* upon instructions from a computer.
2. Equipment which can move the workpiece from machine to machine at the correct time and in the correct posture, again at the behest of a computer.
3. A computer which will link together the machines and material handling equipment.

The consequence of the above is that the cell becomes very much more flexible (Cincinnati-Milacron claim that their Acramatic FMCC (Fig. 16.4) handles in excess of 40 different workpieces in random order) and the need for human intervention is reduced, ideally to zero. There will, clearly, still be the same needs as a conventional GT cell, namely the ability to identify a family (though the FMS family can be larger than the GT family) and to design an appropriate cell to handle the factors. Since human labour can disappear altogether from the cell, longer operating hours are very much more readily achievable.

There is one very substantial difference between GT and FMS, namely that FMS involves *very substantial capital investment*. The consequence of this, of course, is that the installation of an FMS is not a matter to be undertaken lightly. It requires a very thorough study of the anticipated market for at least the next 5 years and a thorough understanding of the objectives of the company. Those who have tried to install FMS without a substantial pre-planning of this sort have found that it has turned into a white elephant which is an embarrassment to everybody as well as being a financial burden.

Recommended reading

Burbidge, J., *The Introduction of Group Technology*, Heinemann, London, 1975.
   A practical book written by one of the great pioneers of GT. As with all Burbidge's work, the writing is lucid and helpful. The serious worker will find it well worth while seeking out papers on GT by this author.
Gallagher, C. C. and Wright W. A., *Group Technology and Manufacturing*, E. Horwood, London, 1986.
   A modern, comprehensive and well-referenced text.
Institution of Production Engineers, *Management Guide to Flexible Manufacturing*, 1986.
   An excellent introduction to FMS. Discusses philosophy rather than technology.

17 Work study I: method study

Work study is '*a management service* based on those techniques, particularly method study and work measurement, which are used in the examination of human work in all its contexts, and which lead to the systematic investigation of all the resources and factors which affect the efficiency and economy of the situation being reviewed, in order to effect improvement'.

This definition indicates clearly where present-day work study differs from earlier job improvement schemes: a systematic discipline has been set up, providing a framework in which to work. Regrettably, work study has been endowed with a glamour which leads newcomers to believe that it is a panacea for all the ills which arise in production/operations. This, of course, is not so: it is one of a number of equally important management tools and cannot replace good management, although it may indicate areas requiring investigation.

Traditionally, work study is associated with 'shop-floor' or direct labour. When applied to indirect work, the term 'organization and methods' (always abbreviated to O & M) is used. The techniques of the O & M man are exactly those of the work study practitioner, but applied to clerical and administrative procedures.

In a Joint Industrial Training Board report on *Training for Work Study Practice*, the following excellent statement occurs: 'Work study attains its benefits through, firstly, investigation of the current situation, examining especially any apparent weaknesses (for example, poor performance by an operating team or machine or the high cost of a job): this diagnosis is followed by the determination and introduction of appropriate improvements in operating methods. The investigation and review will cover operating methods, selection of type of equipment, usage of equipment, layout, supply and usage of materials, availability of ancillary services, e.g. materials handling, organization of work, effectiveness of planning procedures and progress control, and the potential effect of the investigation on overall cost and profitability.'

By virtue of its far-reaching nature, the inception of work study must be undertaken most carefully. For example, in examining the procedures for handling and processing documents, investigations may show that a significant cause of inefficiency is the time the computer takes to process the information. This might appear to be a criticism of the software developed by the data processing department, which in turn may be revealed to be conditioned by the general financial policy of the company limiting the size and power of computer purchased. Thus, what may start as a simple improvement of method programme may call into question the action of a number of senior executives. Such a situation could well cause considerable resentment and in some cases active opposition. An equally difficult situation is the employment of a work study practitioner in a department without adequate managerial support, so that any suggestions or improvements are not implemented. This results in bitterness on the part of the work study practitioner and work study itself being brought into disrepute.

At the outset of any work study programme, therefore, it is vital that all concerned should understand the principles, techniques and limitations of work study. As with any facet of management, success depends upon the co-operation of the people concerned, and positive steps must be taken to obtain the goodwill of those whose work is to be studied. *Secrecy, or the appearance of secrecy, must be avoided at all costs.* The ideal situation is one where work study is not considered as a separate entity but as an integral part of all activities. For this reason, it is highly desirable for 'appreciation' courses to be run for all management down to shop-floor/office supervisor level so that all concerned may learn something of work study. Many technical colleges and polytechnics will run such courses, and a number of employers' organizations and trade unions mount special courses for their members.

Present-day work study includes two closely allied techniques: *method study* of ways of doing work, and *work measurement*, which is the assessment of the time which a job should take. Both are carried out systematically and follow very similar patterns.

Work study

Method study
1. Select task to be studied
2. Record the facts
3. Examine the facts
4. Develop and define the new method
5. Install the new method
6. Maintain

Work measurement
1. Select task to be studied
2. Record the facts
3. Analyse the facts
4. Measure the task
5. Compile the standard time
6. Define method and its related time

By carrying out an investigation along the above lines, the ordinary practitioner will be most likely to achieve useful results. This is not to say that brilliant ideas never occur: of course they will, but their occurrence will be irregular and not to order. A systematic technique will certainly result in an improved method at all times.

Method study

Select

The selection of the task to be studied is a *managerial* responsibility: the attitude 'go and have a look around the production floor or office and find something to deal with' is irresponsible and not likely to produce long-term benefits. As with any other operations activity, a method study—and its subsequent implementation—will cost money, and an estimate of the likely costs should be made before starting. Should these costs exceed probable savings, then the study should only be carried out *if there are other valid, identifiable reasons*. Look particularly carefully at the task which is intrinsically interesting, or about which the managing director has 'a good idea'. Some indications of the possible need for a method study are:

Bottlenecks generating high work-in-progress, long delivery times, or unbalanced work flow.

Idle plant, equipment or people giving rise to an under-utilization of resources.

Inconsistent earnings, where the earnings are tied to output.

Poor or inconsistent quality, which may arise from poor or inappropriate working methods, procedures or conditions.

An injury of any kind may be caused by a poor method of working. It is sensible to method study *every* job at which an accident has occurred.

A critical path analysis of a project will show where effort must be applied to reduce total project time. Activity sampling (to be described in the next chapter) and Pareto analysis (Chapter 6) are also two techniques which can be used to help select the task to be studied.

It is unwise to carry out a study on a job where there is any form of industrial unrest—*the motives for the study will be suspect*. Once a task has been chosen, all involved—however remotely—should be informed, and the reasons for the choice and the desired outcome should be explained. Even quite innocent studies can take on a sinister appearance if the reasons for them are not known and understood.

Record

Once the task is agreed, the study will start by the practitioner concerned *recording the facts* by direct visual observation. 'What the soldier said' is not accepted as evidence either in a court of law or in a method study. This recording requires to be carried out extremely carefully, since important factors may be overlooked or ignored. *All* facts require recording, preferably at the time and place of occurrence. A number of different recording methods are available, and that which is used must be appropriate to the circumstances.

Process charts
These are 'charts in which a sequence of events is portrayed diagrammatically by means of a set of *process chart symbols* . . .' Their purpose is to provide an unambiguous, succinct record of a process so that it may be examined, analysed and—desirably—improved, usually away from the workplace.

Five symbols have been generally agreed and are in current use. These are illustrated in Fig. 17.1.

It is useful to differentiate between two types of operation:
'do' operations where work is actually performed on the material or equipment, resulting in an increase in added value;

○　　Operation:　　'. . . usually the part, material, product or document . . . is modified or changed.'

▷　　Transport:　　'. . . movement of workers, materials or equipment from place to place' without otherwise furthering the process.

▽　　Permanent Storage:　　'. . . a controlled storage . . .'

D　　Delay or Temporary Storage:　　'. . . a delay . . . for example, work waiting between consecutive operations or . . . temporarily laid aside.'

☐　　Inspection:　　'Inspection . . . for quality and/or . . . quantity.'

Fig. 17.1 Work study symbols

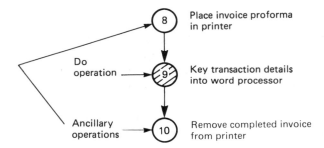

Fig. 17.2

'ancillary' operations where material or equipment is prepared, cleaned down, or put away.

Cross-hatching may be used to emphasize the 'do' operation, as in Fig. 17.2.

Distances are recorded to the left of the transport symbol, and brief descriptions are written on the right of each symbol.

These symbols, combined in a process chart, give a rapid picture of a process, showing clearly where it is worked on, where it is transported and so on. The care with which this recording is done will largely determine the final success of the study.

There are basically two types of process chart, differing in the level of detail recorded:

(a) *Outline process chart*. In this, the overall picture of the sequence of events and of the introduction of materials in a process is given by recording operations and inspections, using only two symbols (the circle and the square) of the five available.

(b) *Flow process chart*. This provides considerably more detail than the outline process chart, and all five symbols are used. Flow process charts refer either to the *man* (or machine/equipment), that is, to the activities performed by the man, or to the *material* (the activities carried out upon the material) and not normally to both simultaneously. Two-handed charts can be drawn, and pre-printed forms (see Fig. 17.3) are often found to be most economical.

Time-scaled charts

These are charts where two or more activities which are proceeding concurrently or simultaneously are shown on a common time scale. Again there are broadly two sets of time-scaled charts, differing in the level of detail:

(c) *The multiple activity chart*. This chart, which may be considered to be a vertical Gantt chart, is used to show the time relationships

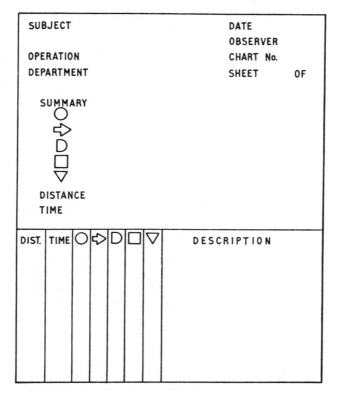

Fig. 17.3 Pre-printed form for flow process chart

between two or more men, machines or materials. Essentially, a vertical column is erected for each of the protagonists, and the work performed is recorded as shading within the column. Time is recorded on the left and a brief description of the activities on the right. From the chart, the ratio of working to non-working time can be determined, and an attempt at balancing can be made.

(*d*) *The simultaneous movement chart* (SIMO chart). In this the movements of two or more parts of a worker's body are recorded. The movements are generally of very short duration—of the order of milliseconds—and the preparation of a SIMO chart usually requires a frame-by-frame analysis of a cine film or video tape of the work being studied. The elements of work may be recorded by *therblig symbols*, which were first used by Gilbreth, hence the name—therblig is Gilbreth spelt backwards (almost!). There are now 17 therbligs covering such elements as grasp, hold, unavoidable delay. There are a number of varieties of SIMO charts which do not use therblig symbols, but employ one or other of the *predetermined motion time systems* (PMTS) codes. These codes usually carry with them time values for the performance of the individual elements being recorded, and the PMTS charts are most frequently prepared as a means of work measurement. These are discussed in more detail in Chapter 18. While SIMO charts can enable imbalances to be detected, they are difficult to prepare, and likely to be expensive both in time and equipment. They are used only if very great justification can be demonstrated.

Movement charts
When movement is to be recorded, one or other of the movement charts is employed:

(*e*) *Travel chart.* In complex situations it is sometimes confusing to try to use a flow diagram, and a travel chart (see Fig. 17.4) can be used. In this, the number of movements made over a period of time can be recorded. Movement is always assumed to start with the left-hand row title and move to the column headings, so that movements from department 7 to department 4 and from department 2 to department 16 are as shown by the two crosses. By adding up the crosses in the rows, the

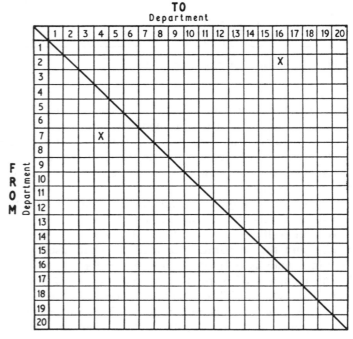

Fig. 17.4 Travel chart

'movements out' can be found, while summing the columns gives 'movements in'.

(*f*) *Flow diagram*. This displays the workplace and the locations of the various activities, drawn to scale. The five standard symbols are used, and the diagrams again refer to man, material or machines/equipment. Effectively, it can be considered to be a flow process chart drawn upon a scale drawing of the workplace.

(*g*) *String diagram*. Here again a scale drawing is used which is mounted upon a wooden panel. A preliminary survey identifies the locations of terminal points, and a fine string is wound between these pins to represent movement, supplementary pins being inserted where directions of movement change. The advantage of string over pencil marks on a piece of paper is that repeated journeys over common paths can be shown without risk of obliteration or confusion. Unwinding and measuring the strings will enable the distances moved to be discovered. The string diagram will display vividly faults in a layout which cause bottlenecks, back- or cross-tracking or other movement difficulties.

Examine and develop

The examination and analysis of the facts and the development of a new method can, and in general should, be carried out away from the place where the task is being performed. It is not easy to separate the development from the analysis, and for this reason these two are considered together.

In order to ensure that a new method is developed, there are two essentials:

(*a*) an open mind, and
(*b*) a systematic approach,

and within particular organizations, a 'laundry list' of possible alternative procedures, methods and materials may be found useful. The open mind is largely a matter of experience and climate within the organization: recriminations about past decisions, and investigations into past reasons and behaviour serve little purpose and invariably generate ill-feeling. The systematic approach can be assisted by the questioning technique.

The questioning technique

The activities in a process are subjected to an interrogation which follows a fixed pattern. It may be thought that 'delays' and 'transportations' should be attacked first, but this is not so: an 'operation' which is eliminated may well cause a 'delay' or a 'transportation' to disappear. Similarly, a modification to a 'do' operation may remove the need for an 'ancillary' operation. Hence *attack 'do' operations first*.

1. *Purpose*   What is being done?
                Why is it being done?
                What else could be done?
                What should be done?

2. *Place*   Where is it being done?
                Why there?
                Where else could it be done?
                Where should it be done?

3. *Sequence* When is it done?
                Why then?
                When else could it be done?
                When should it be done?

4. *Person*   Who does it?
                Why that person?
                Who else might do it?
                Who should do it?

5. *Means*   How is it done?
                Why that way?
                How else can it be done?
                How should it be done?

These questions are asked *in the above order*: if the purpose is dislodged, all other questions are meaningless. If the place is changed, then the sequence, person and means may be altered. If, on the other hand, the means is questioned *first*, then a great deal of effort may be expended in analysing and improving a method which is later found to serve no useful purpose.

From the above recording and analysing, a picture of a new method will begin to emerge. This is a difficult step to systematize, and the speed with which a new method is proposed will depend on the experience, background and ingenuity of the practitioner concerned. Nevertheless, the more closely is the job examined and analysed, the easier it will be to *develop the new method*. Moreover, the first two questions of each of the five sets can be thought of as forming the 'examination' phase, while the second two comprise the 'develop' stage. The technique of 'brainstorming' can sometimes help with this. It may be that the new method will require the design of a jig, tool or other production aid beyond the ability of the work study practitioner. In this case, the assistance of an expert will need to be recruited—for example, a jig and tool designer—and the performance of the device required must be specified in some detail. It must be remembered that the best solution is always the most simple and, if a block of wood with a nail in it will do the job required, a more elaborate device would be undesirable. The new method should be recorded in the same way as the existing one, the two compared, and a summary of the advantages made, along with the cost of the new installation. Any new method must, of course, be inherently safe.

Install

The new method, once approved by the work study man, and the expenditure (if any) authorized by the appropriate person, requires to be *installed*. A process layout must be written and the technique 'sold', first to the supervisor and the management, and then to the operators concerned. Without goodwill the new method may well fail—no system or method is any better than the persons operating it. Many a good idea has fallen down because the operator concerned has not accepted it. In 'selling' the idea, the work study practitioner must first 'sell' himself: this does not mean that he must be offensively 'hearty' or friendly, but he must be respected and trusted by the operators. During the course of a study, the practitioner will have much information thrust upon him and he must not abuse the confidence placed in him by disclosing information intended for his ears alone. Once the idea is accepted, the operator must be trained in it by precept and example, and a habit of good working developed. Training is not considered complete until the productivity expected is achieved.

Maintain

Inevitably, habits of work different from those desired by the work study practitioner will develop unless the method/procedures are *maintained*. This may require continual visits from the practitioner concerned, but it is better if this is done by the operator's immediate supervisor. To be able to˙ do this the method must be written down clearly and concisely and thoroughly understood by the supervisor. If variations in the procedures then arise, he can either correct them or, if they appear desirable, submit them to the work study department for incorporation into the process layout.

Methods improvement and materials handling

The movement of material and documentation from one place to another is found within every organization, and its study—materials handling— is sometimes considered to be a separate discipline. It is, in fact, one aspect of work study, and any materials-handling problem must be solved by normal work study techniques. This section will introduce some of the considerations specific to materials handling. Inevitably, much of this is more relevant to manufacturing than non-manufacturing, although there are some common points.

Costs of materials handling

The costs of materials handling are often difficult to identify: however, it seems likely that in many factories, *at least* one-quarter of the final cost is attributable to the handling of the materials. It is suggested that every manager should cause an investigation to be carried out on the handling costs within his organization. The results would certainly be illuminating and probably alarming. Ignorance of the magnitude of the costs of materials handling is certainly one reason why so little attention is paid to this important subject. It is frequently found that improvements in materials handling provide the quickest and cheapest ways of improving profitability, although attention to this matter should always be given in the initial design and layout of the operating unit.

---

1. Ignorance of costs
2. Poor equipment layout
3. Poor stores layout
4. Excessive manual effort
5. Inadequate/inappropriate equipment

Some causes of high materials handling costs

Unlike many other operations, the movement of materials adds to the cost of the product or service while leaving its value unchanged. It is therefore important first to *reduce the need* for the handling, and second to *reduce the cost* for that handling which is inevitable. Any materials-handling problem must thus start with the layout of the department (the criterion of minimum distance: 'all movements will be both necessary and direct' must be applied), and with the design of the product or service, which should be that, during the various stages of provision, no unnecessary material is transported. This latter aspect coincides with the view that the most economical design is that which requires least material and documentation to be removed. It is often said that the best materials handling is no materials handling.

Aids to good materials handling

Accepting that there is an inescapable need for some handling, attention should be given to:

(*a*) *Correct identification of material and documentation.* The cost and frustration of trying to identify anonymous material and documentation is high.

(*b*) *Correct packing of material and documentation.* Easily damaged material requires careful handling and this in itself is costly. While the use of NCR (no carbon required) paper permits multi-part documentation to be prepared more efficiently, it must be handled carefully if the copies are to be kept legible and unmarked.

(*c*) *Capacity of equipment.* To try to economize by purchasing light or near-capacity equipment is frequently a false economy since it may result in multiple loads being required, rather than single loads.

(*d*) *Size of load.* Always move the largest possible loads, again to avoid multiple handling.

(*e*) *Weight of container.* The heavier the load, the more difficult it is to move. Effort should be expended in moving the material, rather than the container—hence, use the lightest possible container.

---

1. Identification of material
2. Method of packing
3. Capacity of equipment
4. Size of load
5. Weight of container

Check-list when handling material

The reduction of cost of residual movement can be considered under the following four headings.

Use of manpower
The use of manpower for moving material is so flexible that it tends to be used extravagantly. The following rules apply:

1. Do not use productive operators for moving material: use labourers or messengers.

2. Do not move in small quantities: the use of a full wheelbarrow or sack-truck is easier and cheaper than the movement of single items.

3. Do not require loads to be manually raised above shoulder height or set upon the floor. Keep the loads at working height.

Use of gravity
Gravity is always present, and can provide a cheap and reliable source of motive power. Slides, chutes, roller conveyors and ball tables all will assist in the easy movement of material, and roller conveyors can be assembled in very many ways, incorporating junctions, branches, gates and traps of all sorts. A large bottling plant will usually provide an exhilarating view of the adaptability of the roller conveyors. By mounting lengths of roller conveyor on wheeled frameworks, portable unloading conveyors can be made, and these are much used in industries such as

the building industry, where loads have to be deposited at widely different points which vary from day to day.

Use of power

Gravity conveyors are limited in that they will work only on a downward incline and they are not suitable for moving certain types of goods—for example, powders and liquids—without subsidiary containers. For any movements on the level or uphill, therefore, powered conveyors are necessary. The addition of power often permits operations to be carried out by the conveyor system itself, and many multi-stage plants are machines linked by conveyors or conveyors with machines added to them. The power is not only available to carry out the work; it can also control the flow, and precise timing of movements is possible.

Use of packaged loads

Conveyors in general can be used for the continuous movement of goods, and the conveyor itself can be allowed to run whether it is carrying material or not. An alternative method of moving material is by means of devices which convey discrete loads. These have been widely developed and are particularly useful in the storage rather than in the processing of material. They include:

1. *Hoists and cranes.* These are flexible in use, cranes in particular being capable of being moved. Most hoists can run along a fixed line, and the electrically powered block and tackle which can be operated by a hand-held switch is extremely useful in stores, and receiving and despatch departments, where it can be used to load and unload lorries. There are often statutory requirements concerning the maintenance, overhaul and inspection 'by an approved person' of hoists and cranes.

2. *Trucks.* These may be either physically or mechanically propelled, and consist of a platform upon which loads of any shape and size may be placed for onward transmission. Since the platform is fixed, loading and unloading must be performed by hand, when weight becomes significant, or by crane or hoist, where availability of loading equipment is important. This can result in a poor utilization of truck and driver.

3. *Lifting trucks.* These are rapidly replacing ordinary fixed-bed trucks. They are either hand or power propelled, the most common being driven by battery operation, and their use has revolutionized storage and handling of material.

Most lift trucks are of the so-called 'fork-lift' type: lifting is performed by a pair of projecting arms (the forks) which can rise up a pair of parallel uprights. The method of operation revolves around the use of 'pallets', which are portable platforms upon which work is loaded. The forks are inserted below the platform of the pallet, then raised to clear the ground, and the truck moved to the new destination of the material. The essential difference between a pallet and a stillage is that pallets are intended to be stacked upon each other, and herein lies the greatest virtue of the fork-lift truck and pallet. The fork-lift can raise pallets, in some cases up to 20 feet, although heights of 8–10 feet are more common at the moment. By storing loaded pallets on top of each other, maximum use can be made of headroom, and so the floor area of stores can be reduced to a minimum. Gangways must be large enough to allow a truck to operate.

The environment and efficiency

The effectiveness with which work is carried out is conditioned not only by *method* but also by *environment*. Indeed, it is artificial to separate these factors since they are clearly interdependent, and the only justification which can be offered here is that of practical convenience. A further simplification will also be introduced, namely that of considering only the *physical* environment and ignoring the more subtle and probably more important psychological aspects of work.

The study of man in his working situation is known in the UK as *ergonomics*, from the Greek word for work, or, in the USA, as *human engineering*. While the intuitive use of ergonomic concepts is not new, the codification and classification of knowledge received a very considerable impetus from the demands of the armed forces during the Second World War. Regrettably, however, much of the material currently available is either not used or ignored by the designers of machines and equipment, so that it is still not uncommon to find controls so placed that they cannot be conveniently operated, or adjustments which can only be carried out by three-armed midgets.

Man and his dimensions

It is a matter of common observation that man, like all other products of man, is variable. As a consequence, equipment for general use should either be capable of simple and rapid adjustment (for example, the typist's chair) or it should be so designed that it will cater for the majority of persons likely to use it (for example, the access door to a workroom). To be able to ensure that one or other of these conditions is met, it is necessary to know something of the significant dimensions of the human body and how they vary across the population being examined.

There are numbers of anthropometric tables available and, while useful, they must be treated with care as the information set out in them may depend upon many factors, including sex, geographical origin, age and occupation. Thus, the figures obtained from a study of, say, recruits to the City of London Police Force are not likely to be of immediate application when designing equipment for, say, the use of drivers of the Paris Metro.

If a table of dimensions is available from a population which differs from that which is required, then all dimensions can be multiplied by the ratio of the mean height of the initial population to that of the required population. Possibly more useful than the sample tables of human dimensions are the recommendations for equipment dimensions published by the British Standards Institution.

Man at the workplace

Without suggesting that the psychological circumstances of work are not of very great importance, man can also be regarded as a machine with well-known physical requirements. These requirements are frequently ignored, and the ability of man to function in unsuitable situations is quite remarkable. However, to ignore them will inevitably result in stress and discomfort, and therefore any such action should be *as a result of a positive decision* and not as a result of apathy or drift.

Man's physical requirements at the workplace have been, and are still, the subject of considerable research. The results of this research and much experience are here summarized:

1. *Sit rather than stand*. Unless there is some overwhelming reason not to, work should be carried out seated. Even when work demands that the operator stands, then a comfortable seat should be provided for use whenever the work-cycle permits.

2. *Permit a change in position*. The workplace should not be so designed that the working posture cannot be changed. A fixed position is invariably tiring, and should be avoided.

3. *Aim for a natural working position*. Any working position which involves an unnatural posture—a twisted trunk or an extended arm position, for example—will create undue fatigue.

4. *Keep movements symmetrical*. Balanced movements are not only less tiring, they are also more easily controlled.

5. *Ensure adequate working space*. A confined space is not only psychologically distressing, it may increase physical fatigue by causing muscles to be tensed in an effort to avoid the constrictions.

6. *Ensure working area is at a comfortable height*. The correct height of a working area will depend on the nature of the work: fine work (for example, watch assembly) needing to be nearer to the eye than coarse work (for example, ironing in a laundry). Since the possible occupants of a working area differ in size, adjustable heights and distances are desirable.

7. *Use mechanical devices to hold work.* The use of the hands to hold work is generally unnecessary and always tiring. Jigs and/or fixtures can usually be designed to remove the need for the hands to act as clamps. For example, document holders should be provided for operators keying data into a VDU.

8. *Support arms.* Support can often be usefully provided for elbows, forearms and hands. These should be upholstered, adjustable, generous in size and robust.

9. *Support feet.* Feet should, if possible, be placed firmly and comfortably upon the floor. If this is not possible, a robust footrest should be provided. A single bar or an upturned transit box are generally not satisfactory.

---

1. Sit rather than stand
2. Permit a change in posture
3. Aim for a natural working position
4. Keep movements symmetrical
5. Ensure adequate working space
6. Ensure comfortable working height
7. Use mechanical devices to hold work
8. Support arms
9. Support feet

Man as a machine

Man and the machine

Man is essentially a tool-using animal, and the earliest tools, often extensions of their users, were built for an individual's personal use and modified to have the correct 'heft' and 'feel'. Today, tools tend to be much more complex, and the working power provided from sources outside the user. This results in a loss of direct contact between the operator and the workpiece, so that he/she will need to receive information concerning the work and transform this into action by operating some form of control. Care must be thus taken to ensure that the operation of the machine does not become so complex that it is an end in itself and either the work or the operator suffers.

Information

All information provided should be *pertinent, adequate, timely* and *accurate*. Broadly, there are three ways of presenting information: by sound, by vision and by touch.

Sound

Sound signals are extremely useful for alarm and warning purposes, and are most effective if used intermittently. Continuous sound signals—for example, those sometimes used in tuning radio equipment—can become tiring and ineffective, and are best replaced, if at all possible, by visual displays. One advantage of the audible signal is that it can force itself upon the operator's attention, so that a worker engaged upon a task can readily have his attention drawn to a breakdown or malfunction.

Sight

Measurements, except in very special circumstances, are usually displayed visually. Such displays may be *continuous*, where a pointer moves over a scale, or *digital*, where a set of digits is displayed. Where rates of change need to be observed, the continuous display is most useful, particularly where a movable pointer traverses a fixed scale; for absolute readings, digital displays are to be preferred. In addition, warnings may be given by flashing lights or 'blinking' shutters, although these require that the operator's attention be directed to the warning device as they do not 'command' in the same way as sound signals.

Controls

Controls operate by touch, and serve both to communicate information and to operate the machine. The suitability of various controls for different purposes is discussed in the DSIR publication, *Men, Machines and Controls*, by K. A. Provins. The types of controls considered include cranks, handwheels, knobs, levers, pedals, push buttons, joysticks.

Layout of displays and controls

If poorly used, a display or control can lose much of its effectiveness. While man is extremely adaptable and capable of considerable accommodation, it is wasteful to require him to stretch, bend or otherwise contort himself if this can be avoided by sensible layout of the control and display devices. The 'Cranfield Man' was 'created' to use the controls of a lathe in current use—he was required to be 4½ feet tall, 2 feet across the shoulders and have an 8-foot arm span! Regrettably, he is still not yet 'dead'.

Controls should be located so that they are easily handled by the operator. When it is necessary to mount a large number of controls, then locate the 'fine' ones as near to the operator as possible and the 'coarse' ones further away. Try to 'fit' the control devices to the scale of the work: a delicate knob for light work, a more robust one for heavier work.

A display should, if possible, be located near, or in relation to, its control device. Where a number of displays are required, try to:

(*a*) group them according to purpose;
(*b*) differentiate them by colour and/or position.

Wherever possible, try to standardize upon the direction of travel of pointers or scales, and try to align the 'key' points of the display so that they are all in the same direction. Thus if a battery of dials is used in the control of a process, reading is simplified if the 'normal' position of all dials is at 12 o'clock.

Similarly, standardization in computer software usage is important. For example, the field in which the date is entered should always be the same, as should be its format. Designers should avoid requiring data in a format convenient to the computer (870213 for 13 February 1987) which is likely to be confusing for the user.

In the final analysis, a good design is one which 'feels' right, where the hands of the operator fall naturally upon the controls and the eyes fall easily upon the displays. Such an integration is neither easily described nor easily achieved, and however much care is taken in the design stage, testing by *operators of skills comparable to those for which the machine is designed* is most desirable.

Man and the working environment

1. *Lighting*
Good lighting is important: it assists in the efficient performance of work, it allows people to move easily *and safely*, and it creates and displays the character of the item being illuminated. Present illumination technology permits virtually any type of light to be provided, no matter how intense or how constituted. Clearly the aim must be to choose an illumination level which will produce an acceptable visual efficiency, and the definition of '. . . acceptable efficiency' will vary from place to place, '. . . reflecting differences in prosperity, standards of living and the whole national climate' (*Interior Lighting Design Handbook*, published by the IES). The current British IES code is based on the belief that '. . . a visual efficiency of at least 90 per cent in poor conditions of contrast' is 'always justified economically'. The corresponding American code is based upon a much higher requirement for visual efficiency (99 per cent) and Larson (*Lighting and its Design*) discusses the validity of these choices and gives tables comparing recommended intensities in a number of countries.

2. *Glare and contrast*
The overall effectiveness of a lighting system will depend not only on its intensity, but also upon the *glare* and *contrast* generated. Glare is said to occur when the intensity of light is such that it does not contribute to useful seeing, and may arise either *directly*, when it is caused by the

primary light source, or *indirectly*, when it is generated by reflections from surfaces of some sort. Thus, an observer looking directly into the sun suffers from *direct glare*, while if troubled by reflections from a surface suffers from *indirect glare*. It is desirable always to reduce glare, although this is frequently not possible, particularly if the primary designer does not recognize the dangers of indirect glare, and it is not at all uncommon to find multiple reflecting paths giving rise to glare.

Contrast exists when *differences* in brightness occur, and frequently the existence of adequate contrast can enormously improve the modelling of the task being illuminated. Furthermore, a contrast between the task and the general areas can be psychologically very satisfying: the apparently 'simple' solution to the lighting problem of illuminating all areas to a uniformly high level tends to produce a deadly uniformity and mindlessness which is depressing and unnecessarily costly.

3. *Climate*

The 'climate' of work, as used here, is affected by:

(*a*) air temperature;
(*b*) air movement;
(*c*) air pollution;
(*d*) relative humidity of air.

General recommendations for levels of the above factors are clearly impossible since the type of work being carried out will affect the requirements. Thus, a skilled instrument maker, whose work involves little physical effort, considerable precision and much concentration,will demand a higher air temperature than the operator of a heavy press and will tolerate very little air movement. A very active operator will need some movement to help keep cool and will be very sensitive to air pollution—smells—and will wish to avoid too high a humidity.

The measurement of 'comfort' levels for climatic factors is difficult and different authorities recommend different values. In a paper 'An Approach to Environmental Engineering' (*IEE Journal*, May 1972, pp. 167–70), Platts suggests that:

> For comfort, the air temperature should be about 21°C ± 1°C. The mean radiant temperature should not be more than 5°C below the room-air temperature . . . The range [of moisture content] for comfort is quite variable around a relative humidity of about 35–55 per cent . . .

It must be remembered that the climatic factors are invariably better and more cheaply dealt with at the initial design stage of the building, therefore any special requirements concerning climate should be made known to the designing architect. As the use of any building is likely to change throughout its life, provision should be made for the modification and control of environmental factors.

Fortunately, the human body has a high adaptability to climatic conditions, and frequently all that is required is to provide adequate means of heating. If more comprehensive control is needed, it is possible to provide it by means of complete air-conditioning plants.

4. *Noise*

Noise, which is best described as any unwanted sound, will not merely cause annoyance, it may also affect efficiency by inducing stress and may mask communications. The Department of Employment in the UK has been considerably concerned with the problems generated by noise and has published a very thorough *Code of Practice for Reducing the Exposure of Employed Persons to Noise*. This document is so thorough that it would be presumptuous to try to improve upon the recommendations set out therein, and all managers should make reference to it since it contains much sensible advice.

Broadly, it suggests that noise should first of all be reduced wherever possible, and recommendations for doing this are given; and thereafter, where it is not possible to reduce noise, then ear protectors should be worn. While problems with noise tend to be associated with manufacturing, similar difficulties can arise in an office environment. A relatively recent source in this context is the printer attached to a word-processing station.

It is worth noting that too little noise can be almost as great a problem as excessive noise. One of the authors recalls that when engaged upon the design of acoustic devices, he found that working in an acoustically 'dead' room produced feelings of fear which were extraordinarily distressing and which must have affected his work adversely.

Recommended reading

Barnes, R., *Motion and Time Study*, Wiley, 1980.
  A thorough discussion of work study by one of the most respected US workers in this field. The comprehensive text includes detailed material on PMTS. Liberally illustrated.
Currie, R. M., (Revised Faraday, J. E.) *Work Study*, Pitman, 1986.
  An invaluable introduction to work study, giving a comprehensive treatment to both method study and work measurement.
International Labour Office, *Introduction to Work Study*, 1979.
  A valuable introduction, and reference text.

Niebel, B. W., *Motion and Time Study*, Irwin, 1982.
Another basic American text on the subject.
British Standards Institution, *Glossary of Terms Used in Work Study and Organization and Methods (O & M)*, (BS 3138).
Not merely a glossary of terms, it includes explanations of how various terms (such as standard time, performance control . . .) are derived. Now expanded to include material on PBR and performance indices.

18 Work study II: work measurement

Standard performance

Work measurement techniques are intended to reveal the work content of a task. In order that different tasks may be compared, the work content is always measured in the same units, those of *time*, and the time taken to complete any job is considered to be the time which a qualified worker—that is, one who has the necessary physical and mental attributes and has acquired the necessary skill—would take if working without over-exertion throughout a normal working period while applying himself to the job.

Uses of work measurement data

Frequently it is assumed that the principal use of work measurement data is in establishing the basis for financial incentive schemes. How could the production planner schedule work if he did not know how long it was expected to take? How could management establish manning levels for flow lines without knowledge of the work content of the product the line is being set up to produce? There are, in fact, many other uses for work measurement data, some of which are discussed in later chapters, but for convenience are presented below:

1. Scheduling and loading
2. Line balancing and establishing manning levels
3. Efficiency comparisons
4. Comparison of alternative methods
5. Basis for budgetary and cost control systems
6. Estimating future costs and loads
7. Financial incentive schemes

Methods of work measurement

There are a number of different techniques for work measurement, which can be categorized as either *direct*, where actual observations are made of workers, comprising time study and activity sampling, and *indirect*, comprising synthetic timing, predetermined motion time systems (PMTS), and analytic estimating. The best known and probably the most widely used of all of these is:

Time study

An operator is observed to carry out a given task in 6 minutes. This is known as the *observed time* and takes no account either of any allowances or of the ability of the operator—it is just the time which the operator being observed took while actually working, from the moment of starting to the moment of finishing. In order that ability and effort can be compensated for, the operator is *rated*, that is, mentally compared by the observer with a qualified operator working at standard performance.

An observer is thus required to have a very clear concept of the rate at which a worker who possesses the necessary physical and mental attributes, and the required skill, would satisfactorily carry out the task under observation safely, accurately, at the correct speed and without undue strain. Having this concept, the observer then must assess the worker being studied against this criterion. It is clearly an extremely difficult task, since it involves the comparison of a number of different yet dependent features of the subject's work with those of the 'qualified worker'. For example, the subject may be working at the right speed, yet at a lower level of precision or in a less safe manner. Alternatively, the precision achieved may be much higher than necessary, yet the quantity produced may be too low. All the factors concerning the work being carried out must be assessed and integrated into a single rating figure, and this should be done while the task is actually being carried out. Moreover the task may involve a number of different operations which involve different levels of effort. For this reason, and to permit a more accurate study, it is normal to split the task into a number of *elements*, each clearly distinguished from the next by a *break point*. Each element making up the task is then separately timed and rated. So the observed time of 6 minutes for the task may in fact be shown as:

Element	Observed time	Rating
1	1.70	135
2	3.10	90
3	1.20	80

In this illustration it is assumed that on the first element if the operator has been working one-third as hard again as a qualified operator, he would have been rated at 133. In practice, rating is never assessed in increments smaller than 5 units, so the figure of 133 would normally be recorded as 135. The time which a qualified operator would have taken—known as the basic time—is

$$1.70 \times \frac{135}{100} \text{ minutes, that is 2.30 minutes}$$

In practice, it is unusual to establish the basic time simply from a single observation of the task. Normally it will be timed and rated through a number of cycles, and an average basic time calculated for each element. The basic time for the task is then taken as the sum of these: in the illustration assume this is 6.05 minutes. The usual guidelines for the number of cycles to be timed suggest at least 50 for short-cycle jobs, and 20–30 for long-cycle jobs. Strictly, since a sample of work is being observed, the larger the number of cycles in the sample, the better the accuracy of the estimated basic time. It is, in theory, possible to establish statistically the number of cycles to be timed and rated.

The rating is essentially a matter of proper training and considerable experience on the part of the observing work study practitioner, and obtaining consistency in rating both between different practitioners at the same time and the same practitioner at different times is extremely difficult, and is a matter to which much attention has been paid. A common technique for obtaining consistency is by means of *rating films*. In these the same operations are performed at various ratings. The work study practitioner views these, rates the operations, and then compares his rating with that given by the film. He then views the same operation performed as before but in a different sequence, and again rates the operations. This is repeated until consistency is obtained. The whole process is repeated after a convenient interval of time—say one month. By means such as this some considerable degree of consistency is obtained, and it is claimed that ratings can be consistent to ± 5 per cent—a very necessary requirement if an accurate measurement of work content is required.

There are a number of different *rating scales*, just as there are different temperature scales. These differ by the value put on, and the derivation of, the fixed point—the *standard rating* point. This rating corresponds to the average rate at which qualified workers will naturally work, providing that they are properly educated, equipped and motivated. Probably the earliest rating scale is that which assumes that the unmotivated worker (the so-called 'day-worker', one who is paid at 'day-rate' and does not earn any financial incentive) works at a 60 rating, and that the motivated worker will work one-third as hard again, that is at an 80 rating. The standard rating on this '60/80' scale is thus 80. Other scales which are 'pegged' to the 'unmotivated' worker are the 75/100 and 100/133 scales.

The British Standard rating, for reasons which are cogently argued in BS 3138, 'pegs' the rating scale to the performance of the motivated worker, and gives a value of 100 to the standard rating point, making no assumption about the rating of the 'unmotivated' worker. This recommendation has been rapidly accepted by UK practitioners, and it is now becoming rare to find rating scales other than the BS one in British companies.

During a day the operator will need to relax in order to overcome fatigue—whether mental or physical, real or imaginary—and to attend to various personal needs such as drinking a cup of tea or going to the lavatory. These factors are taken into account by adding to the basic time a *relaxation allowance* which has been previously agreed within the organization for each type of work and each circumstance. Within the organization being discussed, let us assume that the relaxation allowance for the task in question is $12\frac{1}{2}$ per cent. The relaxation allowance would thus be:

$$6.05 \times \frac{12.5}{100} \text{ minutes, that is 0.76 minutes}$$

Under some circumstances there may be small irregularities in work—for example, due to small quantities of defective material—for which some allowance should be made. This is done by adding an allowance—a *contingency allowance* for extra work—which in the example might be $2\frac{1}{2}$ per cent, that is:

$$6.05 \times \frac{2.5}{100} \text{ minutes, that is 0.15 minutes}$$

The *work content* of the task is then defined as—

Basic time
   + Relaxation allowance
      + Contingency allowance for extra work

that is:

6.05 + 0.76 + 0.15 minutes, that is 6.96 minutes

This represents the working time for the task being studied throughout the 'attended time'. There are, however, allowances which may have to be made for non-working time before it is possible to calculate the daily output. These allowances arise out of the process itself: for example, there may be a dead period while a machine is slowing down, or there may be idle time due to an overlapping in two machines required for the same task. These are known as 'process allowances for unoccupied time' and 'interference time'. Once these are added to the work content, the average operation time is obtained. This is the *standard time* and is:

Work content
    + Contingency allowance for delay
      + Unoccupied time allowance
        + Interference allowance

Assuming the last three factors are 3 per cent, 2 per cent and 1 per cent respectively, in the example:

$$\text{Standard time} = 6.96 + 0.21 + 0.14 + 0.07 \text{ minutes}$$
$$= 7.38 \text{ minutes}$$

so that if the task were carried out 100 times consecutively, it would take 100×7.38 minutes, not $100 \times$ observed time. The task is said to contain 7.38 standard minutes of work and if, in fact, the actual time taken for 100 repetitions was 680 minutes it would be said that 738 standard minutes were produced in 680 minutes.

Most financial incentive schemes require yet another time, the *allowed time*. This is the time which, if fully used, will earn for the operator no bonus or premium. Any time less than the allowed time generates a *time saved*, and it is very common to gear bonus earnings to this time saved (see Chapter 35). The *allowed time* is derived from the *standard time* by the addition of a *policy allowance*, the magnitude of which depends upon a managerial policy concerning the acceptable level of earnings of the grade of operator concerned. The relations of these various times to each other is shown in Fig. 18.1.

---

1. Confirm the 'best' method is being used
2. Break the task down into elements
3. Time and rate the elements through a number (20–50) of cycles of the task
4. Calculate the basic times of each element in each cycle
5. Calculate the average basic time for each element and, by summing, the basic time for the task
6. Add allowances to the basic time to arrive at work content
7. Add further allowances to give standard time and, if required, the allowed time

---

Steps in time study

It can be seen that time study is a direct observational technique in which an experienced work study practitioner watches a worker, times what is being done, and 'rates' the work. Unfortunately, it is viewed with

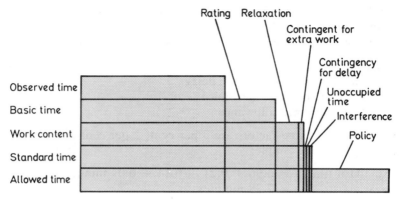

Fig. 18.1

great suspicion by many operators who remember the days of rate-cutting, where the usual reason for using a stopwatch was either to set a rate (that is, a bonus price) or to cut it. On the other hand, it is a completely intelligible technique which can be understood with the minimum of explanation, unlike some other techniques which are so esoteric that they smack of black magic.

Much suspicion will be removed if a clear explanation is given to the person being timed of the reason for the timing, if it is carried out in a perfectly open manner and if the operator has been given ample time to settle into an orderly rhythm of work carried out in accordance with a method laid down by a proper method study. No attempt should be made to carry out a time study if the work is not capable of being done correctly—for example, if the correct tools or the required material are not to hand.

Activity sampling

The British Standard definition of this is 'a technique in which a number of successive observations are made over a period of time of one or a group of machines, processes or workers. Each observation records what is happening at that instant, and the percentage of observations recorded for a particular activity or delay is a measure of the percentage of time during which that activity or delay occurs.'

The technique was developed by a statistician (L. C. Tippett) who was attempting to establish utilization figures for some textile looms in the 1920s. Clearly, to have carried out the large number of time studies (forming a 'production study') required would have been prohibitively expensive. Essentially he made a large number of random observations of the looms, noting the state of each (working, under repair, being set up and so on) on each occasion. This formed the basis of calculating the percentages of time that the looms spent in each of these states. Since the process is only being observed at random points in time rather than continuously, a sample of the activity is obtained and, as such, there is likely to be an element of inaccuracy in the estimates. As the number of observations increases, the accuracy improves. In fact, from an examination of the underlying statistics it is possible to measure the accuracy of the estimate, provided the number of observations made to arrive at it is known.

An exercise would start with discussions with the workers, explaining to them the observation process and the reasons for the study. This would be followed by an examination of the process, establishing the activities to be identified. A preliminary study is normally carried out to confirm that the set of activities identified is complete, and to generate some preliminary results in order to establish the number of observations required in the full study. This preliminary study would normally cover 100–200 observations made at random points during a representative period of time, and could involve the design of a proforma on which to record the data. After the study it is possible to determine the number of observations in the full study using the formula (Appendix 2):

$$N = \frac{4P(100 - P)}{L^2} \text{(for 95\% confidence)}$$

where N = Number of observations
P = Percentage occurrence of desired activity
L = Required percentage accuracy

Suppose this study indicated that 35 per cent of the time is spent on productive work, and in the full study it is felt that an accuracy of 2 per cent is desirable (that is, they want to be reasonably confident that the actual value lies between 33 and 37 per cent, assuming the study confirms the value of 35 per cent), then the formula implies:

$$\frac{4 \times 35 \times (100 - 35)}{2 \times 2} = 2{,}275 \text{ observations}$$

If the work centre concerned has five operators, this implies 455 tours of the centre in the full study. It is now possible to plan the main study with the 455 tours covering a representative period of time.

Having carried out the full study, it is possible to use the above formula, suitably re-arranged:

$$L = \sqrt{\frac{4P(100 - P)}{N}}$$

to establish the actual accuracy in the percentage occurrence of each activity.

---

1. Examination of the process to be sampled
   (*a*) consultation with operators
   (*b*) identification of activities
2. Preliminary study
   (*a*) random observations (100–200)
   (*b*) design of proforma for data collection
   (*c*) confirmation of activities
   (*d*) establish number of observations in full study for desired accuracy
3. Full study
   (*a*) random observations over a representative period
   (*b*) calculate percentage occurrence of activities
   (*c*) calculate accuracies of percentage occurrences

Stages in use of activity sampling

The technique of activity sampling, although quite simple, is very powerful. It can be used in a variety of ways, in a variety of environments, both manufacturing and non-manufacturing. While it can be used to indicate areas which are worthy of further analysis using, for example, method study techniques, it can also be used to establish time standards themselves. While time study requires training and experience before a practitioner can employ it effectively, activity sampling can be used to advantage with much less training. For this and other reasons, the practical considerations in applying it are covered in detail in the next chapter.

Synthetic timing

Within any organization, the same elements of work will reoccur even if the jobs themselves differ. If the work study department comprehensively record the methods for the individual elements making up each job that is studied, together with the composition of the elemental times, this can be used as the basis for the standard times for new jobs. The appropriate elements are identified and the time for the new job established by adding the previously assessed times for these.

Many organizations will build up books of tables of these times, entering new elements as they are discovered. In some cases it is possible to reduce the figures to simple charts. A good classification system for the retrieval of the data is essential, and the master file, carrying the original data, must be carefully preserved. The loss of a set of synthetic data can be extremely serious.

Since working conditions, traditions and work patterns differ from place to place, *it is most unwise to try to transfer synthetic or analytical estimating data from one company to another*.

Predetermined motion time system (PMTS)

In the above techniques (synthesis and analytical estimating), work is broken into coarse elements appropriate to the organization and situation in which the technique is being used. A predetermined motion time system (PMTS) breaks the work down into sets of basic human motions and, by combining these, any task can be synthesized. A number of such systems are available, probably the most widely used being method-time measurement (MTM) in one or other of its forms.

Original MTM (MTM-1) identifies basic motion categories, examples of which are:

Reach
Move
Apply pressure
Grasp
Position
Release
Disengage

For each of these, tables are available giving the time for each motion under various conditions of distance, difficulty or load. The unit of time measurement is a TMU (time measurement unit) where

1 TMU = 0.00001 hours = 0.036 seconds

and all times are 'levelled', that is they are the times taken by an 'average' operator, so that the need for rating vanishes. Thus, MTM-1 shows that to reach to a fixed location over a distance of 20 cm (R20A) would take 7.8 TMUs while to reach over the same distance to a very small object (R20D) would take 11.4 TMUs.

Considerable world-wide experience over many years shows that MTM-1 is capable of giving highly accurate results. It is, however, tedious and time-consuming in its use, and it has been claimed that to analyse 4 minutes can take as long as 10 hours. In the 1960s a second-generation system, MTM-2, was produced that is much faster to handle and which has an accuracy comparable with MTM-1, particularly where the total aggregated time is greater than one minute. The simplification has been achieved by reducing the number of alternative conditions and ignoring movements which occur very infrequently in practice.

A later development is MTM-X which has nine categories:

Category	Description	Code
1 Get	Reach to and grasp an object	GE (easy)
		GD (difficult)
2 Put	Move and position an object	PE (easy)
		PD (difficult)
3 Regrasp	Shift the grasp on an object	R
4 Handle weight	Apply force to move an object	HW
5 Apply pressure	Apply force where no movement is involved	A
6 Eye action	Eye focus and eye travel	E
7 Step	A pace in walking	S
8 Bend down	Bend the trunk	BD
9 Arise from bend	Straighten the trunk	AB

There are three distance codes: N is for near distance (less than 15 centimetres), F is for far, and X is for variable. These simplifications enable the standards to be summarized on a small card:

MTM-X						
		GE	GD	PE	PD	
N		8	17	5	19	
F		16	25	14	28	
X		13	20	9	22	
R	HW	A	E	S	BD	AB
6	5	14	7	18	29	32

WARNING: Do not attempt to use this data unless you have been trained and qualified under a scheme approved by the MTM Association

Despite the enormous simplification in MTM-X compared with the original sets of tables, experience and training are needed in judging complexities. *No attempt should be made to use MTM-X or any other PMTS system without appropriate instructions.*

Unlike synthesis or analytical estimating, the basic data for PMTS can be transferred, not only from company to company, but from one part of the world to another.

Most PMTS data are derived from large-scale studies of elemental movements, the time for an element being taken as the *average* of all the studies. Times, therefore, are said to be *levelled*. However, the studies themselves do not include any ratings of the operators and since it cannot be assumed that all operators were 'standard' operators working 'at standard', a PMTS time does *not* equal a 'BS100 rating' time. In 1969 it was stated, and it was recently repeated to one of the authors, that

$$MTM\ 100 = BSI\ 83$$

that is, that if an MTM study generates a time of, say, 20 seconds, this will be equivalent to a BS100 time of

$$\frac{20 \times 83}{100} \text{ seconds}$$
$$= 16.6 \text{ seconds}$$

Analytic estimating

Usage of this technique normally results from incomplete synthetic data. The time required for the task is built up from synthetic data where possible, but supplemented where such data is not available for particular elements by estimates based on the best available knowledge and experience.

The advantages of the three synthesizing techniques are:

1. Short-run tasks can be work measured.
2. Rating, the most difficult part of a time study, is not necessary.
3. The results obtained are consistent. This is particularly important in small batch production where there are too few repetitions carried out for an accurate time study.
4. A reasonable estimate of work content can be obtained before the task is actually carried out. This is particularly true of synthesis and analytical estimating which are therefore usable in pre-production and estimating work.

The computer and work study

As would be expected, the computer has made its greatest contribution to work study in the area of work measurement. In time study the elemental times and ratings for a job must be recorded both accurately and clearly, without this recording distracting the work study practitioner from his task of observing. The advent of digital stopwatches has improved accuracy. However, clarity is still important when the observed times and ratings have to be extended to derive the standard time for the task. Indeed, some practitioners claim to spend more time on analysis and administration than on observing work. In large departments, where clerks are employed to carry out the analysis, clarity of recording is even more crucial. Microcomputers are now available for this process, at a range of prices offering a variety of facilities. These range from special programs for portable general-purpose computers to specially developed microcomputers built-in to hand-held study boards. These can easily be set up to analyse a particular task. All that is required is the input of the rating and an indication that the break point has been reached. The internal clock automatically records the time this occurs. This establishes the integrity of the time data. Depending on the equipment, the data can be dumped on to some local storage medium (for example, cassette) for later analysis, or the analysis carried out on the spot. This subsequent analysis can frequently be carried out using standard microcomputers (for example IBM PCs), and programs/software are available for a number of different routines, including building up a database of standard element times. It has been claimed that the use of such systems can save over 80 per cent of work study analysis time. Moreover, it appears that typically, analysis and observation might take equal lengths of time.

The purpose-designed microcomputers are normally also capable of handling activity sampling. All the basic calculations relating to accuracy and so on can be carried out, and various report summaries produced.

The reader interested in finding out more about these types of system is referred to the advertising pages of journals and magazines concerned with work study, management services and production engineering. Most vendors provide comprehensive documentation indicating the scope of the systems. Indeed, at the time of writing, one such vendor claimed that their equipment was being used by over fifty different organizations.

Computer databases of element times can easily be set up using such systems. For companies with a geographically widely spread organization, a single database can be built up and accessed from a variety of locations: this contributes significantly to consistency and efficiency. As an alternative to a company building up its own database, these can be obtained ready constructed together with the necessary software to use them. It is claimed that in comparing the time required to prepare a time standard of 45 minutes:

8 hours using conventional work study
40 minutes using synthesis
12 minutes using a computer system

In setting up a computerized database to handle a machine-shop standard times, it is claimed that the synthetic system took 10 weeks compared to an estimated 3 man-years of stopwatch studies. The system cost the equivalent of $1\frac{1}{2}$ years' salary of a work study officer.

Clearly the above is only based on one instance. Comparisons depend on local circumstances, environmental problems and so on.

> *Direct*
> (*a*) time study
> (*b*) activity sampling
> *Indirect*
> (*a*) synthetic timing
> (*b*) predetermined motion time systems (PMTS)
> (*c*) analytic estimating

Techniques of work measurement

Recommended reading

Whitmore, D. A., *Work Measurement*, Institute of Management Services, 1987.
    This definitive text has recently been revised to include discussion of the contribution of microcomputers in reducing the time spent on data collection and analysis in work measurement.
Also see *Recommended reading* for Chapters 17 and 19.

19 Work study III: non-manufacturing examples

The control of indirect labour

Traditionally, work study is associated with 'shop-floor' or direct labour; however, the costs associated with so-called 'indirect' labour are often as high or *very much higher* than the direct labour costs. To control these costs, work study has been applied to indirect labour. The application of work study in the office is frequently referred to as organization and methods (O & M).

Recording methods

While many O & M officers use the standard work study symbols on page 257, some workers have added special symbols of their own devising, a procedure to be deplored. The increasing use of data-processing equipment and the consequent need to analyse data flow systems has brought about a genuine need to produce a set of flow chart symbols for data processing. These symbols were internationally agreed at a meeting in Tokyo in 1965 where representatives of eleven countries were present. The British Standard Specification BS 4058, Part 1, 1966, *Data Processing Problem Definition and Analysis, Part 1: Flow Chart Symbols*, embodies these symbols—some 30 in all—and gives some recommendations upon the conventions to be used in drawing data flow charts. It must be recognized that these charts record the flow of *data* rather than the activities of men or machines, and they thus serve purposes quite different from work study charts.

Work measurement

Work measurement in offices presents—*or is often said to present*—problems of such magnitude and complexity that its use is severely limited. These problems when examined seem to be:

(*a*) *The creative nature of the task*. It is argued that many office workers are involved in creative tasks, and '. . . it's impossible to time thinking'. Upon examination, however, it will be found that the creative content is frequently such a small proportion of the whole that it can be absorbed within an associated physical activity.

(*b*) *The irregularity of the work*. It is true that the work of, say, a secretary may be highly irregular. Thus in the middle of typing a letter she may be required to stop and take dictation, make coffee, welcome a visitor, answer the telephone . . . Frequently it will be found that much of the irregularity is entirely unnecessary, arising principally from the lack of organization and discipline of the supervisor.

(*c*) *Prejudice*. The belief that the office worker is necessarily superior to other employees dies hard and this belief often carries with it the concept that they must not be subjected to such 'indignities' of the shop-floor as the measuring of work. Fortunately more sensible attitudes are replacing these prejudices, but it is obviously vital that the warning against secret work measurement must be heeded. Knowledge is the greatest enemy of prejudice, and any attempt at clerical work measurement must be preceded by full and comprehensive discussion on the purpose of the measurement.

Clearly it is not usually possible *or useful* to measure indirect work as accurately as highly repetitive, large-volume machining work. However, it will often be found that high accuracy is not necessary.

Methods of clerical work measurement

All the techniques of work measurement are available, but it is found in practice that time study—the use of the stopwatch—is rarely satisfactory, partly because of the difficulties of rating and partly because of prejudice. Activity sampling is widely used for departmental studies, while there are a wide range of proprietary PMTS available. These include:

Master Clerical Data (MCD)
Clerical Standard Data (CSD)
Universal Office Controls (UOC)
Clerical Milli-Minute Data (Clerical MMD)
Office Staffing Standards (OSS)
Basic Work Data

All these appear to have been developed from MTM.

Mulligan clerical standards are said to be directly derived from micro-motion studies of clerical work.

Usually and desirably associated with the measurement of indirect labour is some form of control system. These systems, like the PMTS above, often have proprietary names, and are often sold as complete packages by consultants. At one time the 'package' implied a particular type of work measurement technique, but most practitioners now use whichever technique is most appropriate. Among the best-known names in this field are variable factor programming (VFP) and group capacity assessment (GCA).

An example of method study in an office environment

A large insurance broker's office is staffed by a manager and seven assistants. A variety of business is handled for individuals and for companies covering motor vehicles, travel, building and generally all classes of risks.

An existing client's motor insurance has fallen due for renewal. He feels that the renewal premium is too high and calls into the office to see if he can get cheaper cover with an alternative insurance company. One of the assistants comes to the counter to handle his query. Figure 19.1 shows the layout of the broker's office. He retrieves the client's file, consults scales charged by other insurance companies and, with the client, selects alternative cover which offers better value for money. The client writes out a cheque, and is given a receipt and a cover note as proof of the insurance cover until the policy and certificate are prepared by the company. The assistant returns the files and documentation and goes back to his desk.

This and similar operations are carried out numerous times each day. No one questions how efficiently they are being carried out. Indeed, it is difficult to establish this from the brief description above. The techniques of method study provide the tools to examine this situation. Charting techniques can be used to record and present the existing method. Specifically, a flow process chart (Fig. 19.2) presents the detail of the individual activities. This is complemented by a flow diagram (Fig. 19.3), which is simply the plan of the broker's office, showing the activities and the sequence in which they take place. This diagram immediately gives the impression of inefficiency. However, it should be stressed that the casual observer would not see the detail in this diagram from observing the office. What would be seen would be a certain amount of activity, without time appearing to be deliberately wasted. There would be no lines drawn on the floor showing all movements! Together the chart and the diagram can be used as the basis for examining the existing method and developing the improved method. The diagram indicates where inefficiency might lie, the chart provides the detail necessary to critically examine the activities involved. The questioning technique provides a structure for this. Some immediate questions are:

(a) Why is it necessary for the manager to authorize cheques?
(b) Why are the files spread out?

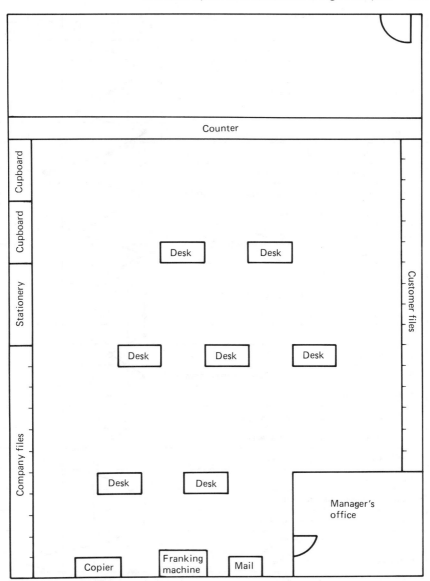

Fig. 19.1 Layout of broker's office

(c) Why is it necessary to collect the receipt book from the assistant's desk?

These and other issues can be analysed using the framework of questions relating to purpose, place, sequence, person and means. It is left

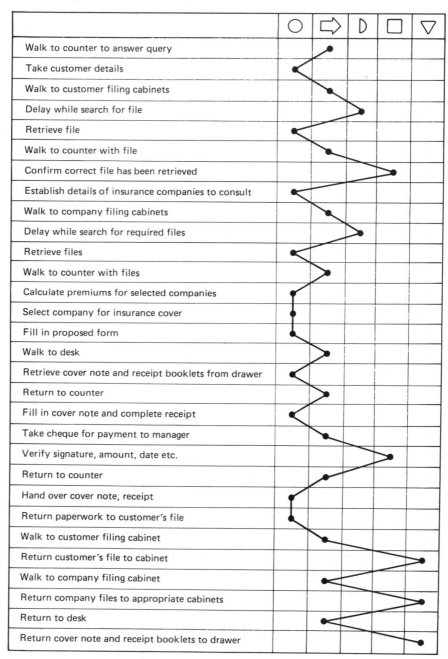

Fig. 19.2 Flow process chart

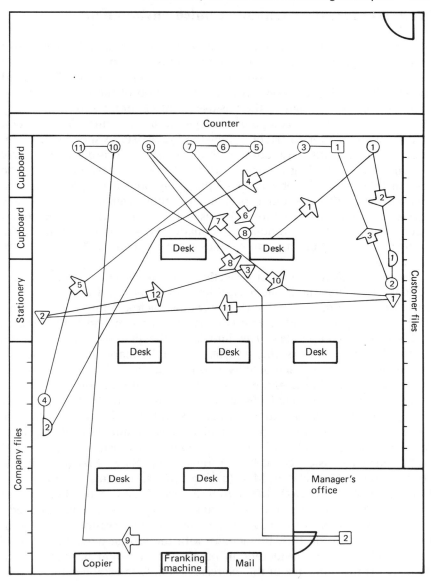

Fig. 19.3 Flow diagram

as an exercise for the reader to complete this process, and to present the appropriate flow diagram and flow process chart for the improved method. Readers may arrive at different charts depending on the interpretation of the situation. It should be noted that for illustrative purposes only the chart and diagram refer to both man and material simultaneously.

Work measurement within an office environment

A small section within the payment services group of a bank handles two major types of transaction: bankers' payments and drafts. Each of these has three processes carried out on it: logging (preparation of a record showing its status and so on); typing (preparation of the basic documentation); and VDU (input of the basic accounting information concerning the transaction into the computer via a visual display unit). The intention is to study the section to establish how the five assistants spend their time. After discussion and consultation with the assistants, it is decided to carry out an activity sampling exercise. Further discussions take place with the section relating to the objectives of the study, and it is agreed that the section head will carry out a preliminary study over a typical two-day period. Random number tables are used to generate the random times when each tour of observation will be made. Activities are identified, the proforma designed and the study takes place as planned. The results are presented in Fig. 19.4.

The proforma for the data collection can take a number of different designs. That illustrated has a high level of detail, and analysis can be quite time-consuming. The work patterns of each assistant can be identified. This might be undesirable (the assistants might find it threatening and refuse to co-operate). The initials of the five assistants could be replaced by the codes of the activities, and tally marks used to indicate the number of times each activity is observed on each tour. This guarantees anonymity but at the expense of loss of information.

It is possible to conclude from the analysis in Fig. 19.4 that miscellaneous activity (MA) should be further subdivided since it occurs relatively frequently (33 per cent of time), and further examination of this non-productive time could lead to improvements in efficiency. In the full study, this subdivision could be (*a*) transaction-related MA (e.g. filing), (*b*) non-transaction-related MA (e.g. meetings, training), (*c*) personal (e.g. toilet, coffee break), (*d*) waiting for work, and so on. For ease of presentation, in this illustration the single activity MA will be retained.

It is now possible to consider the number of observations to make in the full study. To do this, the activity with the largest percentage occurrence (DT) will be considered (in practice, MA would be further subdivided). If the objective of the exercise is simply to establish the current situation, accuracy of 5 per cent in 27 per cent occurrence of DT might be acceptable (i.e. it is necessary to be 95 per cent confident the actual percentage occurrence is between 22 and 32 per cent). If the values are to be used for operations planning and control, 3 per cent accuracy might be adequate (24 to 30 per cent). If the values are to be used for detailed costings, 1 per cent accuracy might be necessary (26 to 28 per cent).

Activity sampling study		Sheet: 1

Preliminary

SUBJECT: Payment Services — Bankers Payments and Drafts section

STUDY DURATION: 2 days

DATE: 25/02/87 - 26/02/87

TAKEN BY: A.P.M

Activities:

Code	Description	Code	Description
PL	Logging Bankers Payments	DT	Typing Drafts
PT	Typing Bankers Payments	DV	VDU on Drafts
PV	VDU on Bankers Payments	MA	Miscellaneous activity
OL	Logging Drafts		

Round Number	Random Time	AB	CF	DJ	HS	BT
1	9.14	PT	DT	DV	MA	DV
2	9.23	PL	MA	PT	DT	DT
3	9.37	DT	PT	DT	PT	MA
4	9.51	DL	OV	MA	MA	DT
5	10.01	MA	DT	MA	DT	OL
6	10.17	DT	MA	DT	MA	DV
7	10.24	MA	PL	MA	MA	DT
8	10.41	DV	PT	DV	PT	MA
9	10.51	PT	MA	DL	PV	DT
10	11.02	MA	DL	DT	MA	MA
11	11.19	DT	MA	MA	MA	PL
12	11.43	DL	DT	PT	DT	MA
13	11.53	MA	MA	DT	MA	PV
14	13.04	DT	PT	PL	MA	DT
15	13.21	PT	DL	OV	DT	PT
16	13.43	MA	PV	DL	PT	DT
17	13.56	PT	MA	MA	MA	MA
18	14.09	MA	DV	PT	DL	DT
19	14.49	PV	DT	DT	MA	MA
20	15.19	DT	MA	MA	DT	DV
21	15.37	MA	PL	MA	MA	DT
22	16.02	DV	MA	DT	DT	MA
23	16.39	DT	PT	MA	DV	DT
24	9.23	DV	DT	DV	PT	DV
25	9.32	PT	MA	MA	MA	PT

Round Number	Random Time	AB	CF	DJ	HS	BT
26	9.47	MA	DT	DT	MA	MA
27	10.03	DT	DV	MA	PL	DT
28	10.19	DV	MA	PT	DT	MA
29	10.32	MA	PT	MA	MA	PT
30	10.49	MA	MA	DT	DV	MA
31	11.17	PL	DT	MA	DT	OL
32	11.25	DT	MA	PL	MA	DV
33	11.47	DV	DV	DT	MA	PT
34	13.17	OL	PT	MA	OL	MA
35	13.39	DT	DT	DL	DT	OV
36	13.52	PT	DT	DT	DV	MA
37	14.23	MA	MA	DT	PT	PL
38	14.52	DT	DT	PT	DT	DT
39	15.18	MA	OL	DV	DV	PT
40	15.29	DV	OV	PT	DT	DT

ANALYSIS

ACTIVITY	NO.	%
PL	9	4.5
PT	28	14
PV	4	2
OL	13	6.5
OT	54	27
DV	26	13
MA	66	33

Fig. 19.4 Preliminary study

Clearly, if the largest percentage occurrence had been much less than 27 per cent, the values of 5, 3 and 1 per cent for the accuracies would need to be revised downward. The derivation of the formulae involved and a discussion of an alternative measure of the accuracy is given in Appendix 2.

In this example, a value of 2 per cent will be taken for the required accuracy. Using the formula from the previous chapter gives:

$$N = \frac{4 \times 27 \times (100 - 27)}{2 \times 2} = 1{,}971, \text{ say 2,000 observations}$$

This will involve making around 400 tours over a representative period of time. It is worth noting that the results of the preliminary study are not included in this. During this earlier period, workers are becoming accustomed to being observed and not necessarily behaving totally normally. Again random numbers are used to establish when the tours should be made. The results of this are shown in Fig. 19.5.

These results give a clear picture of how the assistants spend their time. If potential tasks for method study exercises were being sought, obviously those on which the assistants spend significant percentages of their time are potential targets. However, this data can be used in a much broader context, provided additional information is collected during the period of the study.

Suppose a record is kept of the attendance of the assistants during the period of the study and the number of documents handled. It is then possible to estimate the 'standard times' for the transactions. In fact, all five assistants were working 7 hours per day for the 20 days of the study, and 422 bankers' payments and 1,123 drafts were handled. The steps in allocating the 42,000 minutes across the activities is shown below:

				Activity:			
	PL	PT	PV	DL	DT	DV	MA
Percentage occurrence	4	15	2	7	25	12	35
Total time (min)	1,680	6,300	840	2,940	10,500	5,040	14,700
No. of transactions	422	422	422	1,123	1,123	1,123	
Time per transaction (min)	3.98	14.92	1.99	2.62	9.35	4.49	

However, it is not possible to use these transaction times as they stand since no attempt has been made to handle the time for miscellaneous activity. If this had been associated with specific transactions, it could be added in directly. However, in the absence of any further detail, this time is allocated in proportion to the transaction time, as follows:

Activity sampling study						Sheet:	

SUBJECT: Payment Services, Bankers Payments and Drafts Section	Activities:						

SUBJECT: Payment Services, Bankers Payments and Drafts Section

STUDY DURATION: 20 days

DATE:

TAKEN BY: A.P.m

Activities:

Code	Description	Code	Description
PL	Logging Bankers Payments	DT	Typing Drafts
PT	Typing Bankers Payments	DV	VDU on Drafts
PV	VDU on Bankers Payments	MA	Miscellaneous Activity
DL	Logging Drafts		

Round Number	Random Time	Assistant :					Round Number	Random Time	Assistant :				
		AB	CF	DJ	HS	BT			AB	CF	DJ	HS	BT
1	9.21	MA	MA	DV	MA	DT	26	9.04	DV	MA	DV	MA	PT
2	9.42	DV	PL	MA	DV	DV	27	9.14	MA	DT	MA	MA	PT
3	10.06	PL	MA	PT	MA	MA	28	9.36	PT	PL	MA	PT	DV
4	10.23	MA	PT	MA	PL	MA	29	9.57	MA	DT	PT	MA	MA
5	10.44	DT	MA	PL	MA	PL	30	10.04	DT	DT	MA	PT	PT
6	11.09	PT	PT	MA	DV	MA	31	10.59	MA	PT	PL	DT	MA
		DL	DT	PV	PV	DL	32	11.13	PT	MA	MA	MA	PT
							33	11.39	MA	DL	DT	DT	DL
									PV	MA	DV	MA	DL

Analysis

Activities

	PL	PT	PV	DL	DT	DV	MA
No. of observations	79	299	41	139	501	241	700
Percentage occurrence	4	15	2	7	25	12	35
Percentage accuracy	0.88	1.60	0.63	1.14	1.94	1.45	2.13

Fig. 19.5 Full study

Productive	Non-productive (MA)
65%	35%
'Standard time'	

Hence the factor for non-productive allowance is $35/65 = 0.54$. The time per transaction is multiplied by 1.54 to estimate the standard time. These are shown below in minutes:

Bankers' payments:

Logging	Typing	VDU	Total
6.13	22.98	3.06	32.17

Drafts:

Logging	Typing	VDU	Total
4.03	14.40	6.91	25.34

These figures can now be used for all the purposes discussed in the previous chapter: transaction costing, manpower planning and so on.

Recommended reading

Anderson, R. G., *Organisation and Methods*, Macdonald and Evans, 1983.
   A useful handbook covering non-manufacturing aspects of work study, including clerical work measurement.
Oliver, S., *O and M for First Line Managers*, Edward Arnold, 1975.
   Written for the first line manager, recognizing that he/she is in the front line of O and M activities.
See also *Recommended reading* for Chapters 17 and 18.

20 Control of quality I

In Chapter 8, the corporate implications of a positive quality policy were indicated. In this chapter, the methods whereby that policy is achieved are discussed. In general, the control of quality is achieved by some form of inspection, but it is the point and type of inspection that is critical to the attainment of conformance to requirements.

Inspection

The task of inspection is taken by many to be the passive one of sorting out the good from the bad, when it should be an active device to prevent non-conformance.

When human inspection is used to sift out the result of quality problems, it is frequently found that every item, or element of a service, is examined in an attempt to stop defects reaching or being seen by the customer. In this type of monotonous, repetitive inspection procedure, '100 per cent inspection' generally turns out to be something less than 100 per cent. Monotonous tasks cause people to behave in a certain manner and to stop thinking about the job in hand. Research has shown that, typically, 15 per cent of the defectives present are missed during so-called 100 per cent inspection, and that examination of a sample provides a higher, more consistent detection rate. Some results from this work illustrate the inadequacy of 100 per cent human inspection:

	Percentage missed
Piston ring defects	33
Screw defects	32
Electronic circuit board defects	17
X-rays for tuberculosis	25
Dental X-rays for decay	15
Clerical errors	24

It follows, then, that to be reasonably sure of catching every error in a clerical banking process, for example, 100 per cent inspection must be carried out four times. This should catch 99.6 per cent of the errors.

Clearly any control system based on *detection* of poor quality by post-production inspection is unreliable, costly, wasteful and uneconomical. It must be replaced by a different strategy altogether—that of *prevention*—and the inspection must be used to check the *system* of transformation, not the product. This leads to a 'how-am-I-doing' type of check on the process, which should be carried out by the production operatives, not a separate 'QC police force' dedicated to detection and rejection.

A systematic approach

In the quality improvement process, data will form the basis for decisions and actions, and a thorough data-recording system is essential. If the symptoms of defective output are identified and recorded, it will be possible to determine what percentage can be attributed to any symptom, and the probable result will be that the bulk of the rejections derive from a few of the symptoms (see Fig. 20.1). To improve conformance quality, therefore, the major symptoms (A, B, C in Fig. 20.1) should be attacked first. An analysis of data to identify the major problems is known as *Pareto analysis* after the Italian economist (see Appendix 1). Without an analysis of this sort, it is much too easy to devote resources to removing symptom I, perhaps, because its cause is immediately apparent.

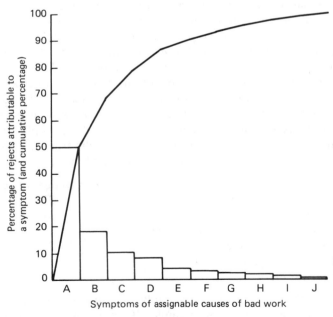

Fig. 20.1 Symptoms of assignable causes of bad work

Of course, any one symptom may be the result of a number of possible causes, and a series of investigations may have to be carried out to determine the effects of the possible causes.

A useful way of mapping the inputs which affect quality is the *cause and effect diagram*, also known as the Ishikawa diagram (after its originator) or the fishbone diagram (after its appearance) (Fig. 20.2). The effect being investigated is shown at the end of a horizontal arrow. Potential causes are then shown as labelled arrows entering the main cause arrow. Each arrow may have other arrows entering it as the principal factors or causes are reduced to their sub-causes, and sub-sub-causes by *brainstorming*. The process is continued until all the conceivable causes have been included.

The proportion of non-conforming output attributable to each cause is then measured or estimated, and a simple Pareto analysis identifies the major causes which are most worth investigating. Cause–effect and Pareto diagrams together provide a most effective means of tackling problems and presenting quality improvement plans or the results of quality improvement programmes.

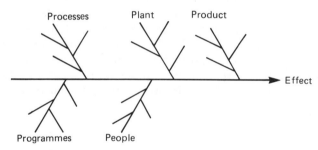

Fig. 20.2 The cause–effect, Ishikawa, or 'herring-bone' diagram

Statistical process control (SPC)

Since the responsibility for output lies with the producing department, the responsibility for achieving the appropriate quality in the transformation process must also lie with production. To fulfil this responsibility, production staff must be provided with the tools necessary to:

(*a*) know whether or not the process is capable of meeting the requirements;

(*b*) know whether or not the process is meeting the requirements at any point in time;

(*c*) make a correct adjustment to the process when it is not meeting the requirements.

Statistical process control (SPC) methods, backed by management commitment and good organization, provide objective methods of process quality control in any transformation process, whether this is in the manufacture of artefacts or the provision of services. A systematic study of a production process provides knowledge of the process capability and the sources of non-conforming outputs. This information can then be fed back quickly to the design and technology functions. Knowledge of the current state of a process also enables a more balanced judgement of equipment, both with regard to the tasks within its capability and its rational utilization.

SPC procedures exist because there is variation in the characteristics of articles and services. The inherent variability in every transformation process causes the output from it to vary over a period of time. If this variability is considerable, it is impossible to predict the value of a characteristic of any single item or at any point in time. Using statistical methods, however, it is possible to take meagre knowledge of the output and turn it into meaningful statements which may then be used to describe the process itself. Hence, statistically-based process control procedures are designed to divert attention from individual pieces of data and focus it on the process as a whole. SPC techniques may be used to measure the degree of conformance of purchased materials, services, processes and products to previously agreed specifications. In essence, SPC techniques select a representative, simple, random sample from the 'population', or the output from a process. From an analysis of the sample it is possible to make decisions regarding the current performance of the processor.

Types of quality data

Numerical information on quality will arise either from:

(a) counting; or
(b) measurement.

Data which arises from counting can only occur at definite points or in 'discrete' jumps. There can only be 0, 1, 2, etc. errors in a typed page, there cannot be 3.89 errors. The number of imperfections on a polished surface, the number of defects in a length of cloth, the acceptability or unacceptability of the lining of a drum are discrete data and are called *attributes*. As there is only a two-way classification to consider, attributes give rise to discrete data, which necessarily varies in jumps.

Data which arises from measurement can occur anywhere at all on a continuous scale and is called *variable* data. The weight of a capsule, the diameter of a piston, the tensile strength of a piece of rod, the time taken to process an insurance claim, are all variables, the measurement of which produce continuous data.

Causes of process variability

At the basis of the theory of process control is a differentiation of the causes of variation in quality during production. Certain variations in the quality of products or services belong to the category of chance or random variations, about which little may be done, other than to revise the process. This type of variation is the sum of the effects of a complex interaction of 'random' or 'common' causes, each of which is slight. When random variation alone exists, no major part of it may be traced to a single cause. The set of random causes which produces variation in the quality of a manufactured product may include: draughts, atmospheric temperature changes, passing traffic or machine vibrations, electrical fluctuations and changes in operator physical and emotional conditions. This is analogous to the set of forces which cause a coin to turn up heads or tails when tossed. When only random variations are present in a process, the process is considered to be *in statistical control*. There is also variation in test equipment and test procedures, whether used to measure a physical dimension, an electronic or a chemical characteristic or any other property. The inherent variation in testing contributes to the overall process variability and is always an important factor. In a similar way, processes whose output is not an artefact will be subject to random causes of variation: the weather, traffic problems, electricity supply, operator performance, etc.

Causes of variation which are large in magnitude and readily identified are classified as 'assignable' or 'special' causes. For the most part, these consist of differences among: plant, equipment, processes, operators, materials and other miscellaneous factors. When an assignable cause of variation is present, process variability will be excessive and the process is classified as *out of control* or beyond the expected random variations.

Control charts

A control chart is a form of traffic signal, the operation of which is based on evidence from the small samples taken at random during a process. A green light is given when the process should be allowed to run. All too often in manufacturing, processes are adjusted on the basis of a single measurement, a practice which can make a process much more variable than it is already. The equivalent of an amber light appears when trouble is possibly imminent. The red light shows that there is practically no doubt that the process has wandered and that it must be stopped and corrected to prevent production of defective material.

Clearly, such a scheme can be introduced only when the process is 'in control'. Since the samples taken are usually small, typically less than 10, there are risks of errors, but these are small, calculated risks and not blind ones. The risk calculations are based on various frequency distributions.

These charts should be easy to understand and interpret. They can become, with experience, sensitive diagnostic tools which can be used by operators and first-line supervision to prevent defective output being produced. Time and effort spent to explain the working of the charts to all concerned are never wasted.

There are different types of control charts for variables and attribute data. The most frequently used charts for variables are mean and range charts which are used together. Number-defective or *np* charts and proportion-defective or *p* charts are the most common ones in use for attributes. Others found in use are moving average and range charts, number of defects (*c* and *u*) charts, and cumulative sum (*cusum*) charts. The latter offer very powerful management tools for the detection of trends or changes in attributes and variable data.

The range of type and use of control charts is now very wide, and within the present text it is not possible to indicate more than the basic principles underlying them. Reference is made in 'Further reading' to some comprehensive texts on the subject.

The control of variables

When dealing with products or services having properties which are measured on a continuous scale, it is important to realize that no two measurements made will be exactly alike. The variation may be quite large and easily noticeable, such as in lengths of pieces of steel sawn by hand. When variations are very small, it may appear that each element of the output is identical. This is in fact due to the limitations of measurement, and 'instruments' with greater precision will show differences.

Process capability

In sampling a continuous variable, e.g. the length of a piece of steel, or the time of arrival of delivery, the main assumption on which the statistical analysis is based is that the variable—the length or time—will be *normally distributed*, i.e. it will be bell-shaped.

For example, on measuring the length of 1,000 steel sheets, it was found that they gave the following *frequency distribution*:

Steel sheet length (mm) (rounded to nearest 0.05 mm)	Number of sheets
60.10	1
60.15	6
60.20	12
60.25	18
60.30	85
60.35	214
60.40	339
60.45	201
60.50	75
60.55	33
60.60	10
60.65	4
60.70	2
	1,000

These values are shown as a *histogram* in Fig. 20.3, and its shape and general symmetry indicate that a normal or Gaussian distribution (Fig. 20.4) conveniently describes the variation in the diameters.

The measure of 'central tendency' most frequently used is the *mean* or *average* (μ) of the process data. The measure of spread of values from the process is given by the *standard deviation* (σ) which is calculated by adding together all the squares of the differences between the measured values and the mean value, dividing the resultant sum by the total number (N) of observations, and then taking the square root of the result, that is:

$$\sigma = \sqrt{\frac{\Sigma (x - \mu)^2}{N}}$$

A simpler method of estimating σ is usually used in SPC.

A process whose average is equal to the nominal or target value is said to be *accurate*. One which has a relatively small spread is said to be *precise*; the smaller the value of σ, the higher the precision. A specification related to variables, therefore, requires a statement on *both* accuracy and precision. Often 'high quality' is associated with high accuracy and high precision, whereas the true requirements may not necessarily imply such a combination.

Suppose the target length of the sheet steel cutting process was 60.4 mm, and that the process was being operated with a mean value, $\mu = 60.4$ mm, and a standard deviation, $\sigma = 0.1$ mm, then from a knowledge of the bell-shape curve and the properties of the normal distribution, the following facts would emerge:

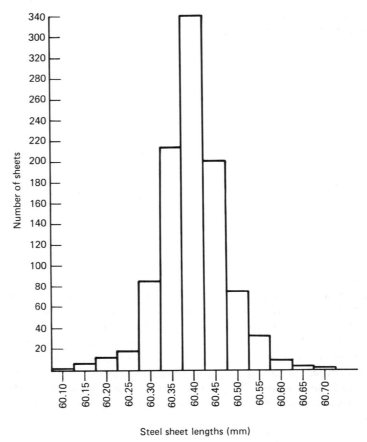

Fig. 20.3 Frequency distribution of steel sheet lengths

68.3 per cent of the sheets produced are within ± 0.1 mm of the average ($\mu \pm \sigma$)

95.4 per cent of the sheets are within average ± 0.2 mm ($\mu \pm 2\sigma$)

99.7 per cent are within average ± 0.3 mm ($\mu \pm 3\sigma$) (Fig. 20.5)

The usual aim in manufacturing is not to achieve every sheet with the same length, but to obtain sheets or products within specified limits or tolerances. No adjustment of the process is called for as long as there is no immediate danger of falling outside the 'tolerance zone'. Ensuring that the tolerance zone exceeds the spread of the distribution is thus an essential prerequisite to avoiding the production of defectives. If tolerances have been set for the sheets of steel at 60.4 ± 0.4 mm, then very few will fall outside them (Fig. 20.6(a)). Conversely, if the spread of the

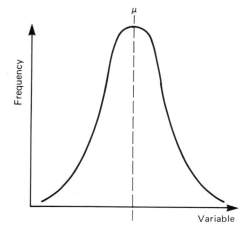

Fig. 20.4 The normal distribution of a continuous variable

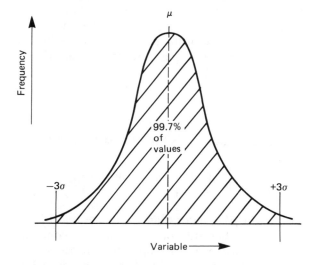

Fig. 20.5 The proportion of output contained in ($\mu \pm 3\sigma$)

process exceeds a specified tolerance, of 60.4 ± 0.2 mm, as in Fig. 20.6(b), then there will be inevitably reject material.

The relationship between process variability and specified tolerances, known as the *process capability*, may be formalized using the standard deviation, σ, of the process. In order to produce within the specified requirements, the distance between the upper specification limit (USL) and the lower specification limit (LSL), i.e. USL − LSL, must be equal

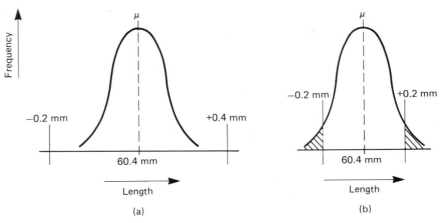

Fig. 20.6 The relationship between tolerances and process variability

to or greater than the width of the base of the process bell, i.e. 6σ.

When a process is in statistical control, i.e. only random causes of variation are present, a *process capability index* may be calculated to relate the actual performance of the process to its specified requirements. The simplest index is *Cp*, which quantifies the spread of the process relative to the specification limits:

$$Cp = \frac{\text{USL} - \text{LSL}}{6\sigma}$$

A second index, *Cpk*, quantifies both the spread and the setting of the process:

$$Cpk = \text{minimum of } \frac{\text{USL} - \bar{X}}{3\sigma} \text{ or } \frac{\bar{X} - \text{LSL}}{3\sigma}$$

Values for *Cp* and *Cpk* greater than 1 indicate that three process standard deviations (3σ) either side of the mean are contained within the specification or tolerance band. To operate a process safely inside the required limits, the values of *Cp* and *Cpk* must approach 2. Clearly, when *Cp* or *Cpk* is less than 1, the process is incapable of achieving the requirements.

Control charts for variables

The standard deviation (σ) of a process distribution is one measure of variation. As the sample size in SPC is usually ≤10, a more convenient measure of spread is the sample range: the difference between the largest and smallest values in the sample. To control the plant or process it is necessary to check the current state of the mean and spread of the distribution, and this may be achieved with the aid of mean and range charts.

If lengths of sheet steel are measured, it is clear that occasionally one will be found which is towards one end of the tail of the process normal distribution. This, if examined on its own, may lead to the wrong conclusion that the cutting process requires adjustment. If, however, a sample of five pieces is taken, it is extremely unlikely that all five lengths will lie towards one extreme end of the distribution. The average or mean length of five pieces will, therefore, provide a much more reliable indicator of the setting of the process. Moreover, the range of the sample will give an indication of the spread of the results from the process.

A capability study

A series of, say, 20 samples of size five ($n = 5$) are taken from a process over a period of time, when no adjustments to the process have been made, say one sample every 15 minutes. Table 20.1 shows the individual lengths of 20 samples of five sheets of steel taken in such a way. The mean and range of each group of five results is calculated and the grand mean of means (process mean, $\bar{X}$) is determined, together with the mean of the sample ranges ($\bar{R}$). The results are as follows:

Process mean, $\bar{X} = 60.5$ mm
Mean range, $\bar{R} = 0.10$ mm

Mean charts

The means of samples taken from a stable process will vary with each one taken, but the variation will not be as great as for single pieces. Comparison of the two frequency diagrams of Fig. 20.7 shows that the spread of the sample means is much less than the spread of the individual sheet lengths.

In setting up a mean chart where samples of a given size (n) are taken at intervals from the process over a period when it is thought to be under control, the sample mean is recorded on a control chart. Providing that the sample size is $n = 4$ or more, then the mean values will be normally distributed even if the original population itself is not truly normal. The standard deviation of the sample means, called the *standard error* to avoid confusion with the standard deviation of the parent population, is smaller than the parent standard deviation:

Standard error of the sample means $= \dfrac{\sigma}{\sqrt{n}}$

Table 20.1 Individual lengths, means and ranges of 20 samples of five steel sheets

Sample number	Length (mm) Piece 1	Piece 2	Piece 3	Piece 4	Piece 5	Sample mean	Sample range
1	60.45	60.46	60.52	60.55	60.55	60.51	0.10
2	60.45	60.55	60.59	60.55	60.52	60.53	0.14
3	60.49	60.49	60.58	60.49	60.54	60.52	0.09
4	60.43	60.43	60.44	60.47	60.51	60.46	0.08
5	60.47	60.50	60.48	60.50	60.44	60.48	0.06
6	60.61	60.58	60.53	60.42	60.46	60.52	0.19
7	60.48	60.56	60.57	60.50	60.43	60.51	0.14
8	60.49	60.49	60.55	60.57	60.54	60.53	0.08
9	60.45	60.47	60.53	60.51	60.46	60.48	0.08
10	60.51	60.43	60.51	60.44	60.49	60.48	0.08
11	60.48	60.50	60.52	60.58	60.49	60.51	0.10
12	60.48	60.56	60.47	60.51	60.54	60.51	0.09
13	60.48	60.54	60.58	60.57	60.54	60.54	0.10
14	60.57	60.49	60.43	60.51	60.49	60.50	0.14
15	60.47	60.47	60.51	60.48	60.43	60.47	0.08
16	60.49	60.41	60.53	60.52	60.54	60.50	0.13
17	60.43	60.48	60.54	60.47	60.48	60.48	0.11
18	60.57	60.47	60.52	60.52	60.53	60.52	0.10
19	60.48	60.42	60.50	60.49	60.48	60.47	0.08
20	60.55	60.52	60.52	60.47	60.55	60.52	0.08

where σ is the standard deviation of the parent population.

Figure 20.8 shows the principle of the control chart for sample mean. If the process is running in control, it can be expected that almost all the means of successive samples will lie between the upper action and lower action lines. These are set at a distance equal to $3\sigma/\sqrt{n}$ either side of the process mean:

Upper action line (UAL) $= X + 3\sigma/\sqrt{n}$
Lower action line (LAL) $= X - 3\sigma/\sqrt{n}$

The chance of a mean falling outside either of these lines is c. 1.5 in 1,000, unless the process has altered. If a point does fall outside, this indicates the presence of an assignable cause and the process should be investigated or the setting appropriately adjusted.

Figure 20.8 also shows warning limits which have been set at $2\sigma/\sqrt{n}$ away from the process mean:

Upper warning line (UWL) $= X + 2\sigma/\sqrt{n}$
Lower warning line (LWL) $= X - 2\sigma/\sqrt{n}$

The chance of a sample mean plotting outside either of these limits is c. 1

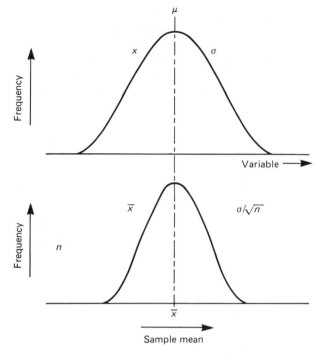

Fig. 20.7 What happens when samples of size *n* are taken and the means are plotted

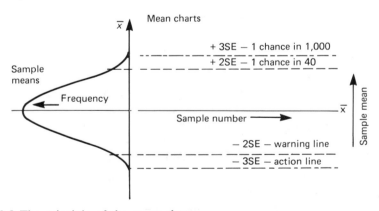

Fig. 20.8 The principle of the mean chart

in 40, i.e. it is expected to happen once in every 40 samples. When it does happen, however, there are grounds for suspicion and the usual procedure is to take another sample immediately, before making a definite decision about the setting of the process. Two successive sample means outside one of the warning lines indicates that action to adjust the process should be taken immediately.

In SPC for variables, the sample size is usually less than twelve, and it becomes possible to use the alternative measure of spread of the process—the mean range of samples, $\bar{R}$. Use may then be made of Hartley's conversion constant (d_n) for estimating the process standard deviation:

$$\sigma = \frac{\bar{R}}{d_n}$$

where d_n is obtained from Table 20.2.

Table 20.2 Hartley's constants for sample size $n = 2$ to 10

Sample size	(n) 2	3	4	5	6	7	8	9	10
	d_n 1.13	1.69	2.06	2.33	2.53	2.70	2.85	2.97	3.08

Using the data already indicated:

Process mean, $\bar{X} = 60.50$ mm
Mean range, $\bar{R} = 0.10$ mm
Sample size, $n = 5$
Hartley's constant, $d_n = 2.33$

Estimate of process standard deviation,

$$\sigma = \frac{\bar{R}}{d_n} = \frac{0.10}{2.33} = 0.043$$

Mean chart:

Action lines $= \bar{X} \pm 3\sigma/\sqrt{n}$
$= 60.50 \pm (3 \times 0.043/\sqrt{5})$
UAL $= 60.56$ LAL $= 60.44$
Warning lines $= \bar{X} \pm 2\sigma/\sqrt{n}$
$= 60.5 \pm (2 \times 0.043/\sqrt{5})$
UWL $= 60.54$ LWL $= 60.46$

Alternative method of calculating mean chart limits
The action lines are at $\bar{X} \pm 3\sigma/\sqrt{n}$
Substituting $\sigma = R/d_n$, the limits become:

Action lines at $\bar{X} \pm \left(\dfrac{3}{d_n \sqrt{n}} \right) \bar{R}$

As 3, d_n and n are all constants for the same sample size, they may be replaced with just one constant, $A_2 = 3/d_n \sqrt{n}$.

The action lines for the mean chart become:

$$\bar{X} \pm A_2\bar{R}$$

The warning lines may be similarly calculated from:

$$\bar{X} \pm \frac{2}{3} A_2\bar{R}$$

The constants A_2 and $\frac{2}{3}A_2$ for sample sizes $n = 2$ to 12 are listed in Table 20.3.

Table 20.3 Constants for use in the calculation of mean chart control limits

Sample size (n)	2	3	4	5	6	7	8	9	10	11	12
A_2	1.88	1.02	0.73	0.58	0.48	0.42	0.37	0.34	0.31	0.29	0.27
$\frac{2}{3}A_2$	1.25	0.68	0.49	0.39	0.32	0.28	0.25	0.23	0.21	0.19	0.18

Applying these constants to the example data, the control limits may now be calculated directly from the values of $\bar{X}$ and $\bar{R}$:

$$n = 5, A_2 = 0.58, \tfrac{2}{3}A_2 = 0.39$$

Action lines at $\bar{X} \pm A_2\bar{R}$

$$= 60.60 \pm (0.58 \times 0.10)$$
$$\text{UAL} = 60.56, \text{LAL} = 60.44$$

Warning lines at $\bar{X} \pm \tfrac{2}{3}A_2\bar{R}$

$$= 60.50 \pm (0.39 \times 0.10)$$
$$\text{UAL} = 60.54, \text{LAL} = 60.46$$

Figure 20.9 shows the mean values of the samples of five steel sheets, given in Table 20.1, plotted on a mean chart.

Range charts

A process is only in control when both the accuracy (mean) and precision (spread) are in control. A separate chart for control of process variability is required, and the sample standard deviation could be plotted. More conveniently, the ranges of samples are plotted on a range chart which is very similar to the mean chart, the difference between the highest and lowest values in the sample being plotted and compared to predetermined limits. The development of a more serious fault than incorrect setting can lead to the situation illustrated in Fig. 20.10, where the process collapses from form A to form B, e.g. due to failure of a part of the process. The ranges of the samples from B will have higher values than ranges in

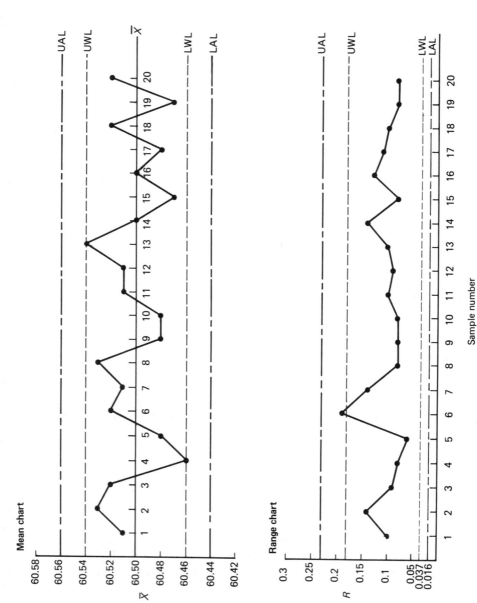

Fig. 20.9 Mean and range chart for steel sheets (Table 20.1, $n = 5$)

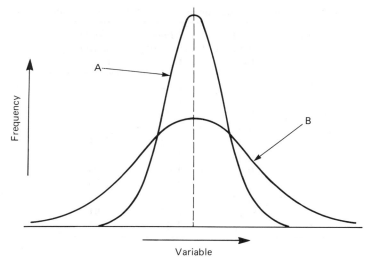

Fig. 20.10 Increase in spread of a process

samples taken from A. If a range chart (Fig. 20.9) is plotted in conjunction with the mean chart, similar action and warning lines can be drawn to indicate trouble.

The range control chart limits are asymmetrical about the mean range since the distribution of sample ranges is a positively skewed distribution. Table 20.4 provides four constants, $D^1_{0.001}$, $D^1_{0.025}$, $D^1_{0.975}$ and $D^1_{0.995}$, which may be used to calculate the control limits:

UAL at $D^1_{0.001}$ $\bar{R}$
UWL at $D^1_{0.025}$ $\bar{R}$
LWL at $D^1_{0.975}$ $\bar{R}$
LAL at $D^1_{0.999}$ $\bar{R}$

For the example data under consideration, the sample size is five and the constants are:

Action	$D^1_{0.001} = 2.34$	$D^1_{0.999} = 0.16$
Warning	$D^1_{0.025} = 1.81$	$D^1_{0.975} = 0.37$

As the mean range, $\bar{R}$, is 0.10 mm, the control limits are:

UAL = 2.34 × 0.10 = 0.234 mm
UWL = 1.81 × 0.10 = 0.181 mm
LWL = 0.37 × 0.10 = 0.037 mm
LAL = 0.16 × 0.10 = 0.016 mm

Table 20.4 Constants used in the calculation of range chart control limits

Sample size (n)	Lower action $D_{0.999}^1$	Lower warning $D_{0.975}^1$	Upper warning $D_{0.025}^1$	Upper action $D_{0.001}^1$
2	0.00	0.04	2.81	4.12
3	0.04	0.18	2.17	2.98
4	0.10	0.29	1.93	2.57
5	0.16	0.37	1.81	2.34
6	0.21	0.42	1.72	2.21
7	0.25	0.46	1.66	2.11
8	0.29	0.50	1.62	2.04
9	0.32	0.52	1.58	1.99
10	0.35	0.54	1.56	1.93
11	0.38	0.56	0.53	1.91
12	0.40	0.58	1.51	1.87

Stepwise procedure

The statistical concepts behind control charts for variables may seem a little complex, but the steps in setting up the charts for mean and range are very simple:

1. Select 20 or so random samples of size n ($n \leqslant 12$)
2. Measure the variable for each of the sample items
3. Calculate each sample mean and range
4. Calculate the grand or process mean, $\bar{X}$, and the mean range, $\bar{R}$
5. Look up the values of: A_2, $\frac{2}{3}A_2$, $D_{0.001}^1$, $D_{0.025}^1$, $D_{0.975}^1$, $D_{0.999}^1$
6. Calculate action and warning lines for the mean and range charts, following the simple formulae given above

Process 'in control'

At the beginning of the section on setting up control charts for variables, it was stated that samples should be taken from the process when it is believed that the process is under control. Before the charts are used to control the process, the initial data is plotted on the mean and range charts to confirm that the distribution of the individual items was stable.

A process is 'in-statistical-control' when all the variations have been shown to arise from random or common causes and none attributable to assignable or special causes. The randomness of the variations may be shown by the plotted mean and range charts when there are:

1. No mean or range values lying outside the action limits.

2. No more than about 1 in 40 values lying between the warning and action limits.

3. No incidences of two consecutive mean or range values lying in the same warning zone.

4. No runs of more than six sample means or ranges which lie either above or below the average control chart line.

5. No trends of more than six values of mean or range which are continuously either rising or falling.

The initial example data under consideration, plotted on the mean and range charts in Fig. 20.9, clearly demonstrates that this process is in control, since all the above requirements are met. If the process examined in this way is not in statistical control, the assignable causes must be identified and eliminated. The process may then be re-examined to test for stability. Having demonstrated that only random causes of variation are present, the next task is to compare the precision of the process with the required specification tolerances. Calculation of the process capability indices Cp and Cpk allows this to be done quickly and quantitatively. In the example, if the requirement was to produce a product within the range 60.20 (LSL) to 60.60 (USL), with the process standard deviation $\sigma = 0.043$ and process mean $\bar{X} = 60.50$:

$$Cp = \frac{USL - LSL}{6\sigma} = \frac{60.6 - 60.2}{6 \times 0.043} = 1.55$$

$$Cpk = \frac{USL - \bar{X}}{3\sigma} = \frac{60.6 - 60.5}{3 \times 0.043} = 0.78$$

The Cp value of 1.55 indicates that the process spread is capable of producing an output within the specified tolerance, but the Cpk value of <1 suggests that the setting of the process is incorrect. In the case of sheets of steel, this will probably require only a simple adjustment to the equipment.

Controlling the process

When the process is shown to be in control, then the mean and range charts may be used to make decisions about the state of the process during production. For example, Fig. 20.11 shows mean and range charts for the next 23 samples taken from the steel sheet cutting process. The process is well under control, i.e. within the action lines, until sample 8, when the mean reaches the upper warning line—a repeat sample required here. Sample 9 shows a mean plotted above the upper action line and corrective action must be taken. This action brings the process back into control but only until sample 11, where the sample mean is again in the

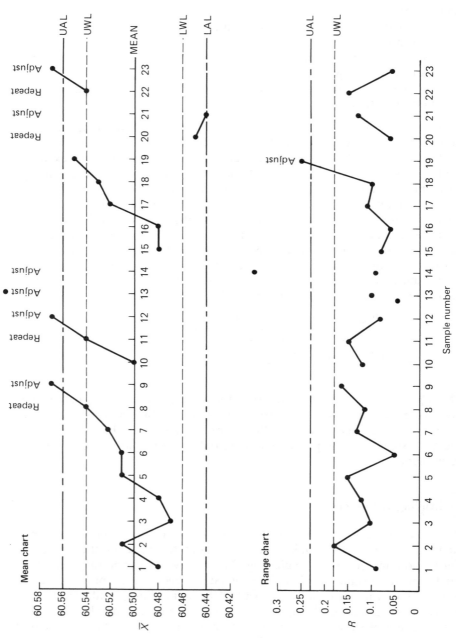

Fig. 20.11 Mean and ranges for next 23 samples of steel sheets ($n = 5$)

warning zone—another sample should be taken immediately, rather than wait for the next sampling period. This sample (12) gives a mean above the action line: corrective action forthwith. But the action appears to be in the wrong direction, and the response results in over-correction with sample mean 14 well below the lower action line. The process continues to drift upwards out of control between samples 15 and 19, at which point the range goes out of control, indicating a serious malfunctioning of the process. The process clearly requires investigation to establish the assignable causes of change in the variability. This situation would not have been identified as quickly in the absence of the process control charts and this simple example illustrates the power of the charts in both quality control and in early warning of equipment trouble.

It will be noted that 'action' and 'repeat' samples have been marked on the control charts. In addition, any alterations in materials, the process, operators or any other technical changes should be recorded on the charts when they take place. This practice is extremely useful in helping to track down causes of shifts in mean or variability.

Recommended reading

Caplan, Rowland H., *A Practical Approach to Quality Control*, 4th edn, Business Books, 1982.
  A very sound introduction to the subject.
Grant, Eugene L., and Leavenworth, Richard S., *Statistical Quality Control*, 5th edn, McGraw-Hill, 1979.
  A very thorough discussion of the statistics of quality control.
Juran, J. M. (Ed.), *Quality Control Handbook*, 3rd edn, McGraw-Hill, 1974.
  A comprehensive work which discusses quality control from particular industrial points of view. Probably on the shelves of most quality professionals.
Oakland, John S., *Statistical Process Control*, Heinemann, 1986.
  One author has a biased view of this book. It attempts to provide a practical, non-mathematical guide to SPC, using real-life examples and data, drawn from a wide variety of industries. The other two authors have been convinced that it does!
Price, Frank, *Right First Time*, Gower, 1984.
  A very readable book on SPC, aimed at senior managers as well as quality control specialists. It treats the subject in a novel way, but gets the message over very simply.
British Standards Institution, *Quality Management Systems—Quality Control*, BSI Handbook 24, 1985.
  Contains eight standards related to quality control: BS 2564 Control Charts, BS 5309 Sampling Chemicals, BS 5700 Guide process to control, BS 5701 Number Defective Charts, BS 5703 Cusum Techniques, BS 6000 & 6001 Acceptance Sampling for Attributes, BS 6002 Acceptance Sampling for Variables.

21 Control of quality II

Process control of attributes

In the case of attributes, e.g. colour, general appearance, surface finish, absenteeism, when it is not possible to measure a product except in terms of 'good' or 'bad', present or absent, the control process is effectively that of determining which one, out of two possible decisions, is appropriate. When this two-way decision involves the classification of whole items or units as defective, the sampling process is governed by the laws of the *binomial distribution*.

If the proportion of the output which is not acceptable (the 'fraction defective') is p, and the 'fraction non-defective' is q (or $1-p$), clearly $p + q = 1$, and when a large number of samples, each of size n is taken, then the average number of defectives which will be found is np. If only one sample is taken, then the probability of finding 0, 1, 2, 3 . . . . defectives in any sample is given by the successive terms in the expansion of $(p + q)^n$, that is:

the probability of 0 defectives $= p^0 q^n = q^n$

the probability of 1 defective $= np^1 q^{n-1}$

the probability of 2 defectives $= \dfrac{n(n-1)}{1 \times 2} p^2 q^{n-2}$

Generally, the probability of x defectives $= \dfrac{n!}{x!(n-x)!} p^x q^{n-x}$

$$= {}_nC_x p^x (1-p)^{n-x}$$

The average number of defectives obtained over a large number of samples is called the *expected number defective* and is given by:

expected number defective $= np$

The standard deviation for the number of defectives in samples of size n, fraction defective p, fraction non-defective q, is:

standard deviation $= \sqrt{npq}$

$$= \sqrt{[np(1-p)]}$$

Thus, if the fraction defective is 0.1 (that is, 10 in 100) and the sample size is 20, then the expected number defective will be:

$$20 \times 0.1 = 2$$

and the standard deviation will be:

$$\sqrt{(20 \times 0.1 \times 0.9)} = 1.34$$

The probability of a single sample containing:

0 defectives will be	$(0.9)^{20}$	$= 0.122$
1 defective	$20 \times (0.9)^{19} (0.1)$	$= 0.270$
2 defectives	$\dfrac{20 \times 19}{1 \times 2}(0.9)^{18} (0.1)^2$	$= 0.285$
3 defectives	$\dfrac{20 \times 19 \times 18}{1 \times 2 \times 3}(0.9)^{17} (0.1)^3$	$= 0.190$
4 defectives		$= 0.090$
5 defectives		$= 0.032$
6 defectives		$= 0.009$
7 defectives		$= 0.002$
8 defectives		$= 0.001$

These probabilities, which have been represented graphically in Fig. 21.1, may also be found by reference to the many sets of statistical tables available.

If, from a population which previously had the above characteristics, i.e. $p = 0.1$, a sample of 20 items is taken and 7 of these are found to be defective, then it can be said that the likelihood of this happening is

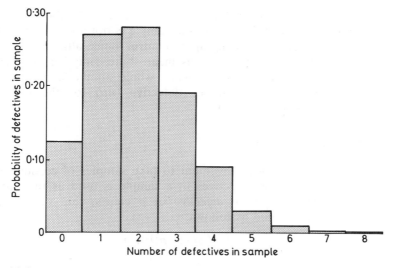

Fig. 21.1

so small (2 in 1,000) that it is extremely likely that the process producing the population has changed.

Number-defective (*np*) charts

The control chart for *number-defective* or *np* charts operates in a similar way to that for variables with warning and action lines. These lines are again set by reference to the average and standard deviation of the number of defectives in the samples, although in the case of the binomial distribution the $\pm 2\sigma$ and $\pm 3\sigma$ values do not present constant risk levels as in the control by variables case. However, to simplify matters, the action lines for the *np* chart may be calculated in the standard manner:

Upper action line (UAL) $= np + 3\sqrt{[np\,(1-p)]}$
Lower action line (LAL) $= np - 3\sqrt{[np\,(1-p)]}$

Similarly, the warning lines may be set at:

Upper warning line (UWL) $= np + 2\sqrt{[np\,(1-p)]}$
Lower warning line (LWL) $= np - 2\sqrt{[np\,(1-p)]}$

For the process producing 10 per cent defectives ($p = 0.1$), with a sample size, $n = 20$:

Action lines $= (20 \times 0.1) \pm 3\sqrt{(20 \times 0.1 \times 0.9)}$
UAL $= 6.02$, i.e. just above 6, LAL $= -2.02$ (omit)
Warning lines $= (20 \times 0.1) \pm 2\sqrt{(20 \times 0.1 \times 0.9)}$
UWL $= 4.68$, i.e. between 4 and 5, LWL $= -0.68$ (omit)

A negative value for the lower lines indicates that they should be omitted and the finding of zero defectives in the sample is not an indication that the process has improved. For the upper control limits, although it is not possible to find fractions of defectives in attribute sampling, ambiguity is avoided by drawing the lines between whole numbers. Figure 21.2 shows a control chart for number defective (*np*) for the situation considered above, $n = 20$, $p = 0.1$.

Proportion defective (*p*) charts

In some situations it is not convenient to take samples of constant size and so the *proportion* of defectives in a sample is used as the quality indicator. In these *proportion-defective* or *p* charts, the warning and action limits are calculated as follows:

Action lines at: $p \pm 3\sqrt{[p(1-p)]}/\sqrt{n}$
Warning lines at: $p \pm 2\sqrt{[p(1-p)]}/\sqrt{n}$

When samples of varying sizes are used to plot *p* charts, the control lines

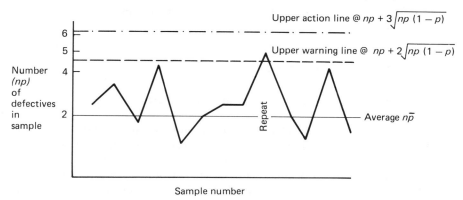

Fig. 21.2 An *np* chart for number defective in a sample of size $n = 20$, when proportion defective, $p = 0.1$

change and unique limits should be calculated for each sample size. For practical purposes, however, an average sample size ($\bar{n}$) may be used in the calculations and the limits obtained are acceptable when individual sample sizes vary from $\bar{n}$ by no more than $\pm \bar{n}/4$. For sample sizes outside this range, separate control limits must be calculated.

Control charts for number of defects (c)

The control charts for attributes considered so far have applied to *defectives*. There are situations, however, where the number of *defects* in the product or service are being counted. In these cases the binomial distribution does not apply because there are no values of n or q for the expression $(p + q)^n$. The *Poisson distribution* describes the results obtained from counting defects, and gives the following equation for finding the probability (P) of observing x defects in a unit:

$$P(x) = e^{-\bar{c}} (\bar{c}^x/x!)$$

where e = exponential constant, 2.7183
      $\bar{c}$ = average number of defects per unit being produced by the process

As with the Binomial distribution, it is not necessary to calculate probabilities in this way, since statistical tables containing this information have been compiled.

The standard deviation of a Poisson distribution is very simply the square root of the process average:

$$\sigma = \sqrt{\bar{c}}$$

and the action and warning lines for a c chart may be calculated in the usual simplified form:

Action lines at $\bar{c} \pm 3\sqrt{\bar{c}}$
Warning lines at $\bar{c} \pm 2\sqrt{\bar{c}}$

Lower action and warning lines on attribute charts

It is sometimes useful to insert lower warning and action limits on attribute charts. If points appear below the lower action limit, there is only a slight chance of this happening unless there has been a significant improvement in the process. In this case, it would be worthwhile investigating the cause of such a change, to discover how the improvement could be made permanent. The only other reason for a point plotting below the action limit would be inaccurate inspection or defectives being passed as good.

Cusum charts

The cusum (cumulative sum) chart is a graph which takes a little longer to draw than the conventional control chart, but which gives a lot more information. It is particularly useful for plotting the evolution of processes because it presents data in a way that enables the eye to separate true trends and changes from a background of random variation. Cusum charts can detect small changes in data very quickly and may be used for the control of variables and attributes. In essence, a reference or 'target value' is subtracted from each successive sample observation and the result accumulated. Values of this cumulative sum are plotted and 'trend lines' may be drawn on the resulting graphs. If this is approximately horizontal, the value of the variable is about the same as the target value. An overall slope downwards shows a value less than the target, and if the slope is upwards it is greater.

Figure 21.3 shows a comparison of an np chart and a cusum chart which have been plotted using the same data—defectives in samples of 100 polyurethane form products. The change, which is immediately obvious on the cusum chart, is difficult to detect on the conventional control chart.

The implementation of statistical process control

One of the first steps in any implementation programme must be the provision of education and training for:

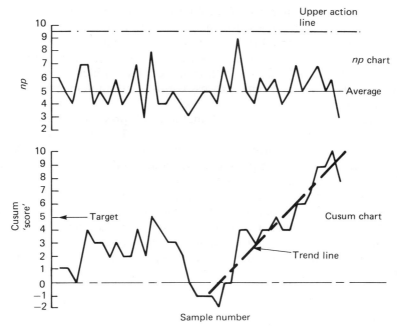

Fig. 21.3 Comparison of cusum and *np* charts for the same data

Managers
Supervisors
Operators, and
Inspection staff

The courses, teaching methods and materials used for this purpose must be very carefully selected, for much harm can be done by the insensitive teaching of 'statistics', which many people in industry and commerce find indigestible. It is possible to learn and apply excellent methods of process control without becoming immersed in heavy theoretical studies.

For the successful introduction of SPC, the training must have follow-up, which can take many forms. Ideally, an in-house expert can provide the lead through the design of implementation programmes. The most satisfactory strategy is to start small and learn through a bank of knowledge and experience. Each technique should be introduced alongside existing methods of quality control (if they do exist): this allows comparisons to be made between the new and old methods. When confidence has been built upon the results of the comparisons, the statistical techniques can take over the control of the process. Improvements in one or two areas of the organization's operations, using this approach, will quickly establish SPC as a reliable tool for control of manufacturing processes.

Sometimes it is necessary to obtain help from outside sources—the prophet is rarely accepted in his own land—and many organizations can offer valuable assistance. Ideally, the people providing the initial training should also be involved in the follow-up activities, which should include 'workshop days' when specific process control and implementation problems are discussed.

The costs of introducing good methods of process control will be greatly outweighed by the savings which accrue. The inevitable reduction in scrap, re-work and correction or rectification costs, together with the increases in people and equipment utilization and production capacity, will directly repay the investment.

The increased confidence and efficiency that derives from greater process knowledge will permeate the whole organization from design and purchasing staff through to sales and marketing. Moreover, the introduction of good process control methods will act as a 'spearhead' to draw through the organization many of the requirements of a good quality system.

Acceptance sampling

The techniques dealt with so far in this chapter and in Chapter 20 are directed towards process control activities. However, there may be a need to carry out a further final check on a batch of finished product, before it reaches the consumer. Alternatively, material or services may be purchased without being able to ensure that the appropriate process control activities are taking place in the supply chain. In these situations, some form of inspection for acceptance or *product control* may be appropriate.

Such an inspection system should be concerned primarily with making sure that the product which passes the inspection point is of the appropriate quality. For this to be possible, it must be quite clear what is required. There are two aspects to a product specification with regard to inspection for acceptance, and there must be specific information on both of these if sensible decisions are to be made. The specification must contain a statement of what constitutes non-conformance. This is an extremely complex issue and demands careful thought before any inspection process gets underway. The various techniques of acceptance inspection will not resolve the problem of an ill-conceived definition of non-conformance, nor can they cope with the absence of one. Unfortunately, the latter situation exists in far too many organizations, where high levels of expenditure on inspection or checking result in frustration and conflict. Sometimes, in cases of subjective assessment, it is necessary to provide samples of acceptable and unacceptable material to aid the decision process.

In addition to the requirement for a definition of non-conformance, there is a need to stipulate, quite categorically, the quantity or proportion which is allowed if the batch of product is to be considered satisfactory. This, of course, may depend very much on the end use of the product or service and often leads to the classification of defects. For example, it may be considered that there are critical, major and minor defects which demand different quantification if customer satisfaction is to be ensured. In the production of aircraft there are obviously different requirements to those found in the manufacture of cast-iron man-hole covers. Similarly, in the assembly of a piece of furniture, one fault, such as a deep scratch on a polished surface, may cause great distress, whereas other, slight imperfections will pass unnoticed by many purchasers. These factors must be considered in the design of the inspection system. Sometimes it is necessary to design different schemes for different fault classifications to operate in parallel.

One hundred per cent inspection is a time-consuming, costly and unreliable method of product control. There are, of course, some situations in which this method is deemed to be an essential part of product control: the aerospace industry relies very heavily on this approach. Wherever it can, the system should move away from human inspection towards automated methods. This is not always possible or economical and some form of human involvement will always be required. In these cases, and where life or death consequences prevail, the only answer is to perform 100 per cent human inspection several times.

Acceptance sampling procedures, if they are applied correctly, will allow the quantification and limitation of risks of making incorrect decisions. In many cases, a properly designed and effectively administered sampling scheme is the most economical and practical way of making acceptance decisions. In cases of destructive testing, some form of sampling is the only acceptable alternative.

In deciding which type of scheme to use, it is first necessary to examine the nature of the quality characteristics which will be employed in the inspection process. Will the product quality be presented in the form of attribute data or variables? There are methods of acceptance sampling for both. Where only attribute data is available there is no choice, but when variables can be measured, two general approaches may be employed: acceptance sampling by variables, or convert the variable data into attribute form and use acceptance sampling by attributes. The advantages associated with using variables are similar to those found in process control: increased sensitivity and smaller sample sizes. The disadvantages concern the extra costs of obtaining the measured data and performing the necessary calculations, and in some situations these may be considerable. The principles of acceptance sampling will be explained using attributes since these are the most frequently used plans. The methods used for variables data are generally very similar and the reader is referred to 'Further reading' for the details of acceptance sampling for variables.

Acceptance sampling techniques are used to decide whether to accept or reject a batch of items based on random sample(s). If a decision is taken to accept, then the remainder of the batch is accepted without further inspection. It must be clear that such a procedure gives no guarantee of the actual quality of the batch; it simply provides a decision-making process.

If a decision to reject the batch is taken, the remainder may be sentenced in several possible ways, depending upon the use of the product and any associated technological or economic factors. A rejected batch may be destined for:

(a) 100 per cent screening to rectify or replace all defectives;
(b) further inspection;
(c) use for lower quality requirements;
(d) return to supplier;
(e) acceptance at discounted price; etc.

Operating characteristics

A characteristic of the mechanism of all sampling plans is that they are associated with risks. There are basically two types of risk derived from the sample or samples not being representative of the whole consignment, batch or production run. There is a risk that a decision may be taken to reject a batch which should have been accepted, i.e. of acceptable quality. This is referred to by statisticians as a *type I error*. Another term, which is more meaningful perhaps, is *producer's risk*. The *type II error* or *consumer's risk* is associated with the acceptance of goods the quality of which is unacceptable.

The efficiency of any sampling plan as a detector of acceptable and unacceptable batches is shown by means of its *operating characteristic* (*OC*) *curve*. This curve, which should be known for every sampling plan used, is derived by plotting:

The chance (or probability) of a batch being accepted	*versus*	The quality offered for inspection (usually measured in percentage defective)

Single sampling plans

The simplest type of acceptance sampling scheme is one where a single sample (size n) is taken from the batch (size N) and the whole batch is

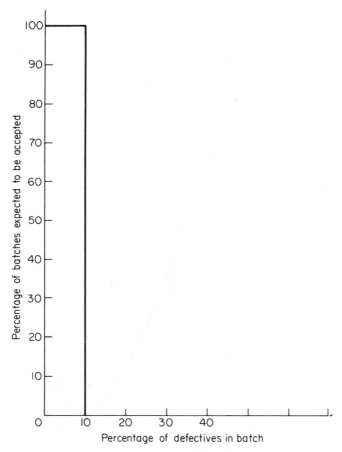

Fig. 21.4 Ideal *OC* curve for AQL = 10 per cent defectives

accepted if the number of defectives found in the sample is equal to, or less than, the acceptance number (*c*). Ideally, the scheme should operate so that *all* batches which have an actual percentage of non-conformance equal to or less than the 'acceptable quality level' (AQL) are accepted on the basis of the single sample, and *all* batches which have an actual percentage greater than the AQL are rejected by the sample. The OC curve of this 'ideal' plan is shown in Fig. 21.4.

In practice, no scheme will offer this perfect discrimination. The OC of most sampling plans follows the curved lines of Fig. 21.5 which shows the consumer's risk at the *lot tolerance per cent defective* (LTPD)—the percentage of defectives which is unacceptable to the recipient.

At a different point on the curve is the producer's risk. This coincides

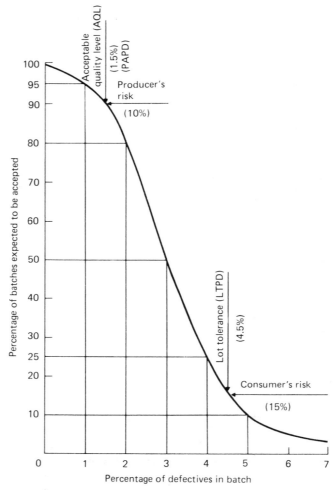

Fig. 21.5 Operating characteristic showing producer's risk, acceptable quality
level, consumer's risk and lot tolerance

with the *process average percentage defective* (PAPD)—the average per
cent defectives being produced by the process when it is considered to
be running at a level which is acceptable. This usually coincides with the
AQL, the maximum per cent defective that can be considered to be
acceptable by the consumer.

To illustrate how an actual OC is generated, consider again the situation set out previously (page 290) where the initial population—in this
case, the batch—had an *actual* proportion of defectives of 0.1, and a
sample of 20 was taken. Assume that the acceptance number c was 1, so
that if 2 or more defectives were found in the sample, then the whole

batch would be rejected, while if 0 or 1 defectives were found, the whole batch would be accepted ($N = 1,000$, $n = 20$, $c = 1$).

From the calculations on page 291 it is known that for this proportion of defectives:

the probability of 0 defectives being found in a sample of 20 is 0.122
the probability of 1 defective being found in a sample of 20 is 0.270
∴ the probability of acceptance (i.e. 0 or 1 defective being found in a sample of 20) is 0.392

Thus, in this sampling scheme, when the actual defective proportion is 0.1, the proportion of batches accepted will be 0.392. Similar calculations can be carried out for other actual defective proportions:

Actual proportions of defectives (p)	*Proportion of batches expected to be accepted* ($P(a)$)
0.01	0.983
0.05	0.736
0.10	0.392
0.20	0.069
0.30	0.008
0.40	0.001

and these give the OC of Fig. 21.6, where the usual convention that 'proportions' are quoted as percentages is followed. (*Note*: in practice it is not necessary to calculate the above values as, again, tables of values are readily available.)

It is useful to consider, in general terms, the effect of the sample size (n) and acceptance number (c) on the discriminatory power of sampling plans. The two parameters n and c may be varied independently. If this is done, the following will be observed:

n The OC curve of a single sample plan becomes more rectangular, that is more discriminatory, as the sample size increases. This is shown very well in the comparison of the two schemes in Fig. 21.7. The ratio of n to c is the same in each case, but the higher sample size gives much better discrimination between good and bad batches. There is an inspection cost penalty for this, of course.

c Lowering the acceptance number lowers the OC curve. Figure 21.8 shows this in the curves for single plans of common sample size with varying c. The scheme with zero acceptance has no inflection in the operating characteristic—the curve is completely concave. This is a feature of all schemes with $c = 0$. What this means, of course, is that $c = 0$ schemes are very poor discriminators. In some organizations, however, it is believed that a plan which rejects batches when a single defect is found is a strong plan. It is evident, from the OC curves, that such schemes will not guarantee defective-free batches, although

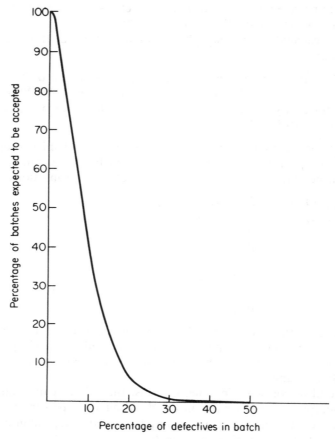

Fig. 21.6 Actual operating characteristic for $N = 1,000$, $n = 20$, $c = 1$

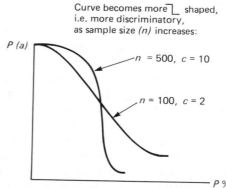

Fig. 21.7 Variation in OC curves with n

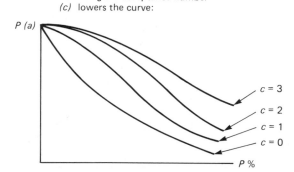

Fig. 21.8 Variation in OC curves with c

many bad lots will be rejected. More importantly, many good lots with low defective rates, which are economically acceptable, will also be rejected. If these are then subjected to 100 per cent screening, then the total inspection costs will increase too.

Average outgoing quality

In many inspection plans, the rejection of a batch is followed by 100 per cent screening of the remainder of the batch which has not been inspected. Whenever a defective is found during the screening, it is removed and replaced by a non-defective item, and this also applies to defectives found during inspection of the sample. This type of sampling plan is known as a rectification scheme.

The accepted batches will contain approximately the percentage defective submitted, although they will be slightly improved by the replacement of any defectives found in the sample. The rejected batches, after screening, assuming perfect inspection, contain zero defectives. For a rectification scheme, it is possible to calculate the average outgoing quality (AOQ) for each percentage defective submitted. A curve may then be drawn through points on a graph of AOQ plotted against percentage defective: this gives the so-called AOQ curve (Fig. 21.9).

$$AOQ = \frac{\text{Actual number of defectives in accepted batches}}{\text{Total number of items in accepted batches}}$$

$$AOQ = \left(\frac{N-n}{N}\right) P(a)p$$

When the initial quality of the goods inspected is high, the outgoing quality will be high since there were few defectives present in the first place; similarly, when the initial quality is poor, the outgoing quality will

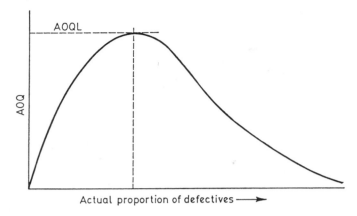

Fig. 21.9 Average outgoing quality (AOQ) curve

again be high, since the sampling scheme will have rejected easily the low-quality batches which are then rectified. A high outgoing quality is represented by a low value*for AOQ. The peak of the AOQ curve represents the highest possible value and this is known as the *average outgoing quality limit* (AOQL) of the sampling scheme.

Together, the OC and AOQ curves give a clear picture of how an acceptance sampling plan may be expected to react, over a series of submitted batches, to changing levels of input quality.

Operation of acceptance sampling plans

It must be fully understood by all who operate acceptance sampling schemes that the individual samples do not give any information about the quality of the remainder of the batch; they simply offer a decision rule—accept or reject (or submit to 100 per cent screening and rectification). It is quite clear, however, that in the operation of a scheme on a series of batches, over a period of time substantial amounts of data will be accumulated. Following the methods introduced earlier in this chapter, this data should be recorded in a systematic way so that additional use may be made of it. It should not go unnoticed, for example, that the proportion of batches being sentenced to 100 per cent screening or returned to a supplier has increased from 5 to 10 per cent. Indeed, when such an increase in rejection rate does occur, the OC curve should be consulted for an indication of the quality level of the input to the scheme, and all batches which have been accepted recently should be quarantined until further investigations take place. A most useful practice is to record the numbers of defectives found in each sample, together with the accept/reject decision. If this data is used to plot a number of defectives (*np*) chart, or a cusum chart, trends or sustained changes in the proportion of defectives present will be detected.

In addition to the single sampling scheme for attributes discussed above, there are in common use double, multiple and sequential schemes and acceptance sampling plans for variables. Standard tables, containing plotted OC curves, are available for assisting in the choice of appropriate sampling schemes for attributes and variables. In the UK, these are: British Standards BS 6000, 6001 and 6002, which have their equivalents throughout Europe, USA and the rest of the world.

Quality index

The quality of a product or service may be monitored by reference to a *quality index*. The product is 'awarded' a mark of, say, 100 and marks ('demerits') subtracted for non-conformances found; for example, 4 demerits for a major, 2 for a minor and 1 for a trivial defect or problem. Clearly, these classes must be carefully predefined. The resulting figure is then compared either with an agreed 'acceptable' figure, with a figure derived from serious competitors, or with previous figures as a monitor of the quality performance.

Recommended reading

See recommended reading for Chapter 20.

22 Costing

While budgets and budgetary control apply to the organization as a whole, costing is the ascertaining of the amount of expenditure incurred on a single item or group of items. There are two principal different types of costing: *historical* costing, where the costs are collected and analysed after the expenditure has taken place, and *standard* costing, where costs are compared as they occur with a predetermined cost, prepared in advance and usually known as the *standard cost*. Both have their place in industry. Standard costing is particularly useful in repetitive manufacture and is a type of control (cost control) exhibiting exactly the same features as other managerial control, namely:

1. *Plan*
2. *Publish*
3. *Measure*
4. *Compare*
5. *Report*
6. *Correct*

In certain types of manufacture, the extraction of costs of individual projects may be more costly than the value of the results obtained—for example, where very few processes are repeated and the time-cycle for a complete task is extremely low. As with any other data-collecting project, consideration must always be given to the use to which the information obtained will be put. Unless there is an immediate need for data, it is probably unwise to collect it: too many files are filled with information which is awaiting analysis. 'The figures will come in useful one day' is heard all too frequently, particularly now that the computer makes the collection and analysis of data easy and relatively inexpensive.

The sources of costing information

No costing system can be any more accurate than the information which is fed into it, although once considerable data is accumulated it is often possible for the cost department to observe probable errors which can then be referred back to the originators. All information used by the cost department originates elsewhere, and it is important to realize this, as often criticisms of the cost department for costs being 'wrong' should in fact be aimed elsewhere. The cost accountant will require to know, when costing a job:

1. The *time spent* and by whom—labour costs.
2. The *material used*—material costs.
3. The *overhead expenses* incurred—overhead costs.

Labour

Time recording is done either by means of time sheets (Fig. 22.1), which are filled in daily or weekly by hand, and which summarize the total hours spent, or by job cards (Fig. 22.2), each job having a separate card, the time spent on the job being recorded on the card by hand or by a clock (a job clock). Increasing use is being made of shop-floor data-collection systems whereby bar codes and bar code readers are used to identify jobs and operators. When job cards are used, the cost department will receive from each operator one card for each job undertaken, and in a jobbing shop with short time-cycles this will result in a large number of cards. However, the assignment of the time to the individual job is much simpler than in the case of the summarized job sheet. In the case of large-scale flow production, where an operator is engaged wholly upon one job for extended periods, the need for individual time recording vanishes.

Name......*J. Brown*............ Dept....*D1*......... W/E.. *7.11.89.* ....

Job No.	Mon.		Tue.		Wed.		Thur.		Fri.		Sat.		Totals
	N	O/T	N	O/T	N	O/T	N	O/T	N	O/T	N	O/T	
4261	2						2		1				5
4773	3		3		3				1				10
3648	1		2		2		3		1				9
4355	1				1				1				3
4343			1				2		1				4
5160	1		2		2	1	1		3				10
Totals	8		8		8	1	8		8				

Fig. 22.1

Description of Job		Job No.	
Assembly of		1001	
F.M.I.		Op. Name	
		J. Brown	

ON	OFF	TIME	
		N	O/T
9.11.81 11.30	9.11.81 12.30	1	
10.11.81 9.00	10.11.81 12.30	$3\frac{1}{2}$	
12.11.81 10.00	12.11.81 12.00	2	
13.11.81 9.00	13.11.81 4.00	6	
Total Time		$12\frac{1}{2}$	

Fig. 22.2 Job time card
(**Note:** 'Time on' and 'Time off' are recorded by means of a job clock)

Where time recording is needed, it must be realized that the accuracy of recording will be low unless there is some incentive towards accurate time booking. This inaccuracy will arise from:

1. Reluctance on the part of an operator to carry out a tedious and often apparently useless task.

2. Reluctance to book 'waiting', 'idle' or 'lost' time, out of loyalty to the supervisor and colleagues.

3. Reluctance to book 'extra' time arising from operations carried out above those anticipated (for example, in rectifying bad material), again out of loyalty to supervisors and fellow workers. Some attempt to prevent incorrect booking can be made by requiring the supervisor to countersign the time records, but this places a considerable strain on the supervisor and can result in a substantial part of the supervisor's time being used signing clock cards.

An incentive bonus scheme, as pointed out in Chapter 35, will usually result in much more realistic time-recording, and this may, in fact, be one of the most substantial advantages of such a scheme.

Material

Material recording is usually carried out by means of requisitions or issue notes (Fig. 22.3) and the general rule to be observed is that no material should be issued from stores without a properly authorized material requisition being presented, this requisition bearing the cost allocation. Care must be taken, however, to avoid cost recording of stock for items of insignificant value, otherwise the cost of costing itself will be abnormally high. This can be avoided by 'bulk issuing' small items and charging the cost of these 'bulk issues' to an overhead or 'spread-over' account.

MATERIAL REQUISITION			
Originator's Signature	*Dept.*	*Date*	*Job No.*
Material Required			*Qty. Required*
Material Issued			*Qty. Issued*
Issuer's Signature	*Date*	*Receiver's Signature*	

Fig. 22.3 Material requisition

Material pricing
The quantity of material being known, it is necessary to assign to it a price. If the price actually paid (the 'specific price') for the material is known, then no particular problem presents itself:

Price charged = Number of units used × Unit price

However, it may happen that quantities of the same material are purchased at different prices, and that 'issues' take place between the various receipts of material. For example:

100 units at 10p a unit are received on 1 January, and there are thus 100 units available in store. 50 and 30 of these are issued on 1 February and 1 March respectively, and clearly the unit price for each of these 'issues' is 10p. On 1 April, a further 100 units are received to give a total of 120 available in store, but unfortunately the unit price for this delivery has risen to 15p. On 1 May, 50 units are issued, and it is impossible to identify the source of this 50—that is, whether it comprises 20 of the original 100, 50 of the second 100, or some combination of the two. What unit price should be set for this issue?

	Received		*Issued*	*In store*
	Unit price (p)	*Quantity (units)*	*Quantity (units)*	*Quantity*
1 January	10	100		100
1 February			50	50
1 March			30	20
1 April	15	100		120
1 May			50	70

There are a number of methods available to deal with this problem:

1. *Weighted average pricing.* Here an average is struck by adding together the values of stock already in store and stock added, and dividing by the total quantity of stock. Thus, on 1 April, the value of stock already in store is 20 × 10p = 200p. To this is added 100 units of stock at 15p a unit = value 1,500p. The total value of stock is thus (200 + 1,500)p = 1,700p and the *weighted average unit price* is:

$$\frac{1,700p}{120} = 14.17p$$

The stock issued on 1 May is thus issued at a price of (50 × 14.17)p = 708.5p. Equally, the remaining 70 items of stock would have a unit value of 14.17p. If now further stock were received—say 100 units at 20p a unit—the weighted average price would be:

$$\frac{70 \times 14.17 + 100 \times 20p}{170} \text{ a unit} = 17.6p \text{ a unit}$$

(*Note*: this averaging should be contrasted with the *simple averaging* method where the price is derived by adding together the unit prices (10p + 15p = 25p) and dividing by the number of orders (in this case, 2) to give the average price: (25 ÷ 2)p a unit. This method has nothing to commend it but its simplicity.)

2. *LIFO pricing*. Here the price charged is the last price paid (hence last-in-first-out). Thus, the 1 May stock is charged out at the last price paid, that is at 15p a unit, so that the total price out would be (50 × 15)p = 750p. If another order for, say, 60 units had to be fulfilled, then 50 would be priced at the last price (15p). This 50 units would have exhausted the April delivery, so that the remaining 10 units would be priced at the next latest price, that is at 10p a unit. Hence, the price out for 60 units on 1 June, assuming no new deliveries, would be:

50 units at 15p = 750p
10 units at 10p = 100p
∴ total price = 850p

3. *FIFO pricing*. Here the price charged is the first price from which the issued material could have been drawn. Thus, on 1 May the issued material would be charged out at 10p a unit for 20 units. The '10p a unit' stock having then been exhausted, the remaining 30 units would have been charged out at 15p a unit, so that the total price out would be (20 × 10)p + (30 × 15)p = 650p.

These three systems would give the following prices out for the 1 May issue:

Weighted average   708p
LIFO   750p
FIFO   650p

4. *Standard pricing*. Here a fictitious price is assumed for the material, and all material issued at this *standard* price. Where the actual price varies from standard, a *variance* is declared, a positive variance indicating that the purchase price is greater than standard, a negative variance indicating that it is less. Standard pricing is only used as part of a complete standard costing system.

5. *Replacement pricing*. Here again a fictitious price is set, this being the price which it is anticipated will be paid when the material is replaced.

The various methods of pricing above each have their own advantages. Probably the weighted average method is most common in the UK except where a complete standard costing system is in use. Whichever method is used, it must be applied consistently and continuously.

Overhead records

Overhead records are derived partly from the normal financial records of the factory and partly from returns from the operating departments. A policy decision is required to decide which items shall be recorded as direct expenses and which as indirect expenses. Those operations which constitute an inherent part of the product are usually considered as direct expenses, so that, for example, the calibration or setting of apparatus is usually a direct expense even if carried out under the supervision of the chief inspector whose own cost is spread over. No general rules can be laid down, however, each case being entirely dependent upon local circumstances.

Other indirect expenses are those which arise from lost time and lost materials. These have been mentioned above very briefly and require very careful consideration. Analysis of both, particularly if reasons can be assigned to the expenses, can be extremely helpful in pin-pointing weaknesses. One method of preparing such analyses is to set up a code of indirect expenses, each common source of such expense bearing a number. For example, idle time may be coded as follows:

W1 Waiting for material
W2 Waiting for drawings
W3 Waiting for fitter
W4 Waiting for maintenance
W5 Waiting for supervisor

and so on. Any idle time is then 'booked against' the appropriate number, and a summary of costs readily prepared against each code. These summaries will then indicate weaknesses; and also show the financial importance of any weakness. This can be of great importance when subsequent decisions on the strength of departments have to be taken. For example, if W3 ('waiting for fitter') has cost the factory £45,500 in one year, there is a strong case for the employment of at least one more fitter.

The location of costs

Data on costs are collected only in order to help the manager control his work. To do this, the figures need to be organized in some useful way, that is, they need to be grouped around *cost centres*. A cost centre is a division, part or function of the whole enterprise wherein *responsibility* can be meaningfully located, for it is only when responsibility can be sensibly identified that control can be properly exerted. There are no simple rules for identifying a cost centre beyond that of requiring an unambiguous definition of responsibility. Clearly the size and complexity of a cost centre will vary from company to company, although it is desirable to make it small enough to enable *rapid* action to be taken if the figures generated indicate a need for this.

The cost centre itself may well include the provision of a number of different activities or the production of a number of different products, and it may also be useful to discover the cost of each activity and/or product, that is, of each of the various *cost units*. As with a cost centre, the definition of a cost unit is a matter of judgement and, again, the overriding requirement is that the results obtained should be *useful*. It should be noted that a cost unit need not necessarily be a unit in the sense of an individual item—it might be a batch of identical items (a dozen, a hundred . . .), or a group of similar products, or a single item. Each organization needs to define its own cost centres and units, although within any industry common practices will probably have grown up and these are often usefully followed.

The recovery of overheads

Consideration of the budget will show that trading expenditure falls into three main categories:

1. Direct labour costs, which can be allocated to specific jobs.
2. Direct material costs, which again can be allocated to specific jobs.
3. Those other costs which cannot be allocated to specific jobs; that is, the aggregate of the indirect material cost, indirect labour cost and indirect expenses. This aggregate is known as the overhead.

So that this overhead charge can be recovered, some method must be available for sharing it among the production. The apportionment of overheads to particular jobs or products is a technical problem of some complexity, and reference needs to be made to a good textbook on costing for a full discussion of the alternatives available. For the purposes of the present text, however, the two most common types of overhead recovery procedure will be briefly described, using the following example:

A company makes and sells during a year 200 units of A (unit selling price £18) and 100 units of B (unit selling price £19). The direct costs in £s are:

	Unit A	B	Total A	B	
Labour	4.0	5.0	800 + 500	= 1,300	
Material	2.5	3.0	500 + 300	= 800	
Totals	6.5	8.0	1,300 + 800	= 2,100	

Assume that:

> The total trading expenditure of the organization is £5,350
> The total income is £(200 × 18 + 100 × 19)   = £5,500
> ∴ the profit is £(5,500 − 5,350)   = £ 150
> the overhead is £(5,350 − 2,100)   = £3,250

Absorption costing

Here, all overhead items are aggregated and the resulting total divided among all products or jobs by means of an agreed rate, the *overhead recovery rate*.

In the example given, the aggregated overhead is £3,250, and one common absorption costing method spreads this over all jobs by adding on a fixed percentage to the wage cost:

Total overhead   = £3,250
Total labour cost = £1,300

$$\therefore \text{Overhead recovery rate} = \frac{3{,}250}{1{,}300} \times 100 = 250\%$$

(as a % of direct labour)

The assigned costs in £s would then appear:

	Unit		Total	
	A	B	A	B
Labour	4.0	5.0	800	500
Material	2.5	3.0	500	300
Overhead	10.0	12.5	2,000	1,250
(at 25% of labour cost)				
Total	16.5	20.5	3,300	2,050
Selling price	18.0	19.0	3,600	1,900
∴ profit	1.5		300	
loss		1.5		150

and final profit = £(300 − 150) = £150

Marginal costing

Here, overheads are divided into *fixed overheads*, being those which do not change with output, and *variable overheads*, being those which do depend on output. Only the variable overheads are assigned to products or jobs, the fixed overheads then being recovered from the contributions to expenses left when the direct costs and variable overheads are subtracted from the selling price. This is sometimes known in the US as *direct costing* or *differential costing*, and the cost figure so produced is sometimes referred to as the *out-of-pocket cost* to express the fact that it is a cost which is only incurred when the activity concerned is actually undertaken. The difference between the selling price and the marginal cost contributes to the fixed costs and to the profit, and is therefore known as the *contribution*.

In the example used so far, the overhead cost was given as £3,250. This is scrutinized to decide how much is fixed (for example, rent, rates . . .) and how much is variable (for example, power to run machines, oil to lubricate tools, cotton waste . . .). Assume the investigation shows:

	£
Variable overheads	650
Fixed overheads	2,600
Total	3,250

Overhead recovery rate expressed as a percentage of wages

$$= \frac{650}{1,300} \times 100$$
$$= 50\%$$

The assigned costs in £s would then be expressed:

	Unit		Total	
	A	B	A	B
Labour	4.0	5.0	800 + 500 = 1,300	
Material	2.5	3.0	500 + 300 = 800	
Overhead	2.0	2.5	400 + 250 = 650	
(at 50% of labour cost)				
Total marginal cost	8.5	10.5	1,700 + 1,050 = 2,750	
Selling price	18.0	19.0	3,600 + 1,900 = 5,500	
∴ Contribution	9.5	8.5	1,900 850 = 2,750	

∴ Final profit = Contribution − Fixed overheads
= £2,750 − £2,600
= £150

In both cases, the final profit figure is the same, £150, and in static conditions, where no changes are contemplated, possible or enforced, there is little to choose between the two methods. However, in the more usual situation of fluidity, marginal costing is more likely to give meaningful answers. For example, if output of B can be increased by 20 units without additional capital charges (that is, from the same plant and equipment), what costs are involved?

Absorption costing would show, at first sight:

Additional costs = £20 × 20.5 = £410

However, this has assumed a constant overhead rate, derived from an output of 200 As and 100 Bs. Since the output of B is being increased to 120, then the overhead rate must be revised. To sweep through a range of alternative levels of A and B becomes a tedious procedure, often more honoured in the breach than in the observance. On the other hand, marginal costing would give immediately:

Additional costs   = £20 × 10.5 = £210
Additional income   = £20 × £19 = £380
∴ Additional contribution   = £170

Again, if examining the product mix, absorption costing would indicate that, by manufacturing 100 Bs, a loss of £150 was being incurred. The deduction that total profit would increase if the number of Bs made and sold were decreased is appealing—indeed, it would seem that total profit could be increased by £150 if B was discontinued altogether. In fact, of course, this would not be so, since the fixed overheads would remain.

These problems, and others of a similar nature, are most readily dealt with by marginal costing, and techniques concerned with changing situations usually need marginal data. The extraction and manipulation of the fixed and variable elements of the overhead often appear difficult, and for this reason marginal costing is not so widely used as the simpler, blunter weapon of absorption costing. Nevertheless, from the operations manager's point of view, marginal costing is much more useful since it allows more ready consideration of the implications of different courses of action.

It must be noted that since the overhead cost contains elements which are the results of managerial decisions (a good example of this would be the rate of depreciation) then the operating cost too will be the result of a managerial decision, that is, cost is a matter of policy.

It is a common failing to assume that high overheads are a sign of inefficiency: this of course is not so, and the relation between cost, direct labour and overheads must be clearly understood. Any increase in direct labour cost must always be accompanied by a reduction in overheads if the operating cost is to remain the same. There is little point in reducing overheads while at the same time causing the direct labour charge to increase. It is not uncommon to find that a reduction in 'overhead' staff will throw more work—and hence greater cost—on to the 'direct' staff, giving an *increase* in total costs. This has given rise to the phrase 'the high cost of low overheads'.

Standard costing

Standard costing is analogous to budgetary control, but deals with cost units rather than the whole organization. Values for all the elements of cost are estimated prior to their commitment, and the actual cost is then shown as the standard cost plus or minus a difference, always known as the *variance*. For example, the standard cost for product C might be made up as follows:

	p
Standard labour cost	20
Standard material cost	30
Standard overhead cost	50
	100

In practice, it might be found that the *actual* costs were:

	p
Labour	37.5
Materials	25
Overheads	60
	122.5

and this could be shown in a standard costing system as:

	Standard (p)	Variance (p)
Labour cost	20	+17.5
Material cost	30	− 5
Overhead cost	50	+10
	100	+22.5

Since the standard values had previously been fixed and recorded, there is no need to repeat them in the report, and so they could be presented as:

	Variance (p)
Labour	+17.5
Material	− 5
Overheads	+10

This method has the advantages of (*a*) giving price estimates of achievable costs, and (*b*) enabling management's attention to be directed to those places where effort is needed, that is, to those places where performance differs significantly from plan.

Variance analysis
The three principal variances (labour, material, overheads) may arise from a number of causes, and the reduction of variances to their consti-

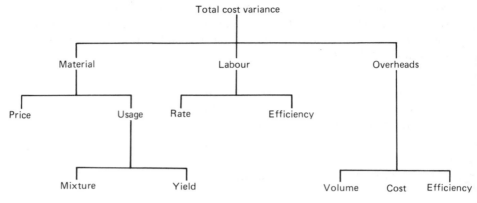

Fig. 22.4 Cost variance pyramid

tuent parts, and the subsequent discovery of reasons for these variances, is known as *variance analysis*. While it is based upon the classic variance pyramid (Fig. 22.4), a complete discussion of this topic is beyond the scope of this text, and recourse to one of the works shown at the end of this chapter is recommended. As an illustration of the method, however, consider the wage variance. This may arise from one or both of two causes:

(*a*) a difference in the time taken for the job (the 'labour efficiency variance');

(*b*) a difference in the wage rate (the 'wage rate variance').

Thus, the standard wage cost of 20p may have been calculated:

Standard time   = 10 minutes
Standard wage rate   = 2p/minute
∴ Standard labour cost = $(10 \times 2)p = 20p$

In practice, however, the *actual* labour cost may have been derived:

Actual time taken   = 12.5 minutes
Actual labour rate   = 3p/minute
∴ Actual labour cost   = $(12.5 \times 3)p = 37.5p$

The labour efficiency variance

$$= (12.5 - 10) \times 2p = 5p$$

The labour rate variance

$$= 12.5 \times (3 - 2)p = 12.5p$$

∴ Total labour cost variance

$$= (5 + 12.5)p = 17.5p$$

and the actual labour cost
> = Standard labour cost + Labour cost variance
> = (20 + 17.5)p
> = 37.5p

a value agreeing ('reconciling') with that previously obtained.

Notes: (*i*) It should not be assumed that a negative variance is necessarily desirable, since although it represents an expenditure less than anticipated—and hence it is a saving—it may also indicate an error in setting the standard. If, as is usual, the standard cost is examined when a selling price is fixed, a high standard cost may result in a high selling price and consequent loss in the volume of sales. (*ii*) As with most 'error signals' generated in a control system, it is the *trend* of the variance rather than the individual values which is of consequence. Thus a substantial variance at one point in time should arouse interest rather than action, but a *series* of variances, particularly if increasing in absolute value, requires investigation.

Recommended reading

Cowe, R. (Ed), *Handbook of Management Accounting*, Gower Publishing Company Ltd., 1987.
> A useful collection of papers by leading authorities in the field of Costing. Expensive but worth obtaining from a library.

Glautier, M. W. E. and Underdown, B., *Cost Accounting*, Pitman Publishing Ltd., 1988.
> Well produced, comprehensive, valuable.

Mott, G., *Management Accounting*, Pan Books, 1987.
> Very useful, inexpensive, simple.

Drury, C., *Management and Cost Accounting*, Van Nostrand Reinhold (UK), 1985.
> An excellent wide-ranging text. Very well produced.

Owler, L. W. J. and Brown, J. L., *Wheldon's Cost Accounting*, Pitman Publishing Ltd, 1984.
> This is the fifteenth edition of the classic *Wheldon's Cost Accounting and Costing Methods*, a text tried and tested by time. Thorough and useful.

Section V **The programmes**

23 An overview

Introduction

Every organization produces—or should produce—a 'hierarchy' of plans to enable it to fulfil its corporate purpose. These plans differ from each other in the level of detail at which they operate, and detail is in itself a reflection of the time-span covered by the plan. The largest time-span is exhibited by the overall company policy as determined by the board of directors. Consistent with this, but spanning a shorter period of time, is the marketing forecast which identifies and quantifies the products or services to be provided over the foreseeable future. It is important that these forecasts are in a form that reflects the resources required (for a building society, this forecast might be to handle 100,000 home loans) rather than in financial terms (to lend £2,500 million). The group within the organization whose responsibility includes examining the resource implications of this forecast is normally called the production control or operations control department (POCD). From the forecast, this department prepares a *schedule* which in turn generates a *load* which is finally translated into action by *supervision* (see Fig. 23.1). It should be noted that the preparation of a set of plans is an iterative process since it may well be found that an inability to achieve a plan at one level may cause a change in the plans at higher levels. Equally, plans must 'interlock' and be acceptable to and agreed with all concerned. Thus a sales forecast must agree with the board's objectives and the production/operations department's abilities.

The POCD is thus one of the planning departments within an organization and, indeed, some writers include planning in its title. In the present text, however, production/operations planning will be reserved for that function which concerns itself with the determination of the method or procedures to be followed, and production/operations control will be understood to comprise *all* the control functions first discussed in Chapter 3, namely:

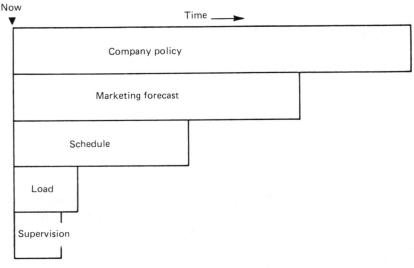

Fig. 23.1

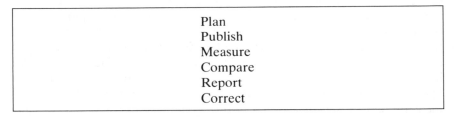

Plan
Publish
Measure
Compare
Report
Correct

In essence, the POCD should be able *at all times* to answer two basic and apparently simple questions:

1. Can a particular task be undertaken and, if so, when?
2. How far have the tasks in hand proceeded?

and in trying to provide these answers, POCD must attempt to organize the most effective use of manpower, materials and equipment. The POCD is likely to generate written instructions, and as a result it is often considered to be the paperwork-producing department, and this is particularly true for manufacturing organizations. It is frequently perceived as being a low level clerical responsibility, indeed one that can easily be taken over by a computer. As such it is much maligned and its duties misunderstood. This misunderstanding is as frequently found at high as at low levels, with the result that staff status and facilities are withheld, duties consequently being ill-performed.

The qualities required of those responsible for production/operations control are no less exacting than those required of, for example, a cost accountant or chief designer, yet it is often found that the staff employed in this area are not adequately equipped by training, experience or innate intelligence to carry out the duties adequately. Working in this area needs a clear brain, capable of dealing with a large number of problems simultaneously, a thorough knowledge of processes, procedures and efficient office organization techniques, an appreciation of the importance of controlling costs, an awareness of the scope and limitations of using computers, and an understanding of mathematical methods and—more important—mathematical reasoning. Moreover, communications skills are also important since decisions in a number of other areas—for example, marketing and purchasing—can have a significant effect on the POCD. In addition, decisions made by the POCD can also influence these other areas. The person responsible must be able to effectively manage these interfaces.

Many of the weaknesses of organizations—for example, excessive material stocks, failure to achieve processing targets, idle time—can be directly attributable to inferior or non-existent production/operations control, while really effective production/operations control can achieve increases in output and efficiency far more spectacular and at a far lower cost than any other management tool. Furthermore, no other activity can show effective results in the absence of good production/operations control. Every work study practitioner or O & M officer must, at some time, have suffered the bitter disappointment of seeing his improved method made ineffectual by the absence of material due to poor production/operations control. In any plan for improving efficiency or reducing losses throughout an enterprise, the organization of a really efficient POCD must come very high in priority: certainly no incentive scheme will work without an effective POCD.

Marketing policy and production control

Broadly, there are two possible ways by which a company can derive its income:

(a) by receiving orders from customers, and thence generating work to fulfil these orders;

(b) by *obtaining* orders from customers, these orders being filled from work generated *before* their receipt.

Thus a restaurant may prepare each meal to each customer's specific requirements. Alternatively, the meal may be ready prepared and cooked, and kept hot prior to a customer's arrival (the principle behind 'fast food'). Some operations are such that the second option is not feasible. For example, a management consultancy cannot generally provide its service by work generated before receipt of the request for assistance; that is, 'storage' of the service is not possible.

Much of the task of production/operations control is concerned with *future* action and, therefore, the more accurately the future can be predicted, the better the chance of making effective plans. An order-receiving policy will inevitably produce greater uncertainty than an order-obtaining policy, which will carry with it greater risk. The marketing department will need to forecast future requirements, and bear responsibility for over-provision if the forecasts are incorrect.

The decision to change from 'order-receiving' to 'order-obtaining' is an extremely important one, whose effects, while felt throughout the organization, are of paramount concern to the department responsible for providing the product or service and to POCD. The value of good market research and sales promotion must not be under-estimated, and failure to align marketing with provision will result, at best, in chaos, and at worst, in failure.

Some of the functions of the POCD are more appropriate in a manufacturing context. In the remainder of this chapter it will be assumed that this type of environment will be considered, although an attempt will be made to indicate the relevance of these concepts where appropriate in non-manufacturing situations.

Outline of the functions of production control

Scheduling and loading

At the time of issuing a marketing forecast (in the case of making for stock), or at the time of acknowledging the receipt of an order (in the case of making to customer's order), marketing will issue an instruction which will authorize the manufacture of a product or group of products. This order is the starting point for all POCD activities concerned with actual manufacture, although POCD should already have assisted marketing in fixing the delivery date shown on the works order.

From the works order a production plan (or programme) is prepared, which involves assessing labour, equipment and material requirements and availability, and thence laying down the dates by which major functions must be complete. This production plan will be issued to the resources control section, wherein labour availability (both men and equipment) is verified, detailed programmes prepared and the various departments *loaded* in as much detail as is useful. At the same time, a copy of the production plan will be passed to the *material control* section, which will check material availability, putting in train whatever action is necessary. The production plan will need to be revised whenever any change in any conditions (demand, materials, facilities . . .) takes place.

Material control

Material control is the reverse of the coin of which facilities control is the obverse. Since the number of items of information is so very much greater in the case of material than in that of labour, the same techniques are not necessarily appropriate. In general, the task of the material controller can be said to be that of assessing the need for material, and then taking appropriate action to see that this need is met. This subject is discussed later in Chapter 28.

The consequences of unavailable materials can be extremely costly. Consider the building society about to increase its interest rates. A formal notice has to be sent to each borrower, but a shortage of envelopes (the requirement for which might be hundreds of thousands) can delay the issuing of this notice and result in consequential loss of interest.

Despatch and progress

At the appropriate time, manufacture is actually initiated by the *despatch* section, which collects together all relevant documents, verifies the detailed availability of labour, materials, tools, equipment and production aids, and issues authorizing documents. Throughout the whole of this time, and during the subsequent manufacture, the *progress* section will observe performance, verifying that the requirements of the production plan are being fulfilled. Any deviations from this schedule are brought to the notice of the appropriate supervision, and any necessary modification to schedule made in order to overcome the results of these deviations. Should the final delivery date appear to be endangered, it is unquestionably the responsibility of the production control department to inform the sales department in order that, if deemed desirable, the customer can be advised.

Avoidance of this simple courtesy will inevitably lead to a severe deterioration in customer relations, which in turn will eventually be reflected in the intake of orders. It will also result in a deterioration in relationships between the marketing and production groups, which in the extreme can threaten the very existence of the enterprise. A delivery date should be considered sacrosanct and every endeavour made to maintain it, but if it proves quite impossible so to do, the customer should be informed, and this information can only originate from the production control department. The despatch and progress tasks are discussed further in Chapter 27.

Parameters affecting the production control function

Organization of production

The way in which production is organized, the technological methods used, the location of plant and the degree of specialization of direct operators, will affect the production control function. Broadly, the smaller the organization, both in physical and organizational size, and the greater the flexibility of the workforce, the easier will be the task of the production controller.

Indeed, if batch manufacturing methods are being used, scheduling work will be an on-going activity, possibly consuming significant resources, with raw material control involving forecasting usage through an examination of requirements for finished production. Contrast this with the situation where flow production methods are being used, when scheduling will be largely 'pre-production' in setting up and balancing the line, and materials control is largely a matter of establishing that materials are available when required, and to specification.

Information and information flow

Production control can only act upon the information that it receives. Regrettably, much of the information is weak:

(*a*) standard times;
(*b*) quantities of stock in store;
(*c*) demand from customers;
(*d*) availability of material from outside suppliers;
(*e*) amount of work already completed;
(*f*) capacities of processing units;

are all liable to be highly inaccurate. There is a considerable reluctance on the part of most members of an organization to pass over information concerning their own activities. This arises frequently because it is assumed that information is required for a punitive purpose—to form a 'do-it-yourself hangman's guide'. Management must make clear to all concerned that a free flow of information is in the best interests of everybody within the organization.

Scheduling system

The heart of the production control function is the scheduling function, which in essence establishes priorities with respect to some criterion measuring performance (for example, meeting customers' processing targets, achieving high labour/equipment utilization) for activities competing for limited resources (workers/equipment). This is a difficult task to carry out and, sometimes with unfortunate consequences, can become a rich field for the mathematically inclined to plough. In the final analysis, the operation of any scheduling system will depend upon the ability of the operatives, administrators and first-line supervisors to understand what is required by the system itself.

Intelligibility, therefore, must be a prime concern: indeed, it is often better to sacrifice 'performance' in order to be able to produce a schedule which is understandable. It is also inevitable that priorities will change, and the scheduling method must be capable of accommodating change extremely rapidly.

The technology of the process

Since the production controller is effectively planning a timetable for the movement of a task through a number of processes or procedures, the technology of the process must be well understood. Usually there will be several alternative ways in which a task can be carried out and it is frequently better to standardize on one particular technological method, for a substantial number of different tasks, than to try to obtain the 'best' from each process. One particularly difficult task to organize is that which prevents material flow taking place in one direction, where material leaves a work station to return to the same work station after other operations have been carried out. Those responsible for setting methods should try to avoid this 'back-passing', or 'back-tracking', and indeed should always consider the effects on production control of their processing requirements. Any apparent loss in technological efficiency may well be more than compensated for by the simplification of the production control task.

The problem is mirrored in non-manufacturing: back-passing of the flow of documents used in processing transactions can add significantly to the complexity of operations planning and control.

Stability of priorities

Every timetable is fundamentally a statement of priorities, and the more frequently priorities are changed, the more frequently will the timetabling need to be changed. It is a common experience for the 'Friday progress meeting' (!) to destroy all the priorities set at a previous meeting, and substitute new ones. This presents an impossible situation for the production controller, who is left in the position of trying to run faster and faster in order to stay in the same position. Clearly, no priority statement can be considered as unchangeable: as circumstances change, so must priorities follow them. However, the common separation between the marketing function and the production/operations function can lead to priorities being set which are themselves unachievable, and a cynical definition of production/operations control is 'the art of trying to reconcile impossible requests with inadequate resources'. While the production/operations department has the responsibility of trying to fulfil the needs of the market, so the marketing department has the responsibility of trying to produce robust forecasts for the production/operations people to act upon.

The myth of plant utilization

One of the most easily observed features of a production unit is the presence of idle equipment and, under pressure from senior management, great efforts are often made to 'keep the machines/equipment working'. The effects of a 'utilization at any price' policy can be disastrous since excessive material and work-in-progress will result. A much more rational criterion is that of velocity of material flow—the more quickly material can be transformed into finished goods, the more rapidly can the initial investment be recovered. A healthy cash flow is an essential prerequisite for a healthy organization.

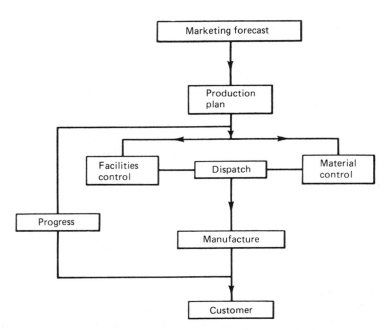

Fig. 23.2 Outline of the functions of the production control department

1. Organization of production
2. Information and information flow
3. Scheduling system
4. The technology of the process
5. Stability of priorities
6. The myth of plant utilization

Parameters affecting production/operations control

Sequence of operations

The sequence of operations is represented in Fig. 23.2, and the five main functions of POCD—scheduling, loading, despatching, progress and material control—will be discussed in detail later. It must be realized that these functions, although separate, are not necessarily carried out by different persons, the detailed organization depending upon the local conditions, such as size of plant, volume and type of work, and the geographical disposition of the plant.

Production control and the computer

The computer is able to store enormous quantities of information and carry out calculations very rapidly, in so-called 'real time', that is, within such a time that information and analyses are available early enough to permit useful action to be taken. Furthermore, the computer will tirelessly repeat calculations for as long as it is required to do so: it will not, if properly instructed, generate mistakes either through fatigue or personal inaccuracy. These characteristics are clearly most valuable to the production/operations control function. The advent of mini- and microcomputers now makes *real-time* access to programs and files a reality, and this speed, combined with distributed terminals, is likely to transform production/operations control in the near future, provided that robust databases are available.

The application of the computer to the production/operations control function offers significant challenge to the computer systems designer and analyst. This covers the data-processing aspects where, for example, it can be necessary to store and retrieve efficiently enormous quantities of information relating to the manufacturing methods for many hundreds or even thousands of tasks, each consisting of numerous operations on a variety of work centres with various machines. The analyst is faced with storing this information efficiently and in such a way that it can be retrieved and analysed in a number of different ways: the machines which are required by a certain task, the tasks which require certain materials, and so on. At the same time, the analyst can exploit the computer's arithmetic capability in such areas, assessing the requirements for common raw materials or components across a variety of tasks, all to be completed at different times, or evaluating the implications of processing a set of tasks in different orders of priority.

Computer manufacturers and computer software consultants have risen to this challenge and produced a wide variety of systems which cover all the functions (and more!) outlined earlier. These tend to be presented in a modular form so that a user (with the consultant's guidance) can build up a system which closely matches requirements. Alternatively (and normally at a significantly higher cost), it is possible to develop (or have developed) a system which perfectly matches requirements. There is the analogous comparison between the off-the-peg and bespoke suit. With off-the-peg, the system is available more quickly, is cheaper, and can normally be seen 'being used in anger' before purchase. With bespoke, the system should be more flexible in that it should meet requirements exactly, involve less change to existing procedures, and be more capable of interfacing with computer applications in other functional areas.

Off-the-peg software:
 (*a*) speed of development and implementation;
 (*b*) cost;
 (*c*) preview before purchase.
Bespoke software:
 (*a*) flexibility;
 (*b*) less change required to procedures;
 (*c*) easier to interface and modify.

Comparison between off-the-peg and bespoke software

The detailed discussions of the role of the computer in the different functional areas of production/operations control will be deferred until the subsequent chapters in which the topics themselves are covered.

Recommended reading

Burbidge, J. L., *Production Planning*, Heinemann, 1971.
    An invaluable book written by a manager turned teacher. He keeps his feet well on the ground, and uses diagrams and descriptions rather than hiding behind mathematical analyses.
Corke, D. K., *Production Control in Engineering*, Edward Arnold, 1977.
    A useful, practical book written by a management consultant.

Tooley, D. F., *Production Control Systems and Records*, Gower, 1985.
   The contents of this text complement much of the material in this chapter.
British Standards Institution, *Glossary of Production Planning and Control Terms* (BS 5191), 1975.
   Defines some 150 terms commonly used in production control, as well as some terms concerning quality and costing. The section titles give an indication of the scope of the glossary: basic production characteristics; process and resource characteristics; production planning terms; load/capacity planning; stock planning; scheduling; general durations; operations durations; production control terms; progress control; stock control; documentation terms; production control documentation; quality control terms; cost control terms. Invaluable in sorting out semantic difficulties and resolving arguments between colleagues.

24 Forecasting

The importance of forecasting in production/operations control

Forecasting is clearly not one of the mainstream activities within the production/operations control function. Nevertheless there are a number of aspects of this function which rely on forecasts of one sort or another if they are to be carried out effectively. Most fundamental is the likely future demand for the products or services being provided by the enterprise. In addition, there are a number of other factors related directly to the management of the conversion process. These include being able to predict the requirements for materials of all types, the times to allow for procurement of these, likelihood and durations of equipment breakdown, absenteeism rates of workers, scrap or error rates and so on. An ability to quantify these factors will clearly improve the quality of the decision-making in the production/operation control area. This quantification can be based on 'guestimates': think of a likely figure, and double it as a margin for error, or it can be soundly based, taking into account all available information and historical data. The purpose of this chapter is to briefly introduce some of the more basic methods of forecasting based on historical data.

The marketing interface

The basic input into the production/operations control function is the forecast by the marketing group of the requirements for the products or services being provided. Without this forecast, planning and control would be extremely difficult, if not impossible, to carry out effectively. A wide-ranging list of factors needs to be taken account of in producing this forecast. This includes: historical pattern of demand—is there a trend or seasonal effect; to what extent is demand influenced by economic considerations outside control (e.g. taxes); is it intended to try and influence demand directly (e.g. through advertising, price variation); and so on.

The basic difference between providing for specific customers' demands and satisfying demand from stock will also influence demand and attempts to forecast it. It is tempting to view all of these interdependent factors and abandon all attempts at a structured approach to forecasting demand. This is unwise: a structured approach should be used wherever possible to support the forecasting process. Moreover, techniques exist for monitoring forecasts, comparing these to actuals, detecting bias, leading to improved prediction.

The materials interface

Predicting material requirements is a subject which is central to the materials management function within production/operations control. However, not only is it necessary to forecast requirements, but also to estimate how long it will take to acquire (or manufacture) the materials. These two pieces of information are necessary inputs into any materials management system. The type of material (raw, work-in-progress and so on) in part indicates how it should be managed, which also establishes how its requirements should be determined. Again a structured approach to the forecasting puts subsequent analysis on a firmer basis. Care should be taken when examining historical requirement figures to establish future demand. Do these historical figures actually represent *demand*, or that part of demand which was satisfied? Is a record kept of occasions when items were required but not available?

Moving averages

In Table 24.1 the usage of copier paper by the local office of a building society is presented. Suppose it is necessary to predict the requirement for paper in order to manage its procurement more effectively. The best estimate of the requirement for week 2, in week 1, is simply the requirement in week 1, i.e. 132. At the end of week 2, it is possible to estimate the requirement for week 3 as the average of the first two weeks' actual requirement, i.e. 147.5. The estimate for week 4, at the end of week 3, would then become 155.3, until the end of week 24, when the estimate for the requirement for week 25 is the average of all the requirements to date. This has the disadvantage that as the process continues there is more and more data to store, and all are given equal weight in estimating the demand in the next period. It is possible to get round this by introducing the idea of a *moving average*, only including a fixed number of the most recent values. Considering a 5-point moving average, the forecast for week 6 is simply:

Table 24.1 Reams of copier paper used per week over 24-week period

Week	Reams used	Week	Reams used
1	132	13	152
2	163	14	170
3	171	15	131
4	148	16	153
5	135	17	137
6	162	18	172
7	107	19	122
8	144	20	142
9	127	21	189
10	193	22	138
11	142	23	161
12	163	24	133

$$\tfrac{1}{5}(132 + 163 + 171 + 148 + 135) = 749/5 = 149.8$$

When the requirement for week 6 is known, it is possible to forecast the requirement for week 7 as the average of the 5 most recent values:

$$\tfrac{1}{5}(163 + 171 + 148 + 135 + 162) = 779/5 = 155.8$$

Alternatively, note that 132 was dropped and 162 was added, a gain of 30 to the total or $30/5 = 6$ to the average.

The remainder of the values, together with the forecasts based on an 11-point moving average, are presented in Table 24.2. Two possibilities exist in presenting this data. It could be argued that the average of the first five values should be shown at the centre, i.e. against week 3, and similarly with subsequent averages (indeed, this approach is followed in the more complex situation proposed in the final section of this chapter). However, since this value is being used as the forecast for week 6, it will be shown against week 6.

These results are shown plotted in Fig. 24.1. The difference between the 5-point and 11-point moving average can be seen clearly. Both averages, as would be expected, damp down the random variation in the requirement. The 11-point average, because it involves an average over a larger number of values, will tend to be more 'stable', but equally will be slow to react to actual changes in level of requirement. The 5-point average, however, will respond more rapidly to actual changes, but is likely to be unduly influenced by random variations. The selection of the number of points in the average aims at achieving a compromise between these factors. It has been suggested for forecasting short periods ahead (4–5 weeks) that the moving average could be over 10–15 values for weekly data, or over 3–5 values for monthly data.

Table 24.2 Forecasts using 5-point and 11-point moving averages

Week	Reams used	Forecast reams used 5-point moving average	Forecast reams used 11-point moving average
1			
2			
3			
4			
5			
6	162	149.8	
7	107	155.8	
8	144	146.6	
9	127	139.2	
10	193	135.0	
11	142	146.6	
12	163	142.6	147.6
13	152	153.8	150.4
14	170	155.4	149.4
15	131	164.0	149.3
16	153	151.6	147.8
17	137	153.8	149.4
18	172	148.6	147.2
19	122	152.6	153.1
20	142	143.0	151.1
21	189	145.2	152.5
22	138	152.4	152.1
23	161	152.6	151.7
24	133	150.4	151.6
25	?	152.6	149.8

A minor modification to this approach is to avoid giving equal weight to all values in the moving average. Suppose it was considered desirable to give more emphasis to more recent values. For the 5-point moving average example, it is possible to choose weights of:

0.4, 0.3, 0.2, 0.07 and 0.03
(note the weights sum to one, and contrast with 0.2, 0.2, 0.2, 0.2, 0.2 with regular 5-point moving average).

These weights give:

0.4 (135) + 0.3 (148) + 0.2 (171) + 0.07 (163) + 0.03 (132) = 147.97

as the forecast for week 6, and

0.4 (162) + 0.3 (135) + 0.2 (148) + 0.07 (171) + 0.03 (163) = 151.76

as the forecast for week 7, and so on.

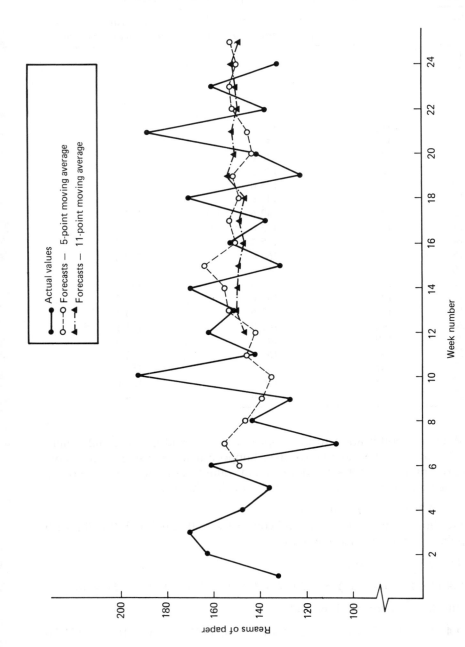

Fig. 24.1 Actual values compared to moving average forecast

However, with *weighted moving averages*, the user has to decide upon both the number of points in the average and the weights to apply.

Exponentially weighted moving averages

The previous approaches either gave each of a fixed number of most recent values equal weight or differential weights in arriving at an average. This approach uses all available historical data, with the weights applied to each getting smaller as the data gets older.

The formula for this approach is:

Forecast for next period = Forecast for last period
$\qquad$ + α (actual for last period − forecast for last period)

where α is the smoothing constant which must lie between 0 and 1. The above formula is a simplification of the basic formula which expresses the forecast as a weighted average of all the actual values to date, with the weights forming an exponential series (see Appendix 3).

Typical values for α lie between 0.1 and 0.2, with an interpretation similar to that placed on the number of points in the moving average. A small value of α results in slow reactions to sudden changes, while a large value can result in an over-reaction to random fluctuations.

Illustrating this method with the data from the previous example, it is necessary to obtain the *first* forecast before the formula can be applied. Initially, this is normally taken to be the straightforward arithmetic mean. The value of α used is 0.1.

So forecast for week 11 = average of requirements for first 10 weeks:

$= \frac{1}{10} (132 + 163 + 171 + 148 + 135 + 162 + 107 + 144 + 127 + 193)$
$= 148.2$

So forecast for week 12 = 148.2 + 0.1 (142 − 148.2) = 147.6
$\qquad$ forecast for week 13 = 147.6 + 0.1 (163 − 147.6) = 149.1

and so on. The calculations are summarized, for both $\alpha = 0.1$ and $\alpha = 0.2$, in Table 24.3.

Again a better picture is obtained by presenting the results graphically: this is done in Fig. 24.2. It is possible to see the forecast using the higher value of α responding more rapidly to changes. Indeed, there is an extension to this approach which allows the value of α to vary depending on the size of the error: actual − forecast. (This is the final term in the formula for exponential smoothing.) If this error is large (indicating a change in level), then α needs to be large to allow the forecast to respond; when the error is small, α again is reduced in size. (This *adaptive smoothing* can offer potential if changes in level are anticipated.)

With exponential smoothing, fewer data elements need to be stored

Table 24.3 Forecasts using exponential smoothing with $\alpha = 0.1$ and $\alpha = 0.2$

Week	Reams used	Forecast $\alpha = 0.1$	Forecast $\alpha = 0.2$
12	163	147.6	147.0
13	152	149.1	150.2
14	170	149.4	150.5
15	131	151.5	154.4
16	153	149.4	149.7
17	137	149.8	150.4
18	172	148.5	147.7
19	122	150.9	152.6
20	142	148.0	146.5
21	189	147.4	145.6
22	138	151.5	154.3
23	161	150.2	151.0
24	133	151.3	153.0
25	?	149.4	149.0

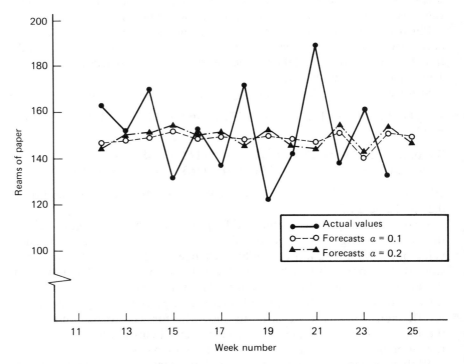

Fig. 24.2 Actual values compared to forecasts using exponential smoothing

(latest forecast, latest actual, α) compared to moving averages (say ten values). In the past this has had an impact on storage requirements for computer application. However, for all but the largest sets of items, this should not cause problems with current computer storage capabilities.

Other techniques

The previous approaches assumed that the level of requirement was relatively static and that there was random variation about this level. The current forecast at any time represents the most up-to-date estimate of that level. Thus the forecasts for weeks 25, 26, 27 . . . are all the same. An estimate of the level of random variation (or forecast error) can be made by averaging the differences between forecasts and actuals (ignoring signs) over historical data. Clearly the situation might arise where there is an increasing/decreasing trend in addition to random variation, see Fig. 24.3. The forecasting method needs to estimate this trend, and the one period ahead forecast will differ from the two or three period ahead forecast. Both the methods described can be extended to handle this situation. With the moving average, this simply involves fitting a line to the points in the moving average. The extension to the exponential smoothing method is slightly more complex.

The second situation which might be encountered is seasonality:

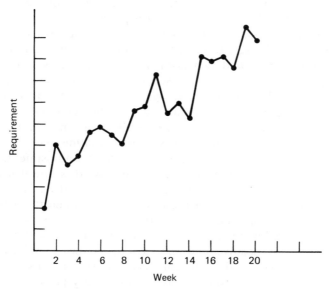

Fig. 24.3 Increasing trend in requirements

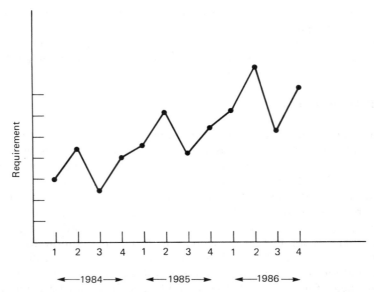

Fig. 24.4 Seasonal influence in requirements

systematic peaks and troughs during particular weeks or months of the year, see Fig. 24.4. Here it is possible to expect requirements to be higher than average in quarter 2, and lower than average in quarter 3, and also subject to a generally increasing trend. Noticing that the seasonal effect follows a four-period (quarters) cycle, it is possible to take a four-quarter moving average to eliminate the seasonal effect and 'isolate' the trend. This is because each average will contain one high value (quarter 2), one low value (quarter 3) and two normal values (quarters 1 and 4); first average: $\frac{1}{4}\,(q1 + q2 + q3 + q4)$; second average: $\frac{1}{4}\,(q2 + q3 + q4 + q1)$, and so on. These moving average values are used to estimate the trend line. The seasonal adjustments can then be made by assessing how much above or below this trend the different quarters are. The forecast for a particular quarter then involves extrapolating the trend to this quarter, and then making the appropriate seasonal adjustment.

A final technique which will be briefly discussed is one which can be used to monitor forecasts rather than to forecast itself. Essentially it involves cumulating the sum of the differences between the actual value and the forecast value each period. If the forecasts are systematically biased above or below the actual values, the differences will be predominantly negative or positive and the *cusum*, as this cumulative sum is called, will either get smaller and smaller, or larger and larger; otherwise the cusum will oscillate around zero. This is a very powerful technique, which has application in a number of other areas, including statistical process control.

This chapter has only really scratched the surface of forecasting techniques. The interested reader is referred to any of the number of texts on forecasting for further details, particularly of those techniques mentioned in this final section.

Recommended reading

Lancaster, G. A. and Lomas, R. A., *Forecasting for Sales and Materials Management*, Macmillan, 1985.

This text is written to provide the non-specialist with a knowledge of forecasting, enabling him or her to apply such knowledge in a forecasting situation. Very readable.

Lewis, C. D., *Industrial and Business Forecasting Methods*, Butterworths, 1982.

This book claims to present the 20 per cent of forecasting models available which are used in 80 per cent of practical forecasting applications.

Makridakis, S. and Wheelwright, S. C., *The Handbook of Forecasting—A Manager's Guide*, Wiley, 1982.

One of a number of texts on forecasting by these authors; here they edit contributions from some of the experts in the area. It is divided into four parts; role and application of forecasting in organizations, approaches to forecasting, forecasting challenges, and managing the forecasting function.

Saunders, J. A., Sharp, J. A., and Witt, S. F., *Practical Business Forecasting*, Gower, 1987.

This book is intended for the manager who uses forecasts and for anyone involved in preparing them. It explains the reasoning behind the various forecasting techniques but avoids the mathematical and statistical detail.

Wheelwright, S. C. and Makridakis, S., *Forecasting Methods for Management*, Wiley, 1985.

A very good reference text.

25 Scheduling and loading

Scheduling and loading

This chapter will examine some aspects of the production/operations control function associated with facilities control. These aspects have a variety of titles given to them in other texts. Here the terms 'scheduling' and 'loading' will be adopted. A schedule is a representation of the time necessary to carry out a task, and should take account of the technical requirements of the task, marketing forecast and available capacity. It is not simply a list of the operations required, since additionally it takes into account the technological relationships between these various operations. For example, the nature of a product may allow several operations in its manufacture to be carried out concurrently, while others may need to be completed before the next can be started. A route or list of work to be done would not show this situation, whereas a schedule would take this into account (see Fig. 25.1). The graphical presentation of the bar chart for the schedule is essential for this clarity. With complex interdependencies between operations, use of a 'precedence diagram' (see Chapter 30) rather than a bar chart may be desirable.

	Route for manufacture of batch of 10 type A chairs	
	Operation	Time (units)
A	Cut metal frame	2
B	Weld frame	3
C	Paint frame	2
D	Cut wood for seat	2
E	Cut foam for seat	1
F	Cut pvc for seat	2
G	Make seat	2
H	Cut wood for back	1
I	Cut foam for back	2
J	Cut pvc for back	2
K	Make back	1
L	Assemble chair	3
M	Pack	2

Fig. 25.1(a) Route for chair manufacture

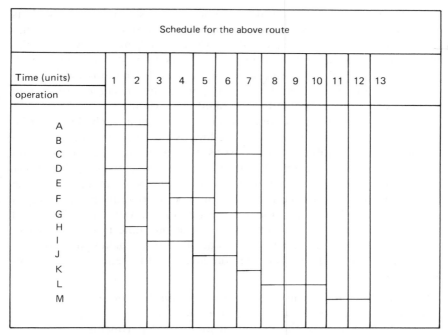

Schedule for the above route

Time (units) operation	1	2	3	4	5	6	7	8	9	10	11	12	13
A
B
C
D
E
F
G
H
I
J
K
L
M

Fig. 25.1(b) Job schedule for chair

Consider a metal-framed chair with padded seat and back rest. Information related to this is presented in Fig. 25.1.

A *job schedule* shows the plan for the manufacture of a particular job. This is the work study input into production/operations control, indicating method and times in sufficient detail for the function to be adequately carried out. Once this schedule has been produced, it need not be changed unless there is a change in either the job (for example in the product being produced) or in the method of manufacture. A company which makes a range of products could draw up a number of schedules which are kept filed and used as the basis for production/operations control. These schedules would show elapsed time—the time between successive operations—rather than specific calendar dates. Once an order for a specific job is received, it is then possible to fix actual dates for the start and finish of each operation making up the job. When producing a schedule, it is important to record upon it:

1. The product to which it refers.
2. The quantity scheduled.
3. The labour used.

Most organizations carry out a number of tasks simultaneously. It is necessary therefore to amalgamate a number of job schedules. This can only be done when the delivery dates for each job are known, and the whole amalgamation will then specify the work to be carried out in each department throughout the period being planned. This process is called *scheduling*, and the result known simply as the *schedule, production schedule* or *factory schedule* for the plant as a whole.

Optimum job conditions obtain when the various job schedules can be transferred on to the production schedule as they stand without modification, so that the job is finished just as it is required and each operation starts just as the operation(s) before it finish(es). However, this rarely happens in practice since a number of jobs will be 'competing' for the same resources, and it would require a number of operations on different jobs to be carried out simultaneously in the same department. This would result in the departments concerned being at one time required to carry out more work than is possible, while at other times being partially idle. The preparation of the production schedule will thus require attention to be paid to:

(*a*) The dates upon which delivery of the finished products are due.
(*b*) The job schedules for the appropriate jobs.
(*c*) The capacities of the various sections or departments.
(*d*) The efficiencies of the various sections or departments.
(*e*) The planned maintenance schedule.
(*f*) Planned holidays.
(*g*) Anticipated sickness/absenteeism/casual holidays.
(*h*) Existing commitments.
(*i*) Availability of raw materials, components, packaging and so on.
(*j*) External priorities set on the individual jobs.
(*k*) Allowances for scrap or re-work.

Not all this information will necessarily be readily available within an organization. It may be necessary, therefore, to set up the systems to record the data and to carry out the required analysis. It is unwise to simply use figures which represent the 'desired' values. Suppose historical records indicate an absenteeism level of 20 per cent, and this is regarded as far too high. The temptation might be to use a value of, say, 5 per cent in calculations, hoping to force it down to this level. However, this will distort the picture produced by the schedule, producing results which are wrong. The correct course of action is to investigate the causes of the level being at its current value, and to tackle these.

It should be noted that while a schedule that completely occupies all work stations at all times gives high utilization of resources, it is accompanied by considerable inflexibility. When the future is known with some security—for example, in an aggressive marketing situation where goods are mass produced and suppliers well controlled—such scheduling may be possible and desirable. In the more usual batch-production conditions, some flexibility is extremely desirable, and this can be built in by deliberately under-loading resources and/or by using sub-contractors. Clearly, such actions generate extra costs and these must be considered as the price which must be paid to be able to handle uncertainty.

The load

Loading differs from scheduling only in terms of detail and time span. A schedule might programme the work for a department for a period of a month, while a load could be the timetable of work for an operator for a day or a week. Not infrequently the final loading—the hour-to-hour assignment of work to the individual operator—is carried out by the first-line supervisor.

The *load* is the work assigned to a machine or operator, and *capacity* is the resource available to complete the available work during any convenient period of time. Both load and capacity should be measured in the same units to make comparisons meaningful. When the load equals capacity, then the department, machine or operator is said to be *fully loaded*. If load is greater than capacity, the plant is *overloaded*; while if load is less than capacity, then the plant is *underloaded* (see Fig. 25.2). It is prudent when drawing up an initial schedule deliberately to *under-load* capacity in order to provide some ability to react to change. The authors' experience is that a 70 per cent load is the maximum which should be aimed for in the first place.

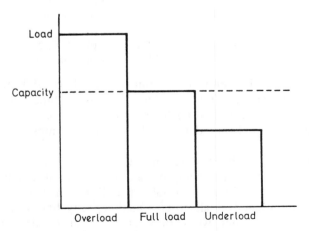

Fig. 25.2 The load–capacity relationship

Loading
The preparation of loading schedules for a processor or operator is capable of providing substantial improvements in productivity. Ideally, every operator should know the tasks which have to be undertaken for as far ahead as is realistic, normally at least one working week. By so doing it will be possible:

1. To make maximum possible use of plant, equipment and personnel.
2. To establish and meet target dates.
3. To establish a case for new plant/equipment.
4. To improve operator morale.

It is frequently possible to express the load on a machine or process in a variety of ways:

Money (a machine is required to produce £ *X* per hour)
Weight (a machine is required to produce *X* tonnes per hour)
Length (a machine is required to produce *X* metres per hour)
Quantity (a process is required to handle *X* transactions per hour)

However, in the context of production control, the only sensible measure of load which can be used directly and universally for comparisons is standard hours of work at a known rate of working.

The load on a machine/operator lays down the work it will complete and the time it will take for the period under consideration, and might well take the form:

Machine 1
Monday	0800–1700	job 131/9	operation 1
Tuesday	0800–1230	job 132/2	operation 2
	1230–1700	job 134/1	operation 1

....

....
| Friday | 0800–1100 | job 138/4 | operation 5 |
| | 1100–1700 | job 134/1 | operation 6 |

This load can only be determined from the schedule, while the schedule can only be drawn up after considering the load. Since delivery dates form a major input in preparing the schedule, the need to consider load when establishing delivery dates is clear. The relationship is shown in Fig. 25.3.

It is folly to set a delivery date without due regard to the load, yet this is done so frequently that it could be said to be general practice. This will inevitably lead to costly usage of labour and broken delivery dates, and should be discouraged at all costs. Once capacity has been filled, it is possible to insert other work only at the cost of delaying existing commitments.

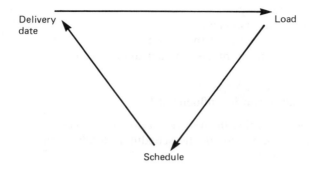

Fig. 25.3

Capacity

The capacity of a unit is its ability to produce that which the consumer requires, and clearly there must be some match between *needs* characterized by market forecast and *abilities* characterized by capacity. A statement of capacity is rarely simple, and it is useful to distinguish between three different capacity levels:

Potential capacity is that which can be made available within the decision horizon of the most senior executive.

Immediate capacity is that which can be made available within the current budget period.

Effective capacity is that which is used within the current budget period.

The production controller is generally concerned with the second and third of these levels, since he must deal with immediate, rather than long-term, problems. Furthermore, it should also be recognized that one of the objectives of the sales programme is to try to ensure that the effective and immediate capacities coincide. It should be noted that the more nearly effective approaches immediate, the more rigid must the organization become: flexibility can only be achieved when immediate capacity is not fully used.

Constraints on immediate capacity
Immediate capacity is limited by:

    (*a*) plant/equipment size;
    (*b*) availability of equipment;
    (*c*) availability of manpower;
    (*d*) availability of cash;
    (*e*) financial policies;

(f) purchasing policy;
(g) sub-contracting policy;
(h) technical demands of the tasks;
(i) number of different tasks being undertaken.

Influences on effective capacity
Effective capacity can be influenced by:

(a) technical abilities in the pre-production stages;
(b) organizational skills in the scheduling/loading stages;
(c) purchasing skills;
(d) sub-contracting skills;
(e) maintenance policies and abilities;
(f) versatility of labour;
(g) efficiency of labour.

Differences between effective and immediate capacities
A great deal of work has been carried out on the utilization of equipment, that is, the differences between effective and immediate capacity. Frequently these studies have involved the use of activity sampling to establish the proportion of time the equipment was being used productively, and to identify the reasons for and quantify the extent of non-productive time. These reasons range across setting-up, planned maintenance, emergency maintenance, idle (no planned work), idle (operator absent), and so on. The picture that emerges is that effective capacity is frequently less than 50 per cent of immediate capacity. While it is unlikely that these two capacities will ever coincide, it is clear that significant increases in capacity are possible, often by improved production control. It is also clear that to measure capacity solely on the basis of available time is likely to give gross errors. Allowance must always be made for current local performance.

Capacity change
Within a production/operations environment, it seems probable that:

1. The ability of an individual to change capacity is directly related to that individual's position in the organization's hierarchy.

2. The time necessary to implement a capacity increase is proportional to the magnitude of the increase.

3. The number of acceptable capacity changes which can be handled at any one time is finite.

Every programme implies a certain level of capacity and, if the above statements hold true, it is important that the implicit capacity decisions are made by an individual at the correct level in the organization. To present the production controller with a programme which requires a capacity change greater than his hierarchical position will permit him to effect can only result in frustration and the non-achievement of the programme. Similarly, if the need for a capacity change is recognized too late, it too will not be achieved, and failure must again result.

The measurement of capacity
Capacity, being the ability to produce work in a given time, must be measured in the units of work, that is, resource-standard time units available in unit time. Thus a work centre with a capacity of 1,000 machine-hours in a 40-hour week should be able to produce 1,000 standard hours of work *of the type appropriate to that work station* during a 40-hour week. To be able to calculate the volume of actual work, it is necessary to know:

(*a*) the work content of the product;
(*b*) the ancillary times involved in the production;
(*c*) the effectiveness of the work station.

The measurement of capacity and the above factors are frequently undertaken by the production engineering departments in manufacturing organizations, and it is useful to confirm these measurements by records of actual performance.

As with load, it is not uncommon to find capacity quoted in terms of quantity of products made in unit time ('. . . 100 dozen pairs a day', '. . . 40 letters of credit per hour'). Such statements should be treated with great caution, changes in methods, procedures, materials, quantities . . . can result in changes in effective capacity. Unless the work unit is dedicated to a single product, it is safer always to refer to units of work rather than units produced.

Finite or infinite capacity loading
In loading and scheduling, two conflicting constraints—time and capacity—have to be considered. If time is fixed, for example by the customer's required delivery date or transaction processing cycle, then it is possible to accept time as the primary constraint and schedule backwards to accommodate these times. However, this can be somewhat difficult in practice, since it is not generally possible to determine beforehand whether all of the tasks can be fitted in with the currently available capacity, and much time can be spent trying to solve an insoluble problem. Indeed, even after recognition that capacity needs to be temporarily increased, the extent of this and its timing still has to be established, with clearly a variety of options open to the decision-maker, all with different cost implications.

Backward scheduling to infinite capacity offers a partial solution to this problem. Many manufacturing and transaction-handling processes go through a number of stages in a sequential manner. If this schedule is being prepared on a period-by-period basis (say week), then the backward schedule can be prepared on the basis of one stage per period. This means that the final stage (operation) of the task is allocated to the period representing the delivery date, the penultimate task is allocated one period earlier, and so on. This produces a slightly more realistic plan of what might happen. This process indicates where overloads are likely to be and gives a far better picture of when and to what extent extra resources will be required. However, to confirm or propose revised delivery dates, a finite capacity schedule must be developed. Generally, it is far simpler to produce a forward (rather than a backward) schedule to finite capacity. For this, tasks are put into some priority order and, following this sequence, added to the schedule in such a way that they are started as soon as possible at each stage, but only using as much resource as is available. Clearly the criterion used for prioritizing the tasks will have a significant effect on the performance of the schedule. This will be discussed in a later section.

The problem of scheduling

The key to efficiency in a production/operations unit is the ability to schedule effectively, and yet *scheduling* is an exercise which is not resolvable in unique logical terms. Two barriers to efficient scheduling exist:

1. *The difficulty in identifying the purpose for which scheduling is being undertaken.* Many criteria exist against which the soundness of a schedule can be judged; for example:

minimum production costs
minimum storage costs

are two possible criteria. It is easy to suggest that the schedule produced should achieve both. However, minimum production costs might imply long production runs of the same product before changing, in order to spread the set-up cost over a large number of units. This will lead to holding high stocks of items and inflated storage costs. There are many more criteria which can be stated and an attempt to satisfy them all can lead to a result which satisfies none. The criteria can be considered to fall under a number of headings: financial, marketing, production/operations; and some examples are listed below.

It is tempting to suggest that these should be combined into a single financial measure. However, a number of intangible problems will still remain, for example is it better to have one job two weeks late or two jobs each one week late? The choice of criterion should be made after careful consideration of the aims of the organization.

Financial:
   minimum production costs
   minimum storage costs
   minimum stock investment
   minimum cash outflow
Marketing:
   achieve delivery dates
   minimize number of late jobs
   maximize customer satisfaction
Production:
   maximum labour utilization
   minimum set-up times
   maximum equipment utilization

Some scheduling criteria

2. *The extremely large number of possible schedules*. If there are N jobs to be processed in sequence through M machines, there are $(N!)^M$ possible schedules. This number can be reduced by requiring that the order of the jobs on the first process should be retained for all the other processes. This produces a so-called ordered schedule, and for N tasks there are a mere $N!$ possible schedules. Thus, for 20 tasks there would be 20! different schedules. It is left as an exercise for the reader to calculate how long it would take even the fastest of modern computers to generate, evaluate all these schedules and to print out the 'best'.

Reducing the scheduling problem
The problem, however difficult, must be solved, albeit in a most imperfect way. To simplify the task, there are a number of fairly obvious common-sense steps which can be undertaken:

1. Reduce the product range if possible. Many companies manufacture products which produce little income and less contribution. As can be seen above, reduction in variety gives a proportionally greater reduction in scheduling complexity.

2. Reduce the component range. Unnecessary variety in components is extremely costly.

3. Examine the available resources. Much equipment is needlessly complex, and uniformity in types of equipment can substantially ease the scheduling problem.

4. Carry out a job enlargement programme. To train staff to carry out a number of tasks rather than only one task will improve flexibility and morale.

5. Investigate the use of sub-contractors. The off-loading of peaks of work can sometimes be very rewarding in terms of the organizational simplification which results.

6. Separate out the 'big' tasks which consume a great deal of labour and 'small' tasks which consume little labour. To try to mix 'big' and 'small' work in the same work areas is usually very difficult, and a 'small order' section organized more informally than a 'large order' section will usually be quite effective.

7. Ensure close liaison between production/operations and marketing. Tension can often be relieved by dialogue with customers.

8. Reduce the size of the organizational units. The difficulty of scheduling—and, indeed, managing—increases considerably with size.

9. Increase the autonomy of work areas. Constraints are often imposed on the grounds that greater 'control' is obtained. Unless a good visible reason can be found for imposing a restriction, it is best left unimposed.

10. Once a forecast and a derived schedule have been prepared *and agreed*, they should only be changed for very compelling reasons. Discipline on all concerned must be accepted.

---

1. Reduce the product range
2. Reduce component range
3. Examine available resources
4. Enlarge all tasks where possible
5. Use sub-contractors
6. Separate 'big' and 'small' tasks
7. Close liaison with marketing
8. Reduce size
9. Increase autonomy
10. Accept need for discipline

Simplifying the scheduling problem

Use of interstage stores

The virtual impossibility in batch production or processing of balancing the load on all stages results in gaps in the work available to a work area or section. To avoid the cost of this inactivity, it is common to find that sub-stores (interstage work-in-progress or buffer areas) are created between sections. These form 'pools' or 'reservoirs' from which succeeding stages can draw work and thus keep all stages at work. While this avoids the 'idle time' cost of an unbalanced load, it substitutes for it the cost of holding the work-in-progress. Since this cost is difficult to identify and quantify, it is often ignored, yet it may well be that the idle-time costs, and the organizational costs to remove them, may in fact be less than the very high costs of holding stock. This area of cost creation may often repay investigation.

Scheduling rules

While the above suggestions may simplify the scheduling task, they will not solve it, and the residual problem is still gigantic. To enable schedules to be constructed in practical circumstances, it is often useful to devise rules which can be used to either put tasks into priority order or to simply select the next task to be handled. These are sometimes referred to as *loading* or *despatching* rules. Essentially they involve examining a particular characteristic of the tasks. Again these characteristics fall under the broad headings of financial, marketing and production. Some of these are shown below:

	Select/order according to:
Financial:	highest value
	highest contribution
Marketing:	earliest delivery date
	least slack time
	least slack time per operation
Production:	least set-up time
	shortest processing time
	earliest date of receipt

Loading/despatching criteria

Clearly the choice of loading rule should be linked to the criteria by which the schedule is measured. Some are easier to operate than others. If works order numbers are issued to tasks sequentially as they arrive, then scheduling by date of receipt simply involves selection of the task with the lowest works order number. This number would be stamped on the documentation accompanying the task. Equally, the delivery date would be recorded on this documentation so that loading by delivery date could also be easily accomplished. However, it may be felt that the amount of free time—the *slack*—is a better measure of the importance of a task. This involves more effort: the work contents of the individual operations making up the task must be added together and subtracted from the delivery date. It is possible to go a step further and to argue that this slack time will be spent queueing before one or other of the processes, so that the measure should be the slack time divided by the number of operations. While the delivery date will normally be fixed throughout the processing of a task, the slack time per operation will change as the task is processed, and needs to be repeatedly recalculated.

None of these rules will always produce the 'best' or 'optimum' schedule. However, they are fairly easy to operate and attractive to the user since they are based on common-sense. They provide a consistency to scheduling which can reflect factors of importance to the organization.

Loading rules and the computer

Loading rules form the basis of the scheduling module of some computer software packages for production planning and control. When deciding which job to schedule next in producing the plan, the computer looks at the various characteristics of the tasks waiting. These characteristics include the factors listed above: value, delivery date, work content, external priority (importance of the customer). These are converted to a common scale (it is not possible to add directly a 'calendar date' to 'pounds value'), multiplied by weights specified by the user, and added together. This 'priority value' is used to select the next job.

Some special methods

1. *Critical path analysis*
One-off jobs can be dealt with by CPA (see Chapter 30). This is particularly suitable for tasks involving complex interdependencies between the individual operations making up the task. However, a multitude of such tasks produces a resource allocation problem just as intractable as the batch scheduling problem.

2. *Johnson's two-machine algorithm*
Where there are only two machines, they can be scheduled to minimize the total throughput time—the *makespan*—by a procedure known by the name of its author: S. M. Johnson. This is easier to use than to derive, so an example will be presented. Consider a series of six jobs (A, B, . . ., F) which all have to pass through two machines in the same order, that is, first through machine I, then through machine II. Processing times (in units) are given below:

Job	A	B	C	D	E	F
Machine I	1	6	5	5	3	6
Machine II	2	4	6	4	2	7

A sequence table is constructed:

Sequence	1	2	3	4	5	6
Job						

The table of job times is scanned and the smallest time identified—in this case 1 (A: I). As this smallest time is on the first machine, this job is put at the start of the sequence; had it been on the second machine, the job would have been put at the end of the sequence. Next smallest is 2 (E: II), hence this job is put at the end of the sequence. As jobs are added into the sequence, their times are no longer considered; the sequence is built up inwards. At this point there is a tie: 4 corresponding to both (B: II) and (D: II), so there are two alternative solutions. The complete solutions can be built up and are shown below:

Sequence	1	2	3	4	5	6
Job	A	C	F	D	B	E
Job	A	C	F	B	D	E

Either of these schedules will minimize the total time taken to process all the jobs. However, in order to find this makespan it is necessary either to produce a table of start and finish times or to draw up a bar chart for the sequence. The use of this approach is rather limited, but could be useful in special circumstances, for example where two consecutive machines are very costly or combine to form a bottleneck. There are also two extensions: the first to certain three-machine problems, and a second to develop a heuristic procedure (one which does not guarantee to obtain the best solution, just a good one) for the more general problem.

3. *The branch and bound approach*

A technique which shows great promise, and which is being increasingly used in scheduling batch production, is the branch and bound approach. The name derives from the ability to display the enumeration of the possible alternative schedules as a tree with many branches. To explore completely the totality of the feasible alternatives would require an examination of all branches; that is, with N jobs, $N!$ branches if only ordered schedules were considered. As previously pointed out, for anything but the very smallest problems this is impractical. However, it is possible to devise indicators (bounds) which show which branches are likely to produce good results and which are not. The branch which appears most promising is followed until a complete solution is obtained. At this stage a large number of other branches can be eliminated, since it can be shown that they cannot produce better solutions. The process continues by exploring other branches which do offer potential for improved solutions. The effectiveness of the approach depends on the method used for calculating the bounds: the 'tighter' these are, the more branches can be eliminated from the search; and the way branches are selected as 'promising' and further developed—branching—the better this is achieved the fewer the steps necessary at arriving at a possibly improved solution. This process offers the further advantage that it can be terminated at any stage (before the optimum solution has been found) and the best solution found so far taken.

4. *Line-of-balance*

Line-of-balance, a special case of CPA, can be used in single batch situations and is particularly useful when delivery rates are not linear with respect to time. Essentially, L-o-B consists of drawing a network for the production of a single unit and calculating the latest finish for all activities. If the delivery activity is taken as the last activity and a previous activity has to be finished four weeks previously, at week N say, the total quantity passed through the previous activity should be equal to the total quantity which should pass through delivery at week $N + 4$. This technique is covered in detail in Chapter 31.

Recent developments

Recent years have seen a number of new methodologies proposed for various aspects of production/operations control. These include material requirements planning (MRP), manufacturing resource planning (MRP II), just in time (JIT or KANBAN) and optimized production technology (OPT). MRP, as its title suggests, concerns primarily the management of materials at a variety of levels within the organization and, consequently, is more appropriately described in the chapter devoted to this topic. MRP II has as one of its central features the MRP framework; however, it comprises much else also, including capacity planning and scheduling at various levels of detail. This will be covered alongside MRP, although both have similarities in part with JIT and OPT.

Just in time (JIT)

This is a manufacturing system developed by the Japanese, normally for use with repetitive manufacture, which aims at a much tighter control of inventories. As mentioned earlier, frequently utilization is a main goal, and it is felt that machines and operators must be kept working at all costs, ignoring the expense of interstage stores. JIT does not accept this: rather it works on the principle that the component should not be made before it is required, *even if this results in operators stopping manufacture* (and perhaps engaging in other activity like cleaning the work stations, quality circle work. and so on). Indeed, this holdup is not greeted with gloom, rather advantage is gained from it since the bottleneck in the process has been identified. Management and operators can now work towards overcoming it. This might involve cross-training of operators, a critical examination of setting-up times and how these could be reduced, and so on. Indeed, JIT systems frequently operate with very small batch sizes and, as a consequence, users have become very skilled at keeping set-up times to a bare minimum. As a result the choice of batch size is of less real economic significance than with the alternative approach of attempting to estimate the costs involved (set-up and holding) and subsequently developing models which minimize these.

In fact, JIT has many similarities with flow line methods in that the whole process is balanced. The starting point is the schedule for the final assembly of the products. This is prepared and normally fixed for the planning horizon—say one month—and is used to derive the daily production rate. This is the only detailed plan produced. The size of the batch produced at any stage can be thought of as limited by the size of the container used to transport the items from one stage to the next. A simplification of the organization is shown in Fig. 25.4. A plant manufactures a variety of products by processing them through a number of work centres. Between each work centre is a store holding containers of components produced by the first work centre waiting to be processed by the next centre in the manufacture of one of the products.

The assembly schedules are derived from the detailed plan. A container of the final components needed in the assembly of the first product is withdrawn from the store after the final work centre in exchange for a card (KANBAN—Japanese for card). This card is the authorization to manufacture a replacement for the container of this component by the final work centre. To manufacture this final component, materials produced by the penultimate work centre are required, and a container is withdrawn from the store after this centre, again a KANBAN is issued to authorize replacement, and so on back down the chain to the initial raw material. A similar process applies to the second product, third product and so on. The assembly schedule thus 'pulls' production through the system. The schedule of work at any work centre is made up of the on-hand KANBANs which have been pushed back down the system by the assembly schedules for the various final products. The order in which the KANBANs have been received at any work centre determines the manufacturing sequence at that work centre, and if no KANBANs are held, no manufacture must take place! Work-in-progress can be reduced and bottlenecks identified and eliminated by systematically reducing the number of components in a container. In this way the manufacturing system is balanced.

Optimized production technology (OPT)

This a relatively new approach which has similarities with some of the

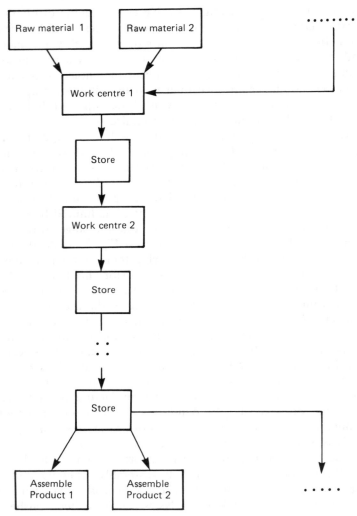

Fig. 25.4 Simplified JIT system

basic ideas behind JIT. However, whereas JIT is essentially a manual system, OPT is supported by computer software. OPT breaks down into a number of distinct steps, shown in simplified form in Fig. 25.5. The information relating to each finished product (process route, process times, set-up times and so on) is stored in network form. An elaborate set of checks and cross-checks, taking in the work centre details, validates this as far as possible. The system takes the marketing forecasts, and backward schedules these orders from their required dates, carrying out

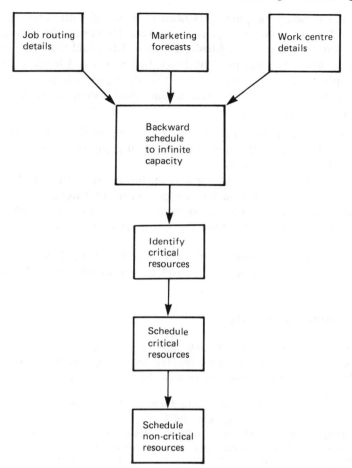

Fig. 25.5 Simplified outline of OPT

this process to infinite capacity. This schedule is used to classify resources as *critical* or *non-critical*, based on utilization. The critical resources can be thought of as bottlenecks. The package then uses what is called a *proprietary algorithm* to optimally forward schedule the orders through the bottleneck resources. Finally, the orders are scheduled through the non-critical resources in such a way that the optimal schedule on the critical resources is not disturbed, and a buffer of safety capacity is included to allow for disruptions.

The heart of this approach was the *algorithm* which carries out the optimal scheduling of the critical resources. It has 'management parameters' which enable it to be fine tuned to specific company objectives.

However, following the plans produced is an act of faith, since the algorithm itself was a closely guarded secret. However, in *International Management*, January 1987, Moshe Eliyahu 'Eli' Goldratt, the 'inventor' of OPT, is quoted as saying: 'the black box was a red herring, the software simply a number cruncher, and the algorithm a huge overkill.'

The creators of OPT state some fundamental principles, some of which are worth mentioning here:

1. Bottlenecks or critical resources determine production for the whole system; the level of utilization of non-critical resources should reflect the needs of the critical ones. So:
   (*a*) An hour lost at a bottleneck is an hour lost to the whole system.
   (*b*) An hour saved at non-bottleneck has no real impact.
2. Bottlenecks determine throughput and inventories, so why manufacture a component faster than the bottleneck can handle it?

At the time of writing, there are insufficient applications of OPT running in the UK to assess its impact on production control systems.

Recommended reading

Baker, K. R., *An Introduction to Scheduling and Sequencing*, Wiley, 1974.
   A sound basic reference covering the models and methodologies in the scheduling field, a desirable prerequisite being some exposure to probability and statistics.
Bellman, R., Esogbue, A. O. and Nabeshima, I., *Mathematical Aspects of Scheduling and Applications*, Pergamon, 1982.
   A comprehensive text on scheduling theory, not for the mathematically weak, with detailed references and a variety of examples.
Goldratt, E. M. and Cox, J., *The Goal, Creative Output*, 1986.
   The OPT principle of manufacturing, developed and presented as a novel.
Reinfeld, N. V., *Production and Inventory Control*, Reston, 1982.
   Chapters on many of the aspects of 'programmes' but particularly planning, processing and scheduling the order, loading and capacity planning, shop-floor control.

26 An example of schedule preparation in a batch production unit

The previous chapter discussed the basic problem of scheduling and suggested that in a large number of cases it was not possible, or even desirable, to try to produce an ideal schedule. In practice, of course, it is essential to produce some feasible schedule, whether it is ideal or not. The problem is probably at its most acute in a batch production unit, and this chapter illustrates some guidelines which will help in the development of such a schedule. It must be stated unambiguously that the solution which is evolved is but one of many. It has the advantage of being workable—that is, it does not produce an overload before any work starts—but there may be many other equally good or 'better' solutions. For illustration, a manual method will be demonstrated for this development; a computer approach will be discussed later.

There are two main situations that occur.

1. Products are manufactured for *stock*, in which case it is possible to prepare the schedule and load at the beginning of the planning period: the 'marketing' situation.

2. Products are manufactured only against *customers' orders*, in which case it is necessary to schedule and load during the planning period: the 'selling' situation.

Frequently, of course, both the above will be found existing side-by-side in the same unit. Often it will be found convenient organizationally to separate the two into different units.

Manufacturing for stock

The sales programme will be effectively in the form:

Delivery by end of week	Product			
	A	B	C	D
1	20			20
2		10		
3			10	15
4	15	10		
5			20	10
6	10	10		
7			20	15
8	20			

From this, works orders, authorizing production, will be issued as follows:

Job number	1001
Product	A
Quantity	20
Delivery required	Week 1

Job number	1002
Product	B
Quantity	10
Delivery required	Week 2

and so on, covering all fourteen jobs shown in the programme.

The production control department will then obtain from the planning department a route and schedule of manufacture for each product. Assuming that the manufacture is simple and that there is neither overlapping nor dead time, the route and the schedule will be identical and would take the form:

Job number			1001
Product			A
Quantity			20
Operation	Department	Time	Number of operators
1	D.1	5 days	1
2	D.2	6 days	1
3	D.3	4 days	1
4	D.4	5 days	1
5	D.5	2 days	1

and, in all, fourteen routes would be required which, when prepared, could be summarized as follows:

					Work content in operator-days in departments				
Product Type	Qty	Job number	D.1	D.2	D.3	D.4	D.5	Job completed by end of week	
A	20	1001	5	6	4	5	2	1	
B	10	1002	10	10	10	10	10	2	
C	10	1003	3	8	5	5	8	3	
D	20	1004	12	24	32	20	12	1	
A	15	1005	4	4	3	4	2	4	
B	10	1006	10	10	10	10	10	4	
D	15	1007	9	18	24	15	9	3	
A	10	1008	3	3	2	3	1	6	
B	10	1009	10	10	10	10	10	6	
C	20	1010	5	15	10	10	15	5	
D	10	1011	6	12	16	10	6	5	
A	20	1012	5	6	4	5	2	8	
C	20	1013	5	15	10	10	15	7	
D	15	1014	9	18	24	15	9	7	

Note: all fractions of an operator-day are rounded up to the next whole number for ease of calculation.

From the production manager the production control department would obtain a statement of the capacity of each department:

Department	Weekly capacity
D.1	12 operator-days
D.2	25 operator-days
D.3	33 operator-days
D.4	20 operator-days
D.5	12 operator-days

These capacities represent the 'maximum theoretical' figures, which must be adjusted downwards to allow for sickness, absenteeism, casual holidays and so on. This adjustment (which can be made as a percentage) will be based on historical figures. In this example, it will be ignored for convenience.

From its own records, POCD would obtain statements of the existing loads, planned holiday periods, maintenance requirements:

Existing load

Department	Loaded until end of week
D.1	46
D.2	47
D.3	48
D.4	49
D.5	49

Holidays
All departments closed for weeks 50, 51.

Maintenance

Department
D.1
D.2   all maintenance
D.3   carried out in
D.4   weeks 50.51
D.5

The chart in Fig. 26.1 (between pages 368 and 369) shows the initial situation in starting to plan work through the departments.

Since delivery dates are specified, it is sensible *in this case* to start by scheduling from completion date backwards to the starting date. As mentioned in the previous chapter, it can be extremely difficult to attempt to schedule backwards and stay within the available capacity restrictions due, at least in part, to the number of different permutations of job orders. Indeed, it may not even be possible to fit all the jobs in before their delivery dates. Consequently the first schedule is carried out to 'infinite capacity'—ignoring any restrictions on capacity—in order to indicate when and where conflicts are likely to occur so that action may be taken where possible to resolve these problems. In order to model the sequential nature of the production route, this schedule is prepared on the basis of one operation per week.

Before any scheduling takes place, POCD should correct the standard times given on the various route cards for any known or foreseeable departmental inefficiencies; for the purposes of this illustration, it is assumed that all work is carried out 'at standard', so no adjustment is therefore necessary. The resultant programme is shown in Fig. 26.2 (between pages 370 and 371). It can be seen that this indicates that severe overloading might occur on a number of occasions.

Overloading is quite unacceptable since it represents a task which is incapable of being fulfilled. There are a number of ways whereby an overload can be reduced, including:

(*a*) increase available resources, either on a short-term basis by working overtime, or on a long-term basis by buying more plant or hiring more men;

(*b*) sub-contracting the work producing the overload: this often results in shifting effort from the direct producing departments to the support departments—for example, to the purchasing department;

(*c*) improving the manufacturing method to reduce work content;

(*d*) changing the product design again to reduce work content or to permit of the purchase of complete parts;

(*e*) negotiating a change in delivery date.

In order to evaluate the effects of increasing the available resources or to establish what delivery dates can be achieved with the available resources, it is now necessary to produce a finite capacity schedule. It is easier to carry this out in a forward direction. However, it is first necessary to decide on the order in which the jobs are to be added into the schedule. Since delivery dates are involved, the order will be determined by these, with jobs with the highest work content having priority in the case of equal delivery dates. Hence the jobs will be scheduled as follows:

Order	Job number	Delivery date (end of week)
1	1004	1
2	1001	1
3	1002	2
4	1007	3
5	1003	3
6	1006	4
7	1005	4
8	1010	5
9	1011	5
10	1009	6
11	1008	6
12	1014	7
13	1013	7
14	1012	8

The result of scheduling the jobs in this order is shown in Fig. 26.3 (between pages 372 and 373). In producing this schedule it is assumed that the time necessary for transport between departments is negligible, and so a job can start in a subsequent department as soon as it has finished in its current department provided capacity is available. Moreover, work has been loaded on to departments without any regard to the number of operators in them and the desirability of having several operators

Week number

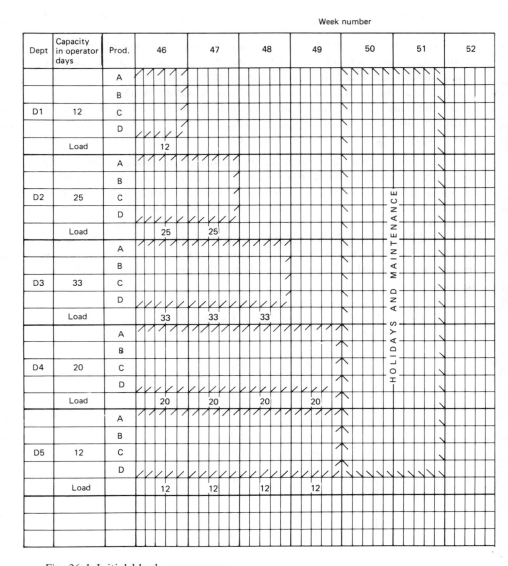

Fig. 26.1 Initial blank programme

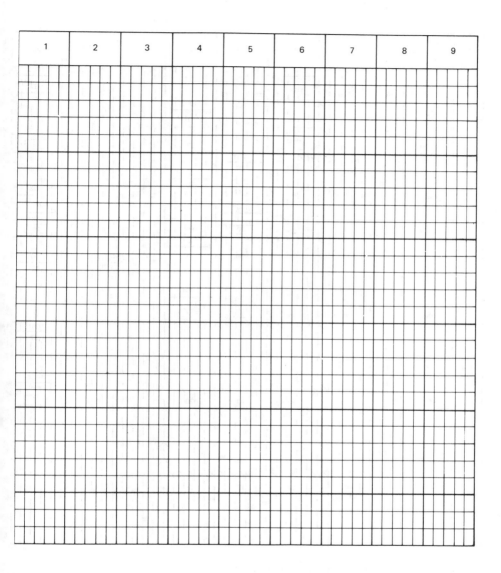

Week number

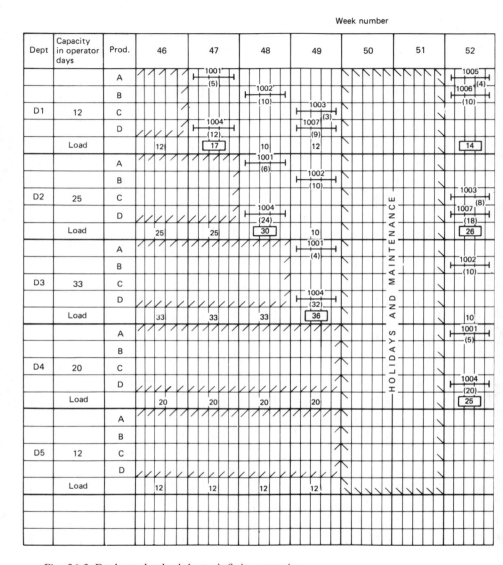

Fig. 26.2 Backward schedule to infinite capacity

1	2	3	4	5	6	7	8	9

1008
(3)
1009
(10)
1012
(5)
1010
1011 (5)
(6)
1013
(5)
1014
(9)
11
13
14
5

1005
1006 (4)
(10)
1008
1009 (3)
(10)
1012
(6)
1010
1011 (15)
(12)
1013
(15)
1014
(18)
14
27
13
33
6

1005
1006 (3)
(10)
1008
(2)
1009
(10)
1012
(4)
1003
1007 (5)
(24)
1010
(10)
1011
(16)
1013
(10)
1014
(24)
29
13
26
12
34
4

1002
(10)
1005
1006 (4)
(10)
1008
1009 (3)
(10)
1012
(5)
1003
1007 (5)
(15)
1010
1011 (10)
(10)
1013
1014 (10)
(15)
10
20
14
20
13
25
5

1001
(2)
1002
(10)
1005
1006 (2)
(10)
1008
1009 (1)
(10)
1012
(2)
1003
1007 (8)
(9)
1010
1011 (15)
(6)
1013
1014 (15)
(9)
1004
(12)
14
10
17
12
21
11
24
2

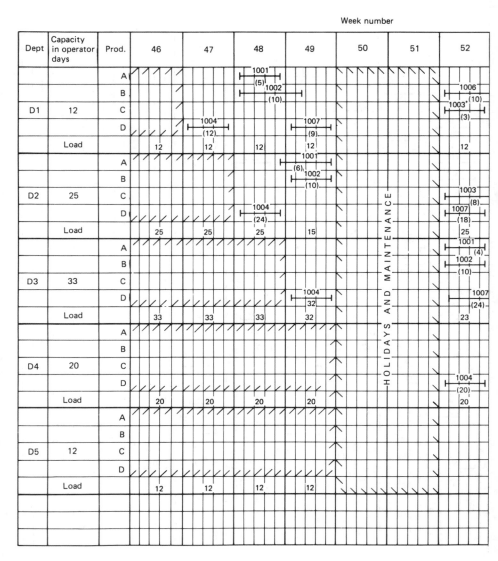

Fig. 26.3 Forward schedule to finite capacity

1	2	3	4	5	6	7	8	9
1005 (4)	1009 (10)	1008 (3)	1012 (5)					
1010 (5)	1011 (6)		1013 (5)					
			1014 (9)					
12	12	12	12					
1005 (4)	1010 (15)	1008 (3)		1012 (6)				
1006 (10)	1011 (12)	1009 (10)	1014 (18)	1013 (15)				
19	23	13	21	18				
1005 (3)	1010 (10)	1008 (2)		1012 (4)				
1006 (10)		1009 (10)		1013 (10)				
1003 (5)		1011 (16)		1014 (24)				
33	13	25	4	33				
1001 (5)	1006 (10)	1005 (4)	1009 (10)	1008 (3)	1012 (5)			
1002 (10)	1003 (5)	1010 (10)	1011 (10)		1013 (10)			
1007 (15)					1014 (15)			
20	20	20	20	11	20	4		
	1001 (2)			1005 (2)		1009 (10)	1008 (1)	
	1002 (10)	1003 (8)	1006 (10)	1010 (15)				1014 (15)
1004 (12)		1007 (9)		1011 6			1014 (9)	
12	12	12	12	12	12	12	12	12

processing the same job. Clearly, local circumstances will determine the significance of these factors in practice. The lengths of the lines associated with each job are not intended to be proportional to its duration or work content, simply to give an indication of the week(s) in which it is planned. This programme satisfies the capacity constraints—no department is overloaded—but at the expense of missing some of the delivery dates.

| | Delivery date—end of week | |
Job number	Required	Planned
1001	1	2
1002	2	2
1003	3	4
1004	1	1
1005	4	5
1006	4	5
1007	3	3
1008	6	8
1009	6	7
1010	5	6
1011	5	7
1012	8	10
1013	7	10
1014	7	8

Clearly, these changes in delivery must be agreed with the customer who, in this case, is the marketing department. The schedule shows periods both when operators are waiting for work and when jobs are waiting to be processed. There is no guarantee that it is the best schedule in any sense, its appeal is simply that it was produced taking account of delivery dates and delivery was considered to be important. Had utilization been important, jobs of similar types could have been grouped together in order to improve 'efficiency', for example, all 'A' together: 1001, 1005, 1008, 1012; then all 'B', and so on. This obviously disregards the delivery requirements. Equally, if it was felt necessary to attempt to achieve more of the delivery dates, then it would be possible to relax the rule which required that a job could only move on to the next department when it had finished in its current department, and consider 'splitting' jobs and sending ahead. Figure 26.4 illustrates the effect of this on job 1002:10A, splitting it into two separate jobs of 5A.

While splitting the job reduces the elapsed time for manufacture and thereby improves delivery potential, it produces a plan which, having gaps, offers less scope for high efficiencies. Moreover, by increasing the number of separate entities to plan and control, it adds to the organizational complexity.

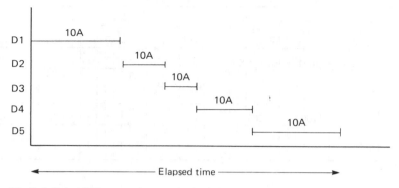

Fig. 26.4(a) Job 1002 treated as a single job

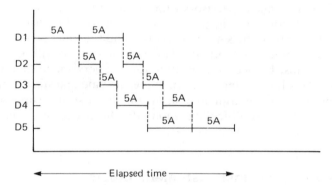

Fig. 26.4(b) Job 1002 treated as two jobs

The load on each department can be read straight off the programme as shown. In turn, the load on individual machines/operators can be readily deduced.

Derived load

Consider department D.1. This has a total capacity of 12 operator-days each week, and this is made up of the work of two operators (Smith and Jones) for six days each week. Their programme of work, that is, their individual loads for weeks 47–2 is represented by Fig. 26.5.

Note: *it must be emphasized again that the solution of Figs. 26.3 and 26.5 is but one of many possible sets of solutions, and no claim is made that it is in any way 'the best'.*

The authors consider that generally it is not necessary to break the load down to individual operators, and the actual allocation of work should

	Week								
	47	48	49	50	51	52	1	2	
	M T W T F S	M T W T F S	M T W T F S	M T W T F S	M T W T F S	M T W T F S	M T W T F S	M T W T F S	
Smith	1004	1001	1002 1007	Holidays		1003 1006	1005	1011	1009
Jones	1004	1002	1007	Holidays		1006		1010 1011 1009	

Fig. 26.5

be left to the first-line supervisors who will have the detailed local knowledge necessary for carrying out this task. Clearly this loading must be recognized as part of the supervisor's task, and time and facilities allowed to enable it to be carried out. If this is not the case, it will be found that much time is lost by operators waiting for a supervisor to find an appropriate job. This loss of time can sometimes assume alarming proportions, besides putting an unreasonable strain on the first-line supervisor, and causing a great deal of ill-feeling among the direct operators, particularly if bonus payments are involved.

Manufacturing against customers' orders

In the problem of manufacturing for stock, the tasks are known before the planning period is started, and time is available to adjust the programme with some precision. In the case of bespoke manufacture, this will be so only if the time-cycle of manufacture is long and the orders received well before production must start. Should the manufacturing cycle be short and deliveries rapid, alternative techniques may be necessary, particularly if the volume of orders is great. Scheduling and loading will not be so accurate, and it is wise under these circumstances to attempt to underload each department by at least 30 per cent in order that any inaccuracies or poor performances will not have too great an effect on the overall performance.

The sales programme will have been prepared in the form of the number of hours' work which it is anticipated will be received by the factory in the form of customers' orders. Under these circumstances it may be convenient to build up a load in diary form, the load increasing as orders arrive. It is clearly not possible to issue a manufacturing programme in detail at the outset of the planning period. The frequency with which a programme is issued will depend on the manufacturing time, the delivery time and the volume of orders, but a factory with a one-week manufacturing cycle and a short delivery should aim to issue a four-week programme each week. Thus, in week 1, a programme covering weeks 1, 2, 3 and 4 is issued. In week 2, the programme will cover weeks 2, 3, 4 and 5, and so on. The setting of delivery dates in this circumstance *must* be a matter for close consultation between the marketing department and the production control department, and unilateral decisions by one or other department can only lead to eventual disaster.

Loading against customers' orders

In this case the loading operation becomes more difficult, since it is necessary to plan the job in detail, preparing a route for each order as it is received. Such a procedure is not, in itself, inherently difficult, becoming so only when the volume of work becomes great. The route having been prepared, there are a number of methods whereby a load is built up. The simplest is a diary, where a series of sheets (see Fig. 26.6) is drawn up, one for each week, and as orders are prepared and planned, work is loaded into the appropriate week. As with all schedules, planning can be carried out either backwards or forwards.

An alternative method is to represent the load graphically on a bar chart of a type exactly similar to Figs. 26.2 and 26.3. This will produce a much more striking effect than the diary: if there are a large number of orders, however, the chart becomes unmanageable and the detail too fine for easy reference. The chart does have the advantage that it can be used, not only as a loading chart but also as a progress chart, and when used in this fashion it is known as a Gantt chart. Progress is shown on a Gantt chart by superimposing a line on the loading line, the length of which is proportional to the work done.

One disadvantage of a bar or Gantt chart drawn on paper is that it is inflexible; that is, that any modifications require alterations to, or complete redrawing of, the chart itself, which in a complex chart can be both costly and difficult, besides being a substantial source of error. To try to avoid this a number of mechanical devices have been designed whereon the work is represented by a card, peg, tape or other device which is held on to a board. Changes are then made by moving the representational devices as required. The ingenuity of these planning boards and their very considerable flexibility command attention, and anyone wishing to install a loading system would be well advised to see all the boards now marketed.

Most computer-based scheduling systems provide the facility to draw a Gantt chart. This enables the calculations required in drawing up a chart like Fig. 26.3 to be carried out accurately and rapidly. Changes in

D.1			D.2			D.3			D.4			D.5			Week no. 28
Total hours available		96	Total hours available		200	Total hours available		240	Total hours available		160	Total hours available		160	
Job no.	Hours	Total hours	Job no.	Hours	Total hours	Job no.	Hours	Total hours	Job no.	Hours	Total hours	Job no.	Hours	Total hours	
2001	20		1984	44		1970	20		1940	24		1920	10		30 June–6 July
2002	15	35	1986	50	94	1972	18	38	1942	30	54	1921	12	22	
2008	24	59	1987	20	114	1973	24	62	1943	15	69	1924	10	32	
2009	18	77	1990	30	144	1974	30	92	1946	16	85	1927	8	40	
2014	14	91	1992	32	176	1977	50	142	1950	25	110	1928	14	54	
			1993	30	206	1978	45	187	1953	20	130	1934	10	64	
						1981	35	222	1956	32	162	1936	8	72	
												1937	12	84	

Fig. 26.6 Diary form of loading

the various parameters, for example, different levels of overtime, can be assessed and different scenarios evaluated. However, the output from such packages is only as good as the data input. So, for example, the use of a computer will not in itself remove the problems associated with an inability to accurately estimate job times.

It must be remembered, however, that no system is any better than the people working it: no method, however good, can make up for inefficient operation on the part of staff. For this reason, if for no other, simplicity should be a primary requirement in any loading/progress system.

Recommended reading

See *Recommended reading* for Chapter 23.

27 Data capture and release

In any sequence of work a great deal of activity takes place prior to the commencement of the actual operations. This will include:

1. Preparing manufacturing drawings/statements of procedures.
2. Designing and making special production/operations aids.
3. Preparing job/operation layouts/routes.
4. Preparing material lists.
5. Purchasing and/or allocating material.
6. Preparing material requisitions.
7. Setting bonus rates and preparing bonus cards.

The actual activities will depend on the environment in which the transformation process is being carried out, and the type of transformation.

Dispatch

All this activity must be coordinated, and this is done most conveniently by the production control department. Once all these preparations are complete, the actual transformation process can start, and the formal act of *releasing* the work is known as *dispatching*. The dispatch section will thus be seen to be the bridge between operations and pre-operations. When all functions are being carried out correctly and to time, the dispatching function will be of least importance, and in large-scale flow production will become vestigial, being a routine clerical task. It is then often found convenient to merge the dispatch function with the progress function, when they are both carried out by a single section.

Responsibilities of the dispatch section

This section will normally be responsible for the following:

1. Checking the availability of material and then taking appropriate action to have it transferred from the main stores to the point at which it is first needed.
2. Ensuring that all production/operations aids are ready when

required and then having them issued to the appropriate departments.

3. Obtaining appropriate drawings/specifications/procedural instructions and material lists. These must be checked to confirm that they are the correct issue required.

4. Withdrawing job/operation tickets, bonus cards, operation layouts, route cards, material requisitions and any other necessary paperwork. These are issued to the appropriate supervisor.

5. Obtaining any inspection/checking schedules. This information is issued to the inspection/control department, along with advice that work is about to commence.

6. Informing the appropriate supervisors and the progress section that work is about to start.

7. At the conclusion, ensuring all process layouts, instructions and so on are returned to their correct location.

The correct time to issue work

It is possible, particularly when using a computer, to schedule work and prepare it for launching far ahead of its required starting date. There is then a temptation for the dispatcher to issue all the work that has been scheduled. However, this should generally be firmly resisted: only those jobs whose starting dates are imminent should be dispatched. Should all jobs be issued, the supervisor will be presented with work which cannot be encompassed in the next planning period and will then have to make a choice among the work, which may well create the undesirable situation of completing work that is not required and leaving undone work that is needed urgently.

Progress

Once work has started, it is necessary to check that it is proceeding according to plan. It might be considered *either* that this is unnecessary (since work is going as anticipated) *or* that it is a tacit admission of inefficiency (since work is not going as anticipated). On these grounds, it could be argued that if a car is being driven along a straight road it is not necessary to watch its progress. Just as the car will encounter irregularities in the road which, although slight, may accumulate to cause it to deviate from its intended route, so it will be found that there are many factors over which the production/operations manager has little or no control which can affect the operations. For example:

1. Materials may be delivered late.

2. Associated departments/sections may be behind in their own operations.

3. There may be excessive absenteeism, beyond that anticipated.
4. The customer may change his requirements.
5. Strikes or 'acts of God' can hold up processing.
6. Breakdowns may be greater than anticipated.

Furthermore, all plans are liable to be in error due to normal human failings; errors due to deliberate malevolence are rare, and are usually readily detected.

The progress chaser

The comparison of performance with plan is the responsibility of the progress department. This is normally staffed by clerical workers (progress clerks) who record, collate and compare information, and by perambulatory staff known as *progress chasers* (in the US 'expediters'). The chaser is responsible for seeing that any details which have been overlooked, or which have not proceeded according to plan, are put right. These details are often of such a nature that they can be resolved only by very detailed investigations, involving much walking and talking. In small organizations, these duties are carried out by the first-level supervisor, but in geographically large units there may be such time taken in going from one section to another that the supervisor is away from his own department an undesirably long time.

Product and process responsibilities

Chasers may either be responsible for processes (that is, for drills, or for data input) or for products (that is, for the progress of a single job from inception to completion). The process responsibility has two advantages: that the chaser becomes very familiar with each individual in his sphere of activity, knowing the strengths and weaknesses of each; and secondly, that he knows intimately the geographic disposition of the department, knowing immediately the places where items are most likely to be mislaid.

On the other hand, with highly complex manufactured products, the effects of variations in production and design can be appreciated only by persons with design experience; as a result, product chasing is often necessary, the chaser being dignified by the name of *project engineer*. The project engineer has an overall view of a project, and can foresee and counteract the effects of weaknesses in any department upon the project as a whole. There is a tendency today to employ product and process chasers simultaneously.

It must be clearly understood, of course, that the chaser supplies an advisory service and has no authority over direct operations personnel.

Informal arrangements may often arise whereby the chaser acts in the supervisor's place, but it must never happen that the responsibility for output, which is unquestionably the supervisor's, should devolve upon the chaser. The chaser should always discuss problems with the appropriate supervisor, never the operator. Should the results of these discussions be unsatisfactory, he should then move up the organizational structure to the person to whom he is next responsible.

The fundamental problems of progress

Ideally, the progress section should always be able to provide detailed information on the location and state of all the work which is in progress. This should be capable of being done from existing records supplemented by detailed knowledge obtained by the chaser at the point of work. This ideal can be very difficult to attain, even in quite small organizations, due to the complexity of the situation which arises from two fundamental problems:

1. *The problem of data capture.* The returning of information from an operations department to POCD is usually regarded by operators and supervisors as an unnecessary and irritating ritual, and is carried out with great reluctance and little accuracy. Furthermore, this information must be in a usable form: surprisingly enough, chasers themselves tend to record information in the most unsatisfactory way, often relying on memory and scraps of paper rather than written records.

2. *The problem of volume.* The information once obtained will be of great volume, yet much of it will excite little interest, since it will relate to work which is, in fact, proceeding satisfactorily. Hence it is necessary to sift and analyse the information obtained.

Data capture

Information can be obtained from an operations department in a number of ways:

1. *Automatically.* If a process is linked to a machine or conveyor, mechanical, electrical or electronic counting and/or recording devices may be used. These can also be employed if it is possible to guarantee that all products pass a particular point. There is a great variety of such devices, many of them being incorporated into the control mechanisms which regulate operations.

2. *Operator's work record.* The operator can be required to maintain a log, showing which operations, and how many of each, he or she has

carried out. This can be done in very abbreviated form, involving little writing, and is probably most satisfactory for repetitive work. It will sometimes require verifying by the supervisor.

3. *Job card*. This is a variation of the work record, in that the operator is presented with a card specifying the work to be done. It is usually prepared in the PCD from the specified route for the work, and can form an authority for the operator to carry out the task specified. The operator will fill in the quantity of the operation carried out, his name and any other information required. The cards are collected daily and returned to the progress section for analysis. This technique is particularly useful in small batch production since the card itself can be used as part of the scheduling system and can instruct the operator in the task he is to carry out and will thus relieve the supervisor of these duties.

4. *Detachable tickets*. If production is repetitive, a ticket can be prepared which accompanies each item. Each ticket will bear the job number of the product, the serial number of the individual item (if applicable) and a list of the operations through which the product will pass. The ticket will be fixed to the product as part of the first operation and, as each operation is completed, the operator will sign the appropriate portion of the ticket and detach it, placing it in a box designated for that purpose. This box is emptied at least daily by the progress clerk, and the results prepared by analysing these tickets. For fast-moving work this can be very useful, since the operator is involved in very little work. A disadvantage is that the tear-off portions can become lost.

5. *Walk-and-count*. This is the most primitive method of all, and relies on the progress chaser's walking round his own sphere of activity and counting the work seen. It would be most unwise to rely solely on this method of collecting information, since it can be very tedious and inaccurate if carried out continuously.

The information obtained above is necessary for the production control department to carry out its duties. It must be pointed out, however, that the information is very similar to that required by the costing department and the wages department if an incentive bonus scheme is in use. If possible, the bonus cards should be used to provide progress information, since they will tend to be filled in promptly and accurately. Organizationally, the turn-round of information must be very rapid since both the progress and the bonus departments require it at the same time. Often these cards go first to the progress section which, after abstracting the required information, will pass them on to the bonus section.

Volume

The volume of information obtained is particularly great when items are being batch produced. Job production clearly presents little difficulty in this respect, while flow production can be considered to be single operation production, where again volume is not so difficult. Furthermore, flow production has the advantage that any difficulties are immediately brought to notice since they affect the whole system.

Batch production not only presents the most difficulty but also has the greatest need for feedback of information. Two methods for reducing the volume of data are suggested below:

1. *Key points.* In any processing sequence there will be found to be a number of key points arising from either the processing method itself or from the geographic layout of the department. Such key points are often found to be inspection or verification points. If information is obtained only at these points, then it will be possible to localize problems without pinpointing them. This type of short-cut will reduce the volume of information considerably, though at the same time sacrificing some detail.

2. *Complete batch.* During manufacture it is found that there is a temptation to move each item of a batch on to the next location as soon as it has been processed. This is particularly so if the batch is 'urgent'. This can result in a batch being spread throughout the whole organization and, as a consequence, information will need to be obtained about each item. If, however, the batch is kept complete, the volume of information is much reduced, since a single return will give all that is required. Moreover, this will also simplify other aspects of production administration, for example material issue and control, and loading. When batches are expected to move through departments at a regular rate, then colour coding can offer the potential of identifying deviations from this regular pattern.

The use of the computer

Computers can play a major role in the areas of dispatch and progress as part of a production control system. If this system is being used to produce a schedule, covering both the resources (operators and facilities) and materials, then much of the information required by the dispatcher is available from the system. The load calculations can be used as a guide to determine the timing of the work to actually release, and the system can actually be used to produce much of the documentation to accompany this release: job cards, route cards, material requisitions, and so on. Use of the computer can significantly improve the quality of this documentation, particularly in the areas relating to legibility and provision of adequate instructions. Indeed, this can go as far as the paperwork which ultimately reaches the customer.

The computer system can also provide the facilities to analyse the data on the progress of the work through the departments. However, it is just as dependent as the clerical systems on accurate and timely feedback of this data. Early systems mimicked manual procedures, relying on keying into the computer once a day information from the job cards returned from completed work. The computer could process the data much faster, but still relied on the operator to accurately fill in the card and speedily return it on completion of the work. With the availability of systems offering on-line real-time access, it has become possible to allow the operator to directly feed back to the computer information on completed work and, if appropriate, to see details of the future load and outstanding work. In this way the computer should always have an accurate and up-to-date picture of the status of all work. Developments in data-capture devices have significantly improved this aspect. The *bar code* is having a significant impact here (see Fig. 27.1).

PROD + OPS MNGMNT 5E

ISBN 0-273-02873-1

9 780273 028734

Fig. 27.1 A bar code

When producing documentation for the release of work, this can include a printed bar code which enables the computer to subsequently identify the job. An operator can then simply use a bar-code reader to quickly and accurately feed back information to the computer on the status of the job as it goes through different sections. Depending on circumstances, this information can be stored locally and part-processed before being fed back to the production planning system, or can effectively be fed directly back. It is claimed that using bar codes, data can be entered three times faster than using a skilled keypunch operator, and that while manual data entry using keyboards might generate one error every 300 characters, with high-quality bar codes the figure is one error in 300 million characters scanned. These, then, offer significant potential to the progress function to overcome the fundamental problems.

Presentation of progress information

The information collected by the progress department will provoke action only when it shows that some task is *not* proceeding according to plan. It is necessary therefore to present the information in such a manner that deviations from plan are made immediately and urgently observable. This is most easily done with the aid of charts or graphs, though the accountant's device of changing the colour of the figures presented can be used.

The type of graph chosen will depend upon the use to which the information is to be put. Broadly, however, charts may be considered as being of two types: (*a*) individual charts, showing some single aspect of operations; and (*b*) overall charts, showing the progress of interrelated functions.

Individual charts

If the output of a single operator, process or department is required to be scrutinized and compared with plan, it can be shown up very readily by means of a cumulative graph. For example, suppose that the planned and actual outputs from allocation are as shown in the following table:

	Output			
	Planned		Achieved	
Day	Daily	Cum.	Daily	Cum.
1	4		4	
2	5	9	4	8
3	6	15	7	15
4	7	22	8	23
5	8	30	9	32
6	8	38	8	40
7	8	46	7	47
8	8	54	8	55
9	8	62	7	62
10	8	70	7	69
11	9	79	8	77
12	10	89	8	85
13	11	100	8	93
14	12	112	9	102
15	13	125		
16	14	139		
17	13	152		
18	12	164		
19	11	175		
20	10	185		
I	II	III	IV	V

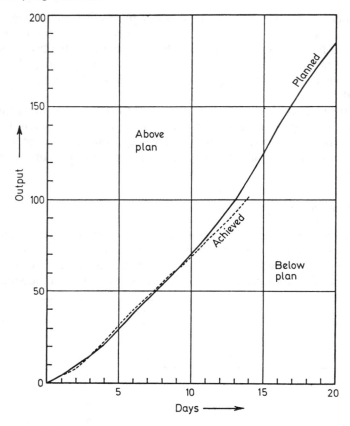

Fig. 27.2 Cumulative output

Examination of daily outputs (columns II and IV) will not readily reveal the failure to meet the plan: the cumulative figures (columns III and V) do in fact show the failure, but if these figures are represened graphically (Fig. 27.2), then the failure becomes more striking. This can be readily understood at all levels, and is very simple to construct and interpret. Care is needed in the choice of scales, but no difficulty will be found after a little practice. This type of graph is ideal for representing output and, with experience, can be very versatile.

Overall-charts

When a number of interrelated functions have to be represented simultaneously, the single line graph is inadequate. Two or three graphs can be drawn on the same axes—beyond this number, the graph becomes cluttered and difficult to interpret. Furthermore, the relationship between various features is difficult to represent. For this reason it is necessary to use some other visual representation, and the most common is the Gantt chart.

When scheduling, it was seen that the simplest method of planning a complex series of functions was to use a chart relating time with required performance. Thus, if operation A is required to start on the fifth day and finish on the fourteenth day of a sequence, while operation B starts on the ninth day and finishes on the twentieth of the same sequence, the chart should be as follows:

DAY	1	2	3	4	5	6	7	8	9	10	11	12	13	14	15	16	17	18	19	20
OPERATION A																				
OPERATION B																				

This shows clearly the interrelation between operations A and B as far as requirements go. The length of the bar represents time: if now it is also assumed to represent performance, the chart will be able to be used to show the relation between actual and planned. Assume that at the end of day 9 only 20 per cent of operation A were complete: this would be represented as follows:

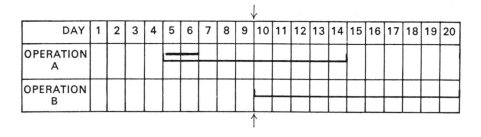

DAY	1	2	3	4	5	6	7	8	9	10	11	12	13	14	15	16	17	18	19	20
OPERATION A																				
OPERATION B																				

The length of the heavy bar represents performance, and it is only 20 per cent of the total length of line A. This shows clearly that operation A is lagging behind target, since after 5 days 50 per cent of the operation should have been completed. On the other hand, assume, that at the end of day 11, operation A was 50 per cent complete while operation B was also 30 per cent complete. This would be represented as follows:

DAY	1	2	3	4	5	6	7	8	9	10	11	12	13	14	15	16	17	18	19	20
OPERATION A					▬	▬	▬	▬	▬											
OPERATION B										▬	▬	▬								

The length of the operation B bar represents 30 per cent of the total length, and since only 25 per cent should have been completed by day 11, it extends beyond the cursor marks.

This simple device, of permitting length to represent both time and performance, is known as a Gantt chart and is widely used in very many applications. By a series of simple annotations, reasons for delays can also be represented, so that the chart can show a comprehensive picture of the state of a department. Most proprietary planning and progress boards are Gantt charts, performance being shown by coloured markers, pegs, tapes or strings; few give information greater than the simple hand-drawn Gantt, although the use of colour may make the representation more vivid, but they often have the advantage of being able to be simply rearranged. Once a hand-drawn Gantt chart requires to be altered, it is necessary to re-draw it—a tedious operation.

Recommended reading

See *Recommended reading* for Chapter 23.

28 Materials assessment

In most organizations the cost of material forms a substantial part of the final selling price of the product. Where the interval between receiving the purchased material and its transformation into profit by selling the completed product is short, then the cost of holding the material is likely to be insignificant. However, material is frequently stored either raw, partly finished or completely finished, and the costs associated with this can be high. There are a number of ways in which these costs can be calculated: it would seem reasonable to consider stock as an investment from which a return is expected. Since no return is forthcoming because the investment, being in materials, is being held like 'cash in biscuit tins under the bed', then these costs can be taken to include the 'loss' represented by failure to earn the expected return. Thus, if company policy requires that any investment should yield a return of 20 per cent of its value each year, then holding stock can be said to cost at least 20 per cent a year of the average value of the stock held. The cost of holding stocks worth £1,000,000 for one year will, therefore, be at least £200,000 when calculated on the above basis. If the money to purchase the stock has had to be borrowed, then the financing charges must be added to the cost.

However great the holding cost as a fraction of the value, it would be unimportant if the value of the stocks held were small. Unfortunately, this is all too frequently not the case. This can be confirmed by consulting any of the government statistics which summarize the various figures (including stock valuation) reported in company balance sheets. Indeed, these summaries are likely to underestimate the true situation since the valuations are frequently taken at one point in time, and it is not unknown for levels to be manipulated to present a more favourable picture.

The task of the materials control department

The materials control department is assumed to be required to maintain an adequate supply of correct material at the lowest total cost. The responsibilities include:

1. Assessing material requirements in agreement with the marketing forecast, and requisitioning that which is required from the buying department.
2. Receiving and storing material safely and in good condition.
3. Issuing material upon receipt of appropriate authority.
4. Identifying surplus stock, and taking action to reduce it.

Buying/purchasing is a function which is not necessarily part of the task of materials control. While it is on occasions claimed that the buyer should be a member of the materials control department, this is largely a matter of local organization and will depend upon, among other things, the value of the material compared to the selling price. For convenience, buying will be treated in a later chapter.

Assessing and requisitioning

Various 'types' of materials may be managed and controlled by an organization:

1. *Raw materials and bought-in items*. These are 'processed' and value added to them to provide the required finished item.
2. *Work-in-progress*. These materials have been part-processed but are not yet in the form required by the customer.
3. *Finished products*.
4. *Service materials*, used in service and maintenance operations, for example cleaning fluid, light bulbs, typewriter ribbons.

Normally, the first and last type are the responsibility of the materials control department. Service materials can be regarded as 'indirect' in that their cost cannot be allocated, but must be apportioned and absorbed by 'cost centres'. Raw materials can be either 'indirect' or 'direct' in that their cost can be allocated.

The responsibility for the management of work-in-progress and finished products may be with the materials control department; equally it could lie with some other section within the organization.

In assessing requirements, it is frequently necessary to forecast usage in the near future. There are a variety of techniques available for this: some are presented in an earlier chapter.

Lead time

A frequently used term in materials management is 'lead time', which may be defined to be the interval between the perception and the fulfilment of a need. Two different but related variants are the procurement lead time and the manufacturing lead time. The former will be dealt with here while the latter will be discussed later. The procurement lead time is not necessarily the same as the delivery time, since it also includes the time required to place 'an order and the time to receive the goods into the appropriate store.

Procurement lead time		
Ordering time	Delivery time	Receiving time

The two components 'ordering' and 'receiving' can be substantial. It is frustrating but not uncommon for an operations manager to raise a purchase requisition and then to discover two weeks later that the purchase order has not been dispatched. Equally, it is not unknown for a buyer to 'phone a supplier to enquire about an apparently late delivery only to discover that it had arrived two weeks ago, but had not been cleared through 'goods inward inspection'.

The cost of this uncertainty in the lead time can be significant, not simply in terms of the annoyance, but because of the higher than necessary stock levels which are frequently maintained to allow for it. These first and last components are within the control of the organization and their careful management can reduce the uncertainty.

Methods of generating purchase or manufacturing orders

There are two broad methods whereby purchase or manufacturing orders are generated. These depend on whether the behaviour of the item of stock itself is being examined (stock point generation)—the independent demand situation—or whether the consequences of an order for finished goods is explored (order point generation)—the dependent demand situation. Order point is an ideal in that stock should be precisely matched to needs. However, the sheer volume of data to handle with this approach can sometimes be prohibitive, unless a computer is used. ABC or Pareto analysis (see Appendix 1) can be carried out on the items stocked, ranking them by average value of annual usage, to establish how the effort in controlling them should be allocated. Materials requirements planning is one method of managing dependent demand items, and will be discussed later in this chapter.

Stock point generation

The trigger which causes the authorization of further purchases of stock, in this case, is the behaviour of the stock itself. Since this decision does not directly depend on the orders placed for finished goods, it is some-times said to be an independent demand system. There are a number of procedures available, details of which can be found in the references. Two of the more common systems will be outlined:

1. *The two-bin or fixed reorder quantity system.* With this, orders are placed when the level of stock has dropped to a previously determined level (the reorder level, or ROL). An order is placed for a, normally, fixed quantity (the reorder quantity or ROQ). The ROL is based on an analysis of the demand and procurement lead time, and it is chosen so that the replenishment order it triggers arrives just as the stock is expected to reach a minimum level. The ROQ is frequently based on economic considerations, one such approach being illustrated later.in this section.

2. *The fixed reorder interval system.* With this, reordering takes place cyclically, that is, an attempt is made to assess the usage and then reorder at fixed intervals of time. The quantity ordered can be either fixed or more usually calculated to bring the stock back to some predetermined maximum level. This cyclical ordering has the advantage that suppliers know well in advance when orders are going to be received; alternatively, if parts are made in the organization's own plant, the production control department can plan machine and labour loads at the beginning of the planning period. It also allows the purchasing department to plan its own work to the best advantage.

Economic batch size

The quantity to be ordered, whether from inside sources or outside suppliers, is dependent on a number of opposing factors. In any purchase or manufacture, there is an element of ancillary cost, either when plant is set up, cleaned or changed over, or when a purchase order is placed. This ancillary cost is spread over the number of items in the batch, and from this viewpoint the larger the batch size, the fewer batches are required per year and the lower the annual ancillary cost. However, with these larger batch sizes, higher average stock levels are held which increases stockholding costs. The calculation of the most economical size of batch to manufacture is extremely difficult involving, among other things, a knowledge of the costs attributable to unused capacity. The purchasing situation, however, is more tractable and the calculation can be usefully carried out.

While all the variations of the basic economic batch size formulation cannot be displayed here, the most commonly performed calculation illustrates the basic concepts. The ancillary cost is, in this case, the marginal cost of raising and servicing an order (the 'purchasing cost') and the simplifying assumption is made that (see Fig. 28.1) the product is

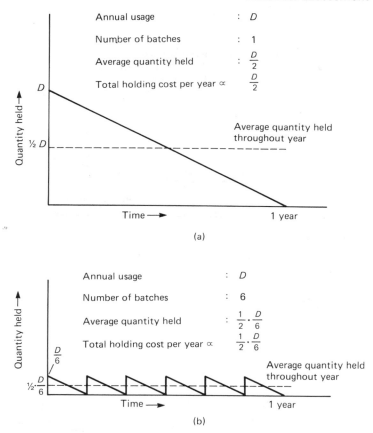

Fig. 28.1 Variation of holding cost with batch size

used uniformly throughout the year. The annual requirement can be either bought in one batch, stocked and used from stock, or it can be bought as a number of batches (six are illustrated), stocked and àgain drawn from stores. In the first case, the average quantity held throughout the year is higher than the average quantity held throughout the year in the second. Consequently, the annual holding cost in the first case is higher than in the second. Since the lead time and requirement are assumed to be constant, stockouts never occur, and there is no stockout cost, so the total annual cost is the sum of the annual holding cost, the annual ancillary cost and the annual purchase cost of the materials. The optimum batch quantity is where the total cost is a minimum, this being known as the economic batch quantity.

This result is illustrated in Fig. 28.2: as the batch size increases, the annual holding cost increases in proportion; whereas if it is assumed that

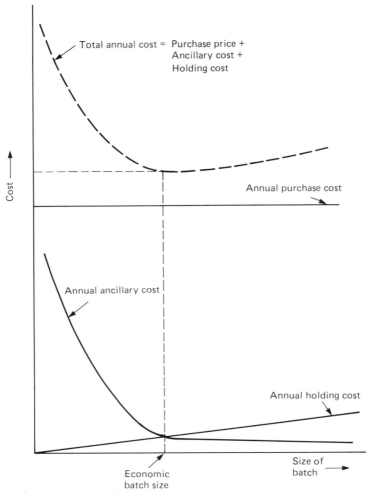

Fig. 28.2 Variation of total cost with batch size

the ancillary cost is constant, independent of batch size, then the annual ancillary cost reduces as the batch quantity increases. The unit purchase price is also assumed constant and independent of batch size, so the total annual cost is the sum of these three components, with the shape of the dotted curve.

The accurate calculation of this economic batch size is difficult, and it has given rise to a number of alternative analyses. These difficulties arise from problems concerning the calculation of the holding cost, since this depends on a number of factors which are difficult to assess, such as the expected return on invested capital, cost of storekeeping, cost of material controlling, wastage, depreciation, obsolescence, insurance, and a number of other factors of varying importance, and from the calculation of the ancillary cost.

The variation of total cost with batch size is illustrated numerically in the following example. As stated earlier, it is assumed that neither unit purchase cost nor ancillary cost vary with the batch size.

Assume purchase price	= £3 each
Assume annual holding cost	= 35% value of goods stocked
Assume purchasing cost for each batch	= £20
Assume annual usage	= 800

Number of batches	Batch size	Average annual quantity stored	Average value of stock	Total annual holding cost	Total annual purchasing cost	Total annual cost (carrying and purchasing cost)*
1	800	400	1,200	420	20	440
2	400	200	600	210	40	250
5	160	80	240	84	100	184
10	80	40	120	42	200	242
20	40	20	60	21	400	421

* For convenience, the fixed annual purchase cost 800 × £3 has been omitted.

The formula for the economic batch size (EBS) Q^* can be shown to be:

$$Q^* = \sqrt{\left(\frac{2SD}{IC}\right)}$$

where S = purchasing cost per batch
   D = annual usage
   I = annual holding cost as a fraction of the stock value
   C = unit price of the item being purchased

Using the values in the example:

   S = £20
   D = 800
   I = 0.35
   C = £3

$$Q^* = \sqrt{\left(\frac{2 \times 20 \times 800}{0.35 \times 3}\right)} = 174.6$$

Let quantity ordered $= Q$

Then number of orders placed per year $= \dfrac{D}{Q}$

And annual purchasing cost $= \dfrac{SD}{Q}$

Average quantity held per year $= \frac{1}{2}Q$

$\therefore$ Annual holding cost $= \frac{1}{2}QCI$

And total annual variable cost T $= \dfrac{SD}{Q} + \frac{1}{2}QCI$

The EBS results from T being a minimum, which occurs when:

$$\frac{\mathrm{d}T}{\mathrm{d}Q} = 0, \text{ and } \frac{D^2T}{\mathrm{d}Q^2} > 0$$

that is, when:

$$-\frac{SD}{(Q^*)^2} + \frac{1}{2}CI = 0$$

that is, when:

$$Q^* = \sqrt{\left(\frac{2SD}{CI}\right)}$$

Note: the above assumes that:

1. The unit purchase price is constant
2. The usage is substantially constant
3. It is not permitted to be out of stock
4. Orders are fulfilled in one delivery
5. Lead time is constant

Derivation of the simple EBS formula

The sensitivity of the EBS

The EBS formula involves a square root and, as a consequence, there can be no guarantee that a 'sensible' result will be produced in relation to purchasing decisions. Indeed, in the earlier example, the formula gave a batch size of 174.6 items! In fact, the total cost curve is normally shallow round the optimum so no serious increase would arise from taking a value of 175. There will always be an element of uncertainty in the cost parameters. Instead of specifying a single value of the batch size, it is possible, after selecting an acceptable allowable percentage increase in minimum total variable cost, to calculate a range for the batch sizes which satisfy this. For the earlier example, if a 5 per cent increase is acceptable, any batch size in the range 127–239 will produce a cost within 5 per cent of the theoretical minimum.

The effect of price breaks on the EBS
It is not unusual for a supplier to offer to reduce the unit purchase price if a minimum quantity is purchased ('. . . if you buy at least 300 units at a time the price will drop to £2.95 each . . .'). The effect of this change in price—the 'price break'—can be seen by comparing the total cost at the EBS at the existing price level and the total cost at the price break level. The total cost curve of Fig. 28.2 then takes the form of Fig. 28.3.

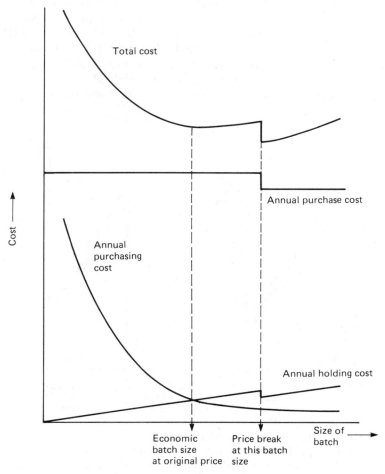

Fig. 28.3

It is also possible to turn the analysis round and answer questions like '. . . What discount must be given on the price of £3 each to result in an order quantity of 500 being preferable to the calculated minimum cost value of 175?'

Insurance or safety stock
The above analysis assumes that the demand and lead time are known and substantially constant; in reality, both are likely to be subject to a mixture of random and predictable variation. In this case, the ROQ can still be estimated using the latest demand forecast as input into the EBS formula.

The ROL is dependent on the number of items expected to be required during the lead time, so in the 'constant' case this causes no problem. In the previous example, if the lead time is given as five weeks, then assuming 50 weeks per year, the ROL is 5 × 16 = 80, and the ROQ of 175 will arrive just as the last unit is used. However, if both the lead time and demand vary, the situation changes: the demand could be higher than anticipated, resulting in a stockout. In setting the ROL it is necessary to have safety stock, in addition to the expected demand in the expected

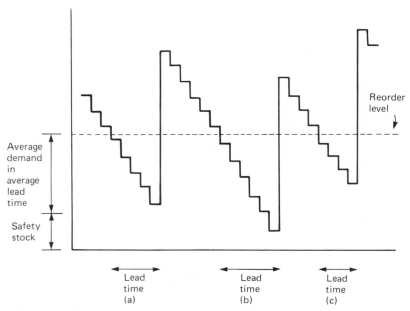

Fig. 28.4 Variable demand in variable lead time
     (*a*) Average demand and average lead time
     (*b*) Higher than average demand, longer than average lead time
     (*c*) Lower than average demand, shorter than average lead time

lead time, to allow for this situation. This is shown in Fig. 28.4. The choice of safety stock level can be related to the risk the manager is prepared to take of running out of stock. This can be viewed in the context of the various costs involved in this, some of which are outlined below:

1. For finished products, this depends on whether the customer is prepared to wait or goes elsewhere for his requirement. It can involve loss of profit, lost goodwill.

2. For raw materials, it depends on the consequences:

(*a*) it may result in idle workers and plant, the cost could be pro- portional to the number of units short and the period of the shortage;

(*b*) production may have to be replanned, a fixed cost largely inde- pendent of the number of items short and the period of the shortage;

(*c*) it may be necessary to buy from an alternative source at a premium price, incurring an additional cost proportional to the number of units short.

The use of safety stock increases the average stock level by this amount, having a consequential effect on the holding cost. If the uncer- tainty can be reduced, the situation can be improved. This can be achieved through a structured collection and analysis of data on demand and lead time, use of forecasting methods, and the tight management of those elements of the lead time which are within the control of the organization.

Order point generation—material requirements planning (MRP)

Stock point generation can operate quite simply and satisfactorily when orders for finished goods are being received at a constant or at least smoothly and slowly varying rate, and this is reflected in the work-in- progress and raw materials requirements. However, when demand for the finished product is lumpy or erratic, then stock point generation may involve holding stocks of work-in-progress or raw materials for excess- ively long periods of time. Under these circumstances if can be desirable to use some form of control of purchasing and manufacturing which is derived from an examination of the orders received for the finished goods. One such form of control is known as material requirements plan- ning or MRP, and since the control depends upon the order for the finished products, the procedure is said to be one of 'dependent demand'.

The approach is best illustrated with a short example concerning a small plant which makes furniture, specifically wooden-framed chairs and two-seat settees. The chair is shown in Fig. 28.5. The method of manu-

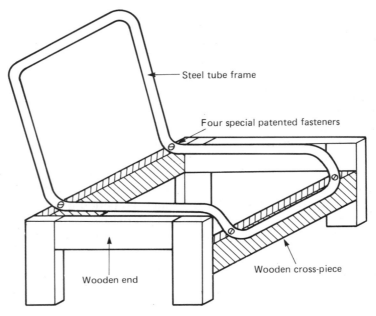

Steel tube frame

Four special patented fasteners

Wooden cross-piece

Wooden end

Fig. 28.5 Wooden-framed chair

facture and materials for both products are very similar: wood (nominally 3 cm by 9 cm) is used to make two ends and two cross-pieces joining the ends. A frame to support the cushions is made from steel tube, rubber webbing and fabric which matches the cushions. Seat and back cushions are made from this fabric and foam chippings. Special patented fasteners are used in the final assembly.

Each seat cushion requires 0.60 metres of fabric and 450 grammes of foam. Each back cushion requires 0.70 metres of fabric and 550 grammes of foam. The chair has one of each type of cushion, the settee two. The end pieces, which are common to both products, each require 2.20 metres of wood, while the cross-piece for the chair is 0.50 metres long, and for the settee 1.10 metres long. The metal frame for the chair uses 3.00 metres of tube, 3.00 metres of webbing and 1.40 metres of fabric; for the settee the figures are 6.00, 6.00 and 2.80 respectively. Four of the special fasteners are used in the assembly of the chair, six in the assembly of the settee.

The relationship between the finished product, its constituent parts and the raw materials can be shown in a product structure diagram, or bill of materials (BOM). This 'parts explosion' is shown in Fig. 28.6 for the chair. Level 0 traditionally refers to the finished product; in this example, there are only two other levels: level 1—sub-assemblies; and level 2—raw materials.

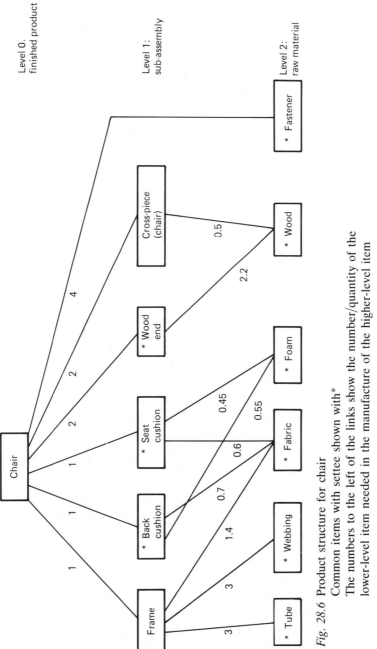

Fig. 28.6 Product structure for chair

Common items with settee shown with*

The numbers to the left of the links show the number/quantity of the lower-level item needed in the manufacture of the higher-level item

Item code	Item description	Unit of measure	Quantity on hand	Lead time	Safety stock
0–0000–01	Chair	each	25	1	20
0–0000–02	Settee	each	30	1	20
1–1200–01	Wood end	each	50	2	0
1–2000–02	Cross-piece — settee	each	65	1	0
1–1000–03	Cross-piece — chair	each	70	1	0
1–2000–04	Metal frame — settee	each	25	2	0
1–1000–05	Metal frame — chair	each	5	2	0
1–1200–06	Seat cushion	each	45	2	0
1–1200–07	Back cushion	each	45	2	0
2–4500–01	Webbing	metre	50	3	50
2–1230–02	Wood	metre	65	2	100
2–4567–03	Fabric	metre	95	3	50
2–6700–04	Foam	kilo	110	2	50
1–1200–08	Fastener	each	98	1	200
2–4500–05	Steel tube	metre	84	2	50

- An order for 100 metres of wood is due to arrive at the start of week 3
- An order for 500 fasteners is due to arrive at the start of week 2
- An order for 20 kilos of foam is due to arrive at the start of week 2

- Lead time is weeks to procure for raw materials (level 2)
- Lead time is weeks to manufacture/assemble for levels 1 and 0

Fig. 28.7 Stock status at week 1

It is also necessary to have information relating to the current stock position with respect to all items. This is shown in Fig. 28.7.

It is currently week 1, and there are orders for 200 settees for week 8, 350 chairs for week 9, and 100 replacement seat cushions for week 7. These requirements are 'exploded' down through the bills of materials, and the implications for the sub-assemblies and raw materials assessed.

This process starts with the level 0 items: in general the gross requirements (GR) are taken, and the net requirements (NR) calculated taking account of the on-hand stock (OH), the orders due (OD) and the required safety stock (SS). The planned orders (PO) are then the NR offset by the lead time, known as 'time phasing'. The PO for the level 0 items provide the basis of the GR for the level 1 items, taking account of the product structure diagram, and the process repeats for all the level 1 items, cascading down the levels.

For chairs,   GR = 350 (week 9)
                       NR = GR − OH − OD + SS = 350 − 25 + 20
                       = 345 (week 9)
                       Since the lead time is 1 week, PO = 345 (week 8)
For settees,   GR = 200 (week 8)
                       NR = GR − OH − OD + SS = 200 − 30 + 20
                       = 190 (week 8)
                       Since the lead time is 1 week, PO = 190 (week 7)

Cascading down to the level 1 items, *all* should be considered, but for the purposes of this illustration only cushions will be considered.

For back cushions,   (1) GR = 190 × 2 = 380 (week 7)
                       (resulting from the PO for 190 settees in week 7, each settee requires 2 back cushions)
                       NR = GR − OH − OD + SS = 380 − 45 = 335 (week 7)
                       Since the lead time is 2 weeks, PO = 335 (week 5)
                       (2) GR = 345 (week 8)
                       (resulting from the PO for 345 chairs in week 8)
                       NR = GR − OH − OD + SS = 345 (week 8)
                       PO = 345 (week 6)
For seat cushions,   (1) GR = 190 × 2 + 100 (week 7)
                       (resulting from the PO for 190 settees in week 7, each settee requires 2 seat cushions, plus order for 100 replacements)
                       NR = GR − OH − OD + SS = 480 − 45 = 435 (week 7)
                       Since the lead time is 2 weeks, PO = 435 (week 5)
                       (2) GR = 345 (week 8)
                       (resulting from the PO for 345 chairs in week 8)
                       NR = GR − OH − OD + SS = 345 (week 8)
                       PO = 345 (week 6)

When all level 1 items have been analysed, it is possible to cascade down and consider all level 2 items. For the purposes of this illustration, only foam will be considered.

For foam,   (1) GR = 335 × 0.55 + 435 × 0.45 = 380 (week 5)
                       (resulting from the PO for 335 back cushions in week 5, each requiring 0.550 kilos of foam, and PO for 435 seat cushions in week 5, each requiring 0.450 kilos of foam)
                       NR = GR − OH − OD + SS = 380 − 110 − 20 + 50 = 300 (week 5)
                       Since the lead time is 2 weeks, PO = 300 (week 3)

(2) GR $= 345 \times 0.55 + 345 \times 0.45 = 345$ (week 6)
(resulting from PO for 345 back cushions in week 6, and PO for 345 seat cushions in week 6)
NR $=$ GR $-$ OH $-$ OD $+$ SS $= 345$ (week 6)
PO $= 345$ (week 4)

These calculations can be seen summarized in Fig. 28.8, each block

	Time period (week)								
	1	2	3	4	5	6	7	8	9
Chair (safety stock = 20)									
• on hand	25	25	25	25	25	25	25		
• orders due									
• gross requirement									350
• net requirement									345
• planned orders								345	
Settee (safety stock = 20)									
• on hand	30	30	30	30	30	30			
• orders due									
• gross requirement								200	
• net requirement								190	
• planned orders							190		
Back cushion									
• on hand	45	45	45	45					
• orders due									
• gross requirement							380	345	
• net requirement							335	345	
• planned orders					335	345			
Seat cushion									
• on hand	45	45	45	45					
• orders due									
• gross requirement							480	345	
• net requirement							435	345	
• planned orders					435	345			
Foam (safety stock = 50)									
• on hand	110	130							
• orders due		20							
• gross requirement					380	345			
• net requirement									
• planned orders			300	345					

Fig. 28.8 Partial MRP calculation

being referred to as the 'material requirements plan' for the item concerned.

It is sometimes argued that safety stock need not be used in MRP. However, it is sometimes incorporated into the finished product stock levels to allow for uncertainty in the requirements. Scrap, rework and uncertainty in manufacturing lead times are sometimes used to justify safety stocks of sub-assemblies. Uncertainties in procurement lead times are sometimes quoted as reasons for raw materials safety stocks.

The overall structure of the MRP system is summarized in Fig. 28.9.

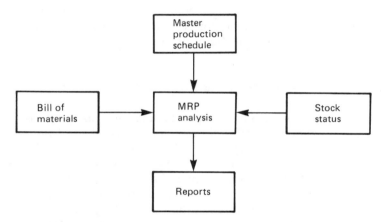

Fig. 28.9 MRP structure

The three major inputs are the bill of materials for all level 0 products (illustrated in Fig. 28.6), stock status information for all items (including lead time; basic data illustrated in Fig. 28.7) and the master production schedule (MPS). It is normal to have a forecast of the requirement for each level 0 item (finished product) for each time period over the planning horizon (rather than the single requirements in the earlier illustration): this forms the gross requirement for the level 0 items, and is called the master production schedule.

In the illustrations presented above, the calculations were trivial. In practice, however, there may be many level 0 items, each having a product structure with hundreds of parts at levels 1, 2 and so on; these structures may have many common items. The plan may extend over a number of periods. The calculations cease to be trivial, and substantial computing facilities are required. Moreover, significant volumes of data need to be stored. The basic reports include the material requirements plans for each item, summaries of planned orders, stock status, and the ability to trace materials back to the level 0 items in which these are used, and relate this to the net requirements. Many computer packages are available for MRP, running on a wide range of sizes of computer. These offer the user the ability to re-run the analysis as circumstances (requirements, manufacturing capacity, time) change. In fact, if products are analysed into A–B–C categories on cost of usage, it can be possible to carry limited 'what if' MRP type analysis rapidly for the 'A' items using a spreadsheet on a microcomputer.

The importance of accurate input data cannot be stressed enough. Sales forecasts forming the MPS must be as good as possible, inventory transactions must be routinely incorporated into the stock status data, and product changes must result in modifications to the product structure data. Many of the problems reported with the implementation of MRP have data inaccuracy as contributory factors.

Manufacturing resources planning (MRP II)

The basic MRP procedures simply handle the materials aspects of production/operations control. No real account is taken of the resources available, apart from the inclusion of the manufacturing lead times in the analysis. Indeed, these are normally assumed to be constant, independent of the quantities being manufactured and other factors likely to influence them. MRP has been 'extended' in a number of directions. Rough-cut capacity planning is incorporated at the start, linking with the MPS. This can be used to evaluate the implications of the MPS for resources at the aggregate (department/section) level. There is no point in working with a MPS which places impossible demands on the manufacturing resources. This enables the MPS to be replanned or extra resources made available where necessary. The MRP is used to produce both detailed capacity plans and detailed materials plans, which in turn are implemented enabling shop-floor control and purchasing control to be carried out. A simplified overview is shown in Fig. 28.10. An essential element of this is the feedback of information, relating to manufactured items, purchased items and so on. This 'model' can now be used for much more than planning manufacture as it now contains much of the information necessary to plan and run the organization. It is possible to evaluate the effect of decisions in many of the other functional areas: financial factors and cash flow, marketing decisions and sales, and engineering/research and development. This is the essence of manufacturing resources planning (MRP II).

Clearly there are similarities between MRP/MRP II and just-in-time (JIT), in that both approaches aim to produce/purchase items only when they are required. JIT is a manual system whereas MRP/MRP II is generally computer-based. MRP/MRP II *pushes* the requirements for

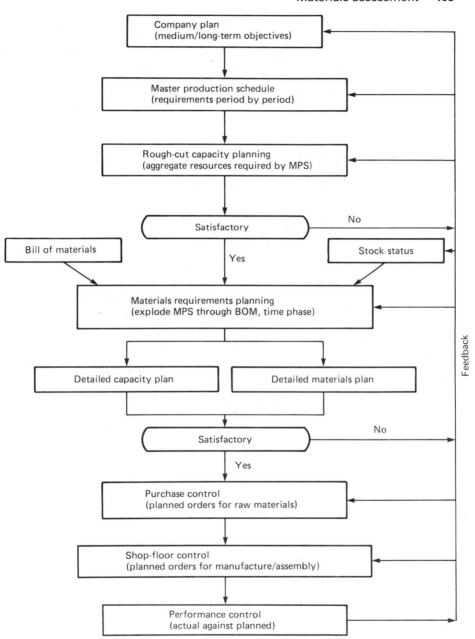

Fig. 28.10 Simplified MRP II

finished items back through the manufacturing process and, using lead times, generates works orders and purchase orders. JIT uses a *pull* approach whereby when there is a requirement for parts at one stage, these are pulled from the earlier work centre, generating a requirement to manufacture at that stage. This process repeats itself down through the manufacturing chain, pulling production forward right back to purchasing.

Recommended reading

Dudick, T. S. and Cornell, R., *Inventory Control for the Financial Executive*, Wiley, 1979.

Looks at stock control from a somewhat broader perspective, but including much material of interest to the production/operations manager.

Love, S. F., *Inventory Control*, McGraw-Hill, 1979.

A comprehensive coverage of a variety of models with emphasis on those which are most readily applicable. Rather mathematical.

Orlicki, J., *Material Requirements Planning*, McGraw-Hill, 1975.

The first authoritative treatment of time phased material requirements planning. Many examples and illustrations are used to show exactly how an MRP system works.

Vollman, T. E., Berry, W. L., and Whybark, D. C., *Manufacturing Planning and Control Systems*, Irwin, 1984.

Covering the latest developments in this area (including JIT, OPT, MRP, MRP II), as well as the basic concepts. Recommended.

British Standards Institution, *Guide to Stock Control* (BS 5729), 1981.

A five-part guide covering the management of stock control, demand, assessment, replenishment of stock, data processing and storekeeping.

29 Materials management

Materials control documents

There are three major documents in any manual materials control system, namely:

1. *The materials (or stores) requisition.* This is a document which requires the stores department to issue material. It should bear at least the following information:

(*a*) date of origin;
(*b*) originator's identification;
(*c*) cost location;
(*d*) material required, preferably with its code or part numbers;
(*e*) quantity of material required;
(*f*) material issued;
(*g*) quantity of material issued;
(*h*) date issued;
(*i*) issuer's identification;
(*j*) receiver's identification.

Depending upon the use to which the requisition is put beyond that of an issuing device, the materials requisition can also bear cost information (that is the cost of the material issued) and stock control information.

2. *The purchase requisition.* This is a request to the buyer to purchase material, and may be originated by any department. There is usually a restriction on those signing purchase requisitions (for example, heads of department only may be allowed to sign them) and the bulk of them should originate from the materials control department.

These requisitions should bear the following minimum information:

(*a*) date of origin;
(*b*) originator's identification;
(*c*) cost location;
(*d*) material required with full specification;
(*e*) quantity required;
(*f*) date by which it is required;

and under no circumstances should the entries be vague: thus the description 'as previously supplied' should not be used, nor should the date of requirement be 'as soon as possible'. These requisitions may be the only information upon which the buyer acts, and he must not be handicapped by lack of information. In some organizations, purchase requisitions involving purchase of capital equipment require to be sanctioned by the board or a nominated director, while in others all requisitions involving spending sums of money greater than a specified amount must be countersigned by designated persons.

3. *The stock record card*. This is the central record within the material control area. The information for each item can be thought of as falling into four broad areas:

(a) Issues	— date	
	— works order number	
	— quantity issued	
	— balance	
(b) Purchases	— date of order	
	— purchase order number	
	— quantity ordered	
	— delivery date	
	— quantity delivered	
	— price	
(c) Allocation	— date allocated	
	— job number	
	— quantity	
	— date issued	
(d) General	— description	
	— code number	
	— unit of measure	
	— minimum level	
	— maximum level	
	— order quantity	

Each time a transaction occurs, it is posted against the appropriate areas (a), (b) or (c), and the adjustment made against the balance.

The above list is not exhaustive and will have to be tailored to local circumstances. For example, some organizations may not use an allocation system—'earmarking' stock for a particular job before actually issuing it to the job. Some types of items go into 'quarantine' on arrival in stock, only to be free for issue when some tests have been successfully completed. Sometimes it is necessary to be able to trace the materials issued to a job back to a particular delivery (lot-traceability). Stocks of some items may be held at several locations. Various different costing options may be required.

Other materials control documents

As well as the major documents listed above, there are others which are often used, for example:

1. *A materials return* or *credit note*, which permits unused material to be returned from the manufacturing department to the stores.

2. *A materials transfer note*, which allows material to be transferred from one location to another or from one job to another.

3. *A scrap note*, which records the scrap generated and permits it to be handed in to the stores in exchange for good material. This usually requires to be countersigned by an inspector.

4. *A shortage note*, which is issued from the stores to a requisitioner, informing him that material required is not available and citing the action being taken.

The stock record information can be held on a computer. If an integrated package is used, the production control module might access the stock record information to generate the materials requisitions, and the stock control module could produce the purchase requisitions. However, it is stressed that it is imperative that a detailed specification is produced for a potential computer application, identifying *all* the data to be stored and the transactions to be handled. Generally, manual systems are cheaper to modify after implementation than computer systems; moreover, the data is more 'visible' with a manual system. A very wide variety of 'off-the-shelf' computer packages is available for stock control.

Carrying out a materials reduction programme

The stock valuation figure should include all stock except that which has been declared valueless and 'written off'. Often the so-called valuable stock includes much that is of little or no real worth despite the valuation placed upon it, and the authors recall a factory where one-third of the total stock was worthless due to obsolescence, over-ordering, incorrect ordering and similar causes.

Despite the lack of worth, the storage and 'annoyance' costs may be substantial, and any reduction in stock can have substantial real benefits, some of which are:

1. Holding costs will be reduced.

2. Floor space will be available for manufacture rather than for storage.

3. More cash will be available for use in other ways.

4. Reduction in administration and clerical effort.

The following technique is suggested as one which has been usefully used in carrying out a materials reduction programme:

1. Carry out an A–B–C analysis (see Appendix 1) of the value of stock held against the number of items of stock. This can either be done from the auditor's stock valuation sheets or from the materials control cards; some computer-based stock management systems include the facility to carry out this analysis.

2. From the analysis, decide on the A, B and C categories, the A items being those few which represent the bulk of the value, the C items being those many items of trivial value, and the B items being those of moderate value between A and C. *Note*: if there are too many items to handle conveniently, select 100 at random, carry out a Pareto analysis on this sample, and hence determine the A–B–C boundaries appearing; for example:

A items—total value of £1,000 or more
B items—total value between £100 and £999
C items—total value less than £100

If this sampling is used, then as records are handled to record transactions, they are examined and 'flagged' appropriately.

3. Examine the 'A' group to determine:

(*a*) dead items—those which have not been used for two years;
(*b*) slow-moving items—those which have been used in the last two years but have not moved in the last six months;
(*c*) current items—those used within the last six months.

(*Note*: the definitions of these categories will vary from company to company and will depend upon the technology of the company concerned.)

4. Test the 'dead' items against the following:
(*a*) can they be used in place of current stock?
(*b*) can they be transferred into current stock?
(*c*) can a demand for them be predicted or stimulated?

If the answer to all the above is 'no', then the items should be written off and sold or given away. The arguments that they 'will come in useful one day' or 'we can't afford to get rid of them' are specious and must be resisted vigorously. Particularly frustrating is the 'policy' which limits the value of stock that may be written off in any one financial year so that, for example, no more than a total of £1,000 can be written off in a year, whatever the circumstances. Such a policy is neither useful nor prudent, and serves only to mislead the shareholders.

5. Repeat (4) for slow-moving items.

6. Test the 'current' items against the following:

(*a*) Is the coverage $= \dfrac{\text{Units available}}{\text{Average units used/Unit time}}$

excessive? If so, then some part of the stock should be treated as 'dead' stock.

(*b*) Can the unit price be reduced? Try (i) value analysis, (ii) work study of the manufacturing methods, (iii) alternative suppliers.

(*c*) Can any item be made common with or interchangeable with other items? A good coding system is invaluable here.

(*d*) Can the lead time for any item be reduced? The shorter the lead time (that is, the time between the decision to place an order and its subsequent fulfilment) the lower the average value of stock which may be held. It may be that a supplier, hitherto discarded on price, may benefit the purchaser on grounds of a shorter, and more predictable, delivery.

(*e*) Is the authority to purchase appropriately controlled? Where there are large numbers of orders to be placed, the authority to sign them is often given to assistant buyers and buying clerks. Item 'A' purchases are often better authorized only by senior members of the organization. The resulting inconvenience in getting such orders signed will, in itself, tend to discourage demands and purchases.

(*f*) Is the stock-holding reviewed frequently enough? A perpetual inventory causing second stock checks of 'A' items can be of assistance here.

7. Repeat the above for 'B' items.

8. To try to carry out the above for 'C' items is usually quite impossible, since the number of items is likely to be extremely large and the rewards obtained small. 'C' items, therefore, should be scrutinized only when stock cards are withdrawn for normal recording purposes. When (7) above is completed, the whole process should be started again.

The above procedure will certainly reduce the obesity in the stores, and may even result in some cash inflow from the sale of surplus stock although this should not be considered to be the prime purpose of the programme. On the other hand, supplementing the above by a reduction in stock purchases can result in valuable financial gain, since the savings in cash will be real and immediate. A reduction in stock purchases of 5 per cent out of a total of £100,000 will immediately release £5,000, whereas a reduction of 5 per cent in a work content of £100,000 may only result in a saving of £1,000, due to the inability to use less than a complete person, and by a general ability of supervisors to use all the time available on jobs other than direct production jobs.

Materials specification and numbers

For a control system to be effective, all material should be accurately and unambiguously described; that is, it should be specified. The responsibility for making this specification is usually upon the designer, who should be in a position to detail the requirements of his design. This matter has been discussed in detail in Chapter 10. At the same time, all material should be given a number in order that it can be easily and unequivocally referred to. The design of a code numbering system is of great importance to the efficiency of the organization as a whole; here it is only necessary to say that every code number should be unique, that is, that it should refer to one type of material only. The importance of the choice of a code numbering system is so great that it is considered in some detail in Chapter 5.

Storekeeping

Storekeeping is an important aspect of materials management and, for the purposes of this volume, the storekeeper will be assumed to be responsible not only for the stores but also for the goods inwards or receiving department. This is not invariably so: in some cases it is combined with goods inwards inspection and made a part of the inspection department, while in others it is part of the purchasing organization or the materials control department.

Duties of a goods inwards department

All goods entering a unit should pass through a goods inwards department in order that their arrival should be recorded. The duties of this department are:

1. Recording the receipt of (or 'booking-in') all goods in a ledger often known as a goods received (GR) book. This is effectively a simple list of goods recorded as they arrive, and it is not a record of goods received against the order authorizing them.

2. Unpacking all goods and checking them against the originating order both for quantity and quality. While the qualitative checks can only be carried out by goods inwards inspection, which is part of the inspection department, the work itself will certainly be geographically located within the receiving area.

3. Returning all defective goods to the suppliers responsible. These should be covered by a reject note, giving the reason for the rejection. This note will originate in the goods inwards inspection department, and

is either sent off by the goods inwards department with the goods or passed to the purchasing section for onward transmission. In either case, it is imperative that a copy of the rejection note is passed to the buyer.

4. Informing the purchasing and materials control departments of the receipt of all goods. This is conveniently done by means of a goods received note (GRN), a copy of which can be used to transfer goods to the next location—for example, stores.

5. Returning all chargeable packing to the supplier.

---

1. Receiving and recording all deliveries
2. Unpacking and checking against orders
3. Returning defectives
4. Circulating statements of receipts
5. Returning chargeable packing

Usual duties of a goods inwards department

Duties of a storekeeper

Organizationally, the responsibility for the stores may be in the hands of the accountant, the buyer or the materials controller. Furthermore, the duties of the storekeeper also vary greatly with the company concerned: in some organizations the storekeeper is virtually a materials controller, keeping comprehensive records and raising all purchase requisitions, while in others the storekeeper has no tasks beyond the receiving, storing and issuing of goods. Whatever the organizational situation, care must be taken to give the position its due importance.

It is assumed here that the stores is part of the materials control department, and that the duties of the storekeepers are:

1. Receiving and storing in good order and condition all goods including raw materials, purchased parts and components, and partly manufactured items. This may involve a routine handling of material—for example, tins of paint often require to be inverted monthly. Special regulations are in force governing the storage of certain chemicals, spirits and cellulose paints, and detailed information on this topic should be obtained from the local factory inspector.

2. Issuing goods against authorized requisitions only. The storekeeper should never issue material (except for such items as have been declared 'free issue') without a requisition signed by a duly authorized person.

3. Marshalling goods against sets of documents. It is frequently convenient for the storekeeper to assemble together all the materials required for a particular works order. This material can then either be issued against a summarized materials requisition or against a single pack containing all the individual documents. Stores are often provided with

special 'job' trolleys on which the marshalled goods are placed for subsequent issue.

4. Maintaining such records as may be required of him. This matter is dealt with in more detail later.

5. Carrying out any physical stock-taking as necessary. This also is dealt with later.

---

1. Receiving and storing all goods
2. Issuing goods against authorized requisitions
3. Marshalling goods against sets of documents
4. Maintaining appropriate records
5. Physically checking stock

Usual duties of a storekeeper

Stores records

A knowledge of exactly what material is available is essential to the running of the production control department and, accordingly, a stock records section is always part of, or very closely associated with, that department. From the records held therein it must be possible at all times to know accurately the stock in stores. Similar records are sometimes maintained in the stores itself in the form of bin cards. These are cards placed in the store bin itself, recording the movements of stock held in the bin. In the absence of a properly maintained stock record card the bin card is essential, since it will be the only statement of stock in the company. However, if a stock control department is functioning properly, then the bin card is an unnecessary and confusing device which takes up some considerable time on the part of the storekeeper. It is argued that the bin card is a simple means whereby the stock records can be checked, but this is an admission of weakness which should not be tolerated. A better method of ensuring the accuracy of stock is by carrying out a perpetual inventory, and if this is in being then the stores need not carry bin cards. Increasingly, stock records are maintained on computer files, access to them being by means of remote terminals.

Stock-taking

Stock needs to be correctly recorded not only in order that the unit may be run efficiently, but also in order that the trading results shall be calculated accurately. When goods are continually being moved in and out of the stocks it is inevitable that inaccuracies creep in and, though a control account held by the costing department might indicate probable errors in total, it is clearly necessary to minimize the effect of mistakes. This is normally done by carrying out a stock-taking, stock check or inventory, when a physical count of stock is taken and the results checked against the entries on stock record cards. Errors found are investigated and, if necessary, alterations are made to the records to bring them into line with the actual stock. Stock checks can either be carried out annually (at the end of the company's trading year) or continually throughout the year, a few items being checked each day.

Annual stock-taking
Even in a small organization the taking of an annual stock is a big undertaking likely to occupy a substantial number of man-hours. For this reason it is imperative that all goods must be immobilized, and it is therefore usual to carry out the annual stock-check over a weekend or during a holiday, when operations are not proceeding. To ensure that the whole operation is carried out expeditiously, it must be very carefully planned. Instructions to all personnel (many of whom will not normally be associated with the stores) must be issued in writing and in as great a detail as possible. Cards or lists of material should be pre-typed, leaving only the minimum clerical work to be done during the stock-taking.

Perpetual stock-taking
A perpetual inventory involves much less disorganization and is much simpler to organize than an annual stock-taking. Briefly, each day a number of items are checked so that by the year's end the whole stock will have been counted two or three times.

One method of organizing a perpetual inventory is as follows:

1. Withdraw all internal stores records (bin cards). This will prevent a storekeeper copying the quantities from the bin cards on to the stock-check lists, a temptation which is great when the storekeeper is hard pressed or the items very difficult to check. As pointed out above, bin cards serve no useful purpose if the stock record cards are correct.

2. Daily, the material control clerk presents to stores a list of items to be checked. This can be handwritten on a standard form, the part number, description and location being filled in by the stock controller, the storekeeper having only to fill in the quantity found, his signature and the date checked.

3. The storekeeper completes the form and returns it to the materials control department each day.

4. The materials controller checks the stock found against the record card and immediately causes significant discrepancies to be investigated. The stock record card is marked with the date and result of the stock check, and this figure becomes the basis for all future action.

A technique such as the above has the advantage that the choice of item to be checked is in the hands of the materials control department, who will be able to ensure that any items requiring special care are checked frequently. If the choice is left to the storekeeper, items which were easy to check might be verified frequently while difficult items might be overlooked. In large organizations the checking of stock might be a sufficiently large task to permit the full-time employment of one person. This person (sometimes called a stores auditor) would be a member either of the materials control or the accounts departments, and not a storekeeper. Such an independent check not only has a psychological advantage, but it is likely to be acceptable to the company's auditors, who would probably admit the results if incorporated in the company's financial statements.

Advantages of a perpetual inventory
1. No dislocation of stores or operations.
2. It is cheaper than an annual inventory, since the work is usually part of the stores' staff's normal activities and will occupy so little time during a day that it can be carried out during any quiet periods.
3. Results are produced more quickly: during an annual check the comparison of actual with recorded stock may take some considerable time, during which stock movements may confuse the results.
4. Important items can be checked as frequently as desired: stock record cards are likely, therefore, to be more accurate than in the case of the annual inventory.

Recommended reading

Crompton, H. K., *Supplies and Materials Management*, Macdonald and Evans, 1985.
    This book is intended for all staff involved in supplies and materials management. Its scope is wide, including purchasing provisioning, stock control, administration, properties of materials, handling.
Jessop, D. and Morrison, A., *Storage and Control of Stock*, Pitman, 1986.
    This text describes in detail stock control and storage from the elementary principles and simplest manual methods to the most sophisticated automated operations.
Lewis, C., *Managing with Micros*, Blackwell, 1986.
    A practical and interesting little book with a chapter on stock control.

30 Critical path analysis

The operations manager, even in a flow-production factory, is frequently concerned with 'one-off' or 'job production' tasks, which will include:

Maintenance programmes
Overhaul procedures
Installation of new plant, or processes
Laying out, or re-laying out, workshops
Testing equipment or systems
Designing and making operating aids

For the planning and control of these, and any similar tasks with an identifiable start and finish, critical path analysis can be used.

Critical path analysis (CPA) is one form of network analysis, and it is by far the most commonly used. In essence, the activities in any task are represented by *arrows*, and inter-relationships are shown by the positioning of one arrow relative to another. This arrow representation of activities gives rise to the generic name, 'Activity-on-Arrow' (A-on-A) networking. Alternative but closely associated forms represent the activity by a box (or 'node'), and these systems bear the family name, 'Activity-on-Node' (A-on-N) networking. This chapter will discuss CPA extensively, and briefly explain A-on-N systems.

The basic elements of CPA

Every task must have a recognizable beginning and an end in order to be susceptible to CPA planning. These two points in time are represented by two 'nodes' (usually drawn as circles), and the constituent parts of the task (the 'activities') are drawn as arrows located somewhere between the start and the finish nodes. The start and finish of any activity, or group of activities, is also represented by a node circle, and the dependency of one activity upon another is shown by the dependent activity emerging from the node at the head of its preceding activity. These nodes are sometimes called 'events'.

Consider, for example, the problem of moving one piece of plant (X) to a new site, and installing in its place another piece of plant (A). The first step is to define the starting and finishing situations.

Start. The project will be considered to start when the budget for removing and relocating X and A, and obtaining any associated material handling equipment and tools, has been agreed.

Finish. The project will be considered to be completed when X and A are in position, tested and ready to run.

These definitions will then enable two simple arrows to be drawn, as in Fig. 30.1.

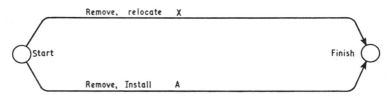

Fig. 30.1

The 'Remove, relocate X' arrow can be considered to comprise four activities:

Clear site for X
Remove X
Re-install X
Test X

Of these, 'clear site' must precede 'Remove X' since X must be placed somewhere once moved. Similarly, it can only be re-installed when removed, and testing must follow re-installation, so that the single arrow would break into a chain of four, as in Fig. 30.2.

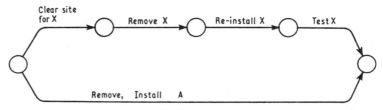

Fig. 30.2

The 'Remove, install A' activity can be considered to comprise activities:

Remove A
Install A

Test A
Obtain tools for A
Obtain associated material handling equipment

Here again, 'test', 'install' and 'remove' follow each other. However, the act of obtaining tools for A does not depend upon A at all—it can start as soon as the budget is approved, that is, at the START node, but it must be completed before testing can start. The material handling equipment is similarly not dependent upon anything but budget approval (that is, START), and does not influence testing or installation, the only requirement being that it must be available when A is ready to run—that is, by FINISH, so the diagram develops as in Fig. 30.3.

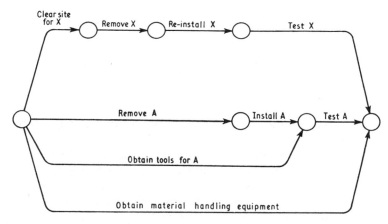

Fig. 30.3

A closer examination of this diagram indicates that A is installed without its site having been prepared so there is an activity 'Prepare site for A', which is missing. A is going to occupy the site previously used by X and thus the activity 'Prepare site for A' cannot start until X is removed, and it must be complete before A can be installed. See Fig. 30.4.

Dummy activities

The fundamental convention used in drawing the network is that if one activity must follow another they will be shown as in Fig. 30.5.

In some situations a 'dummy' or 'dummy activity' is used to avoid ambiguities and illogicalities, a 'dummy' being an activity which *shows only a dependency*—it requires neither time nor resources. For example, if the act of 'Prepare site for A' generates rubbish which must be cleared,

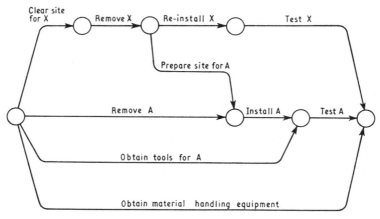

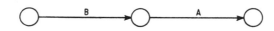

Fig. 30.4

Fig. 30.5

an activity 'Cart rubbish' would need to be drawn emerging from the head of 'Prepare site for A', but to draw it as in Fig. 30.6 would indicate that 'Cart rubbish' depended on both 'Prepare site for A' *and* 'Remove A', and since the rubbish arose from the act of 'Preparing the site', not the act of 'Removing A', this is an unnecessary restriction. A dummy can be inserted, as in Fig. 30.7, which removes the false dependency, and shows 'Cart rubbish' depending only upon 'Prepare site for A' and *not* upon 'Remove A'. A dummy is an activity of zero duration, and is usually drawn as a 'broken' arrow. The complete network can be seen in Fig. 30.8.

A dummy may also be needed to remove the ambiguity which arises from two activities having the same start and finish—for example, in Fig. 30.9 two activities ('Obtain tools' and 'Obtain materials') have the same head and tail nodes. If these nodes are numbered, then both activities have the same head and tail numbers—they are *both* activity 2–3. To release this ambiguity a dummy is inserted at the beginning or end of either activity—see, for example, Fig. 30.10.

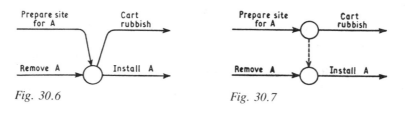

Fig. 30.6   *Fig. 30.7*

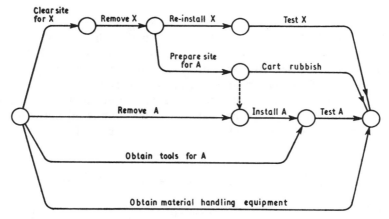

Fig. 30.8

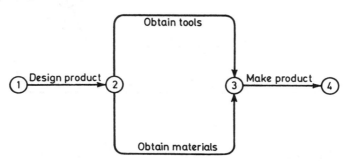

Fig. 30.9

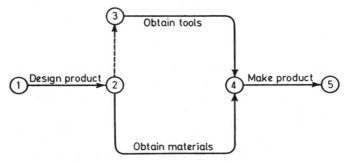

Fig. 30.10

Activity times

The network so far shows only the *logic*—that is, the necessary techno-logical requirements—of the project. To this must be added the times required for each activity, and these are shown as subscripts to the activity arrows. Dummy activities require no time, and by convention no subscripts are added to them. Numbers are inserted in the nodes to permit simple reference to the activities. The completed network, with duration times and node numbers, is shown in Fig. 30.11.

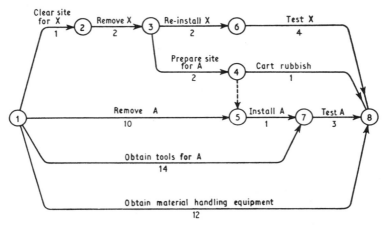

Fig. 30.11

Analysis of the network

The total time for the whole task is found by carrying out a *forward pass*, that is, by adding activity times together, starting at the first node. The 'spare' time available in any activity is then deduced from a *backward pass*, when activity times are subtracted in succession from the total project time.

The forward pass
In essence, the forward pass determines the earliest times at which activi-ties can start. Assume that the present time is written as time 0. The earliest time at which any activities emerging from the first node can start is 'now' and this is shown by an E = 0 at event 1.

Note: this does not imply that *all* the activities leaving event 1 *must* start at time 0, but that they *may* start at time 0.

The earliest time at which activity 2–3 may start is $0 + 1 = 1$, hence E = 1 at event 2. The earliest time at which activities 3–4 and 3–6 may start is $1 + 2 = 3$—hence $E = 3$ at event 3. Events 4 and 6 will both have times $E = 5$. Activity 5–7 cannot start until activity 4–5 is completed—at time $5 + 0 = 5$—and activity 1–5 is finished—at time $0 + 10 = 10$. To satisfy both activity constraints the later time (10) is necessary, so that $E = 10$ appears at event 5. By a similar argument, the earliest time by which activity 7–8 can start is 14. The total project time will permit all entering activities to finish. Thus:

> Activity 6–8 can finish by time $5 + 4 = 9$
> Activity 4–8 can finish by time $5 + 1 = 6$
> Activity 7–8 can finish by time $14 + 3 = 17$
> Activity 1–8 can finish by time $0 + 12 = 12$

and the earliest time which allows *all* these to finish is time 17—hence $E = 17$ at event 8, so that the total project time is 17.

The backward pass
In the backward pass, the latest possible time for the completion of each activity is determined. Assuming that the total project time of 17 is acceptable, then all final activities must be finished by time 17, and an $L = 17$ is written at the final node. If activity 6–8 must finish by time 17, then activity 3–6 must finish by time $17 - 4 = 13$, and an $L = 13$ is written at event 6. Similarly, $L = 14$ will appear at event 7, and $L = 13$ at event 5. Activity 3–4 must finish by such a time that activity 4–5 finishes at time 13, and activity 4–8 at time 17, so the latest finishing time for activity 3–4 must be time 13. Similarly, activity 2–3 must satisfy activities 3–4 ($13 - 2 = 11$) and 3–6 ($13 - 2 = 11$)—hence $L = 11$ at event 2. The latest possible time by which all the activities can start is:

> for activity 1–2 time $9 - 1 = 8$
> for activity 1–5 time $13 - 10 = 3$
> for activity 1–7 time $14 - 14 = 0$
> for activity 1–8 time $17 - 12 = 5$

and for all activities considered together, the smallest of the above, that is, time 0, and $L = 0$ is entered at event 1.

Calculation of activity times
Every activity now has two limiting times associated with it—the earliest starting time, given by $E =$ at its tail node, and the latest finishing time, given by $L =$ at its head node, so that in effect activity i–j is bounded by two times:

> E_i = the earliest starting time
> L_j = the latest finishing time

This can be seen in Fig. 30.13.

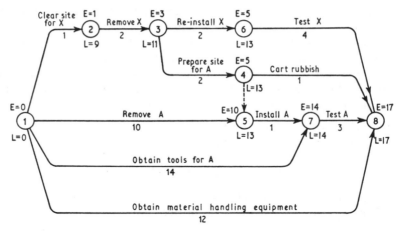

Fig. 30.12

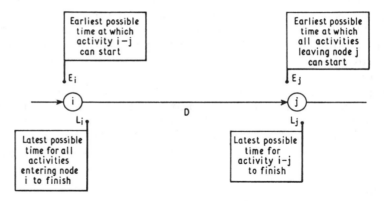

Fig. 30.13

Knowing the duration D, it is possible to carry out the following calculations:

$E_i + D$ = the earliest finishing time
$L_j - D$ = the latest possible starting time

or, diagrammatically, as in Fig. 30.14

The activity can thus slip or 'float' from an early position to a late position, the amount of float being shown by the hatching.

The float is calculated as follows:

$$\text{Float} = L_j - E_i - D$$

or in words:

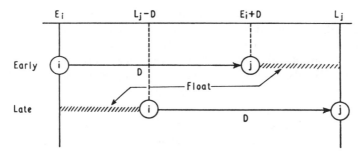

Fig. 30.14

> Float = Latest finish − Earliest finish

or:

> Float = Latest start − Earliest start

or, if $L_j - E_i$ is defined as the *time available*, and D is defined as the *time required*:

> *Float = Time available − Time required*

With these calculations, it is possible to construct the following table:

Nos.	Activity		Start		Finish	Float
	Description	*Durn.*	*Early S*	*Late Early S*	*Late*	
1–2	Clear site for X	1	0	8 1	9	8
2–3	Remove X	2	1	9 3	11	8
3–6	Re-install X	2	3	11 5	13	8
6–8	Test X	4	5	13 9	17	8
3–4	Prepare site for A	2	3	11 5	13	8
4–8	Clear rubbish	1	5	16 6	17	11
4–5	Dummy	0	5	13 5	13	8
1–5	Remove A	10	0	3 10	13	3
5–7	Install A	1	10	13 11	14	3
1–7	Tools for A	14	0	0 14	14	0
7–8	Test A	3	14	14 17	17	0
1–8	Obtain material handling equipment	12	0	5 12	17	5

Note: The columns headed *S* refer to scheduled times, and these will be determined later.

In the above table two activities (1–7 and 7–8) have no float, so that any changes in their duration times will affect the total time for the whole project. Hence, these activities are 'critical' in that they determine total time, and the sequence of critical activities is known as the *critical path*.

In some situations the project is given a 'target' or 'acceptable' time, and in this case the backward pass will start with this target time. Under these circumstances the critical path may itself have float (*positive* float if the target time is greater than the final E = figure, *negative* float if the target time is less than the final E = figure). Criticality is measured by the size of the float:

> The critical path in a network is that
> path which has least float

Reduction of total project time

The total project time can only be reduced by reducing the total length of the critical path. This can be done by using the critical examination technique of the work study engineer (Chapter 17) and/or by changing the logic, that is, changing some of the decisions inherent in the network. It must be remembered that if the reduction in the critical path is *greater than* the next lowest value of float, a new critical path is created. Thus, if activity 1–7 is reduced by more than 3 units of time—to, say, 10—then the sequence 1–5–7–8 forms a new critical path, the original one now becoming non-critical in part.

Representing the network as a bar chart

The network can be translated into a bar chart in a number of ways. One method is to 'square' the network as in Fig. 30.15, and the similarity between this representation of the project and the original arrow diagram is sufficiently great to make a description of a method of drawing unnecessary. In drawing this or any other form of bar chart it is useful to remember that the node numbers effectively describe the logic of the situation, so that any activity whose tail number is M *must* follow *all* activities whose head numbers are M.

The bar chart representation is very useful in three ways:

(*a*) it illustrates the physical meaning of float;
(*b*) it is often more readily understood than the arrow diagram;
(*c*) it can be used to assist in the disposition of the various resources used in the project.

Resource allocation

In most situations, the resources available are limited, and it is obviously essential to see that the resources required are never greater than those

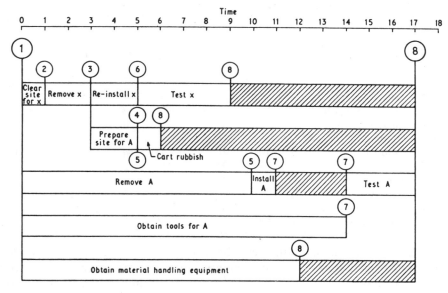

Fig. 30.15

available, as pointed out on page 347. Critical path analysis, while not resolving this situation uniquely, provides useful assistance in achieving an acceptable solution, since it shows which activities can be 'moved' without increasing the total project time, and also the effect of moving time-limiting activities. In the project so far considered, there are two 'removal' activities:

Activity 2–3   Remove X
Activity 1–5   Remove A

Assume that both of these are going to be carried out by the same gang, then, as drawn in Fig. 30.15, *two* gangs are required during days 2 and 3, and if only *one* gang is available, then Fig. 30.15 represents an impossible situation. However, it will be observed that both activities possess float (activity 2–3, 8 days, activity 1–5, 3 days), so that either can be moved. To start activity 2–3 after activity 1–5 has finished would increase the total project time by 1 day, but to start activity 1–5 after activity 2–3 has finished would use up float, but would not increase total time. Hence, the removal gang must carry out the sequence 'Remove X' then 'Remove A'. This would mean that the earliest and latest start and finish times would disappear—the activities concerned would be 'scheduled'—the analysis table appearing:

Nos.	Activity Description	Durn.	Start Early	S	Late	Finish Early	S	Late	Float
1–2	Clear site for X	1	~~0~~	0	~~9~~	~~1~~	1	9	~~8~~ 0
2–3	Remove X	2	~~1~~	1	~~8~~	~~3~~	3	11	~~8~~ 0
3–6	Re-install X	2	3		11	5		13	8
6–8	Test X	4	5		13	9		17	8
3–4	Prepare site for A	2	3		11	5		13	8
4–8	Clear rubbish	1	5		16	6		17	11
4–5	Dummy	0	5		13	5		13	8
1–5	Remove A	10	~~0~~	3	~~3~~	~~10~~	13	~~13~~	~~3~~ 0
5–7	Install A	1	~~10~~	13	~~13~~	~~11~~	14	~~14~~	~~3~~ 0
1–7	Tools for A	14	0		0	14		14	0
7–8	Test A	3	14		14	17		17	0
1–8	Obtain material handling equipment	12	0		5	12		17	0

This type of manipulation can be very difficult if there are a large number of activities and a large number of resources, as the number of possible 'moves' increases factorially with the number of activities. To allow a systematic procedure to be followed, a set of decision rules must be generated. These rules, which will differ from organization to organization, will not necessarily produce a 'best' or 'optimum' solution, but they will tend to produce 'feasible' or 'workable' solutions in a reasonable time.

Decision rules for resource allocation

All sets of rules depend upon resolving a 'conflict' for resources by means of arbitrary decisions. For example, if two (or more) activities require more resources than are available, a *conflict* is said to exist which is resolved by, perhaps, awarding the resources to the activity which has least float, then to the activity which has the next smallest value of float, and so on. If conflict still exists, then resources are awarded to the activity with the greatest work content, and so on, down through a ladder of rules. It is not possible to prove that any one set of rules produces a better answer than any other set, and the rules quoted below, though they have an intuitive appeal, are derived from R. L. Martino's work and are quoted only as an example of one possible set of rules. Other sets may be more appropriate in particular circumstances.

Control using CPA

Control upon the progress of a task can be exerted in basically two ways:

(*a*) by using a derived bar chart and marking 'achievement' against 'plan';

When conflict for resources arises, award resources according to the following rules:

First priority	in order of float
Second priority	in order of work content
Third priority	in order of size of resource
Fourth priority	in order of priority of resource
Fifth priority	in order of latest finish date
Sixth priority	in order of 'j' number

Rules for resource allocation following R. L. Martino

(*b*) by inserting into the network the actual activity time and examining the effect upon float.

The detailed working out of either method will be found in any of the more advanced texts. In many cases, the simplest method is to compare actual finish dates with the L = figure on the network. For complex or frequently checked networks, a computer re-run ('update') with actual rather than estimated activity times may be appropriate, particularly if there is ready access to the computer.

Activity-on-node networking

In A-on-N systems, an activity is represented by the node, and the arrow is used to denote only dependency. The subscript to the arrow, in the most commonly used A-on-N system, gives the dependency time—that is, the time which must elapse between the *start* of one activity and the *start* of the next. This eliminates the need for dummy arrows, and simplifies the representation of overlapping activities (see Fig. 30.16).

The forward and backward passes in A-on-N systems are carried out in precisely the same way as in CPA. The result of the forward pass is unchanged—it gives the earliest starting time of the activity. The backward pass, however, gives the *latest starting time* of the activity, *not* the latest finishing time. The example used earlier in this chapter is shown drawn as an A-on-N network in Fig. 30.17.

All the manipulations described for conventional CPA can be carried out in A-on-N networking. The main advantage of A-on-N is its freedom from dummies, which newcomers to the subject sometimes find difficult. On the other hand, more arrows are generated, and the diagram may be found to be rather more difficult to read. In practice, neither system appears to have overwhelming advantages, and the choice between them seems largely a personal one. Computer programs to deal with A-on-N are readily available commercially.

SITUATION	C.P.A.	A-o-N.
Activity B depends on Activity A	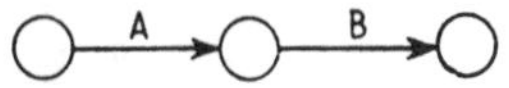	
Activity C depends on Activities A and B	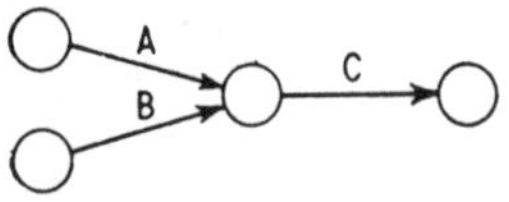	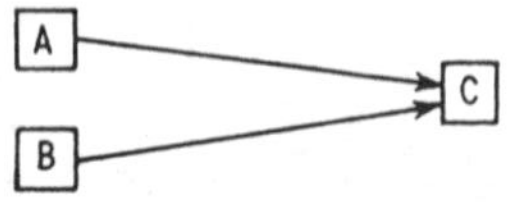
Activities C and D depend on Activities A and B	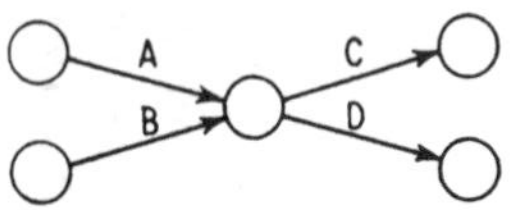	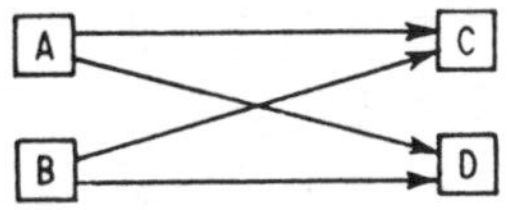
Activity C depends on Activity A; Activity D depends on Activities A and B	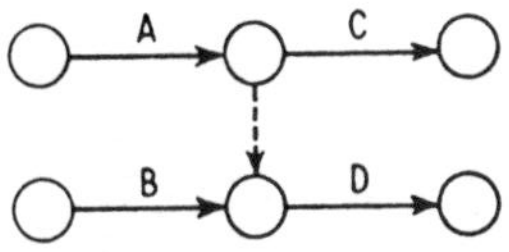	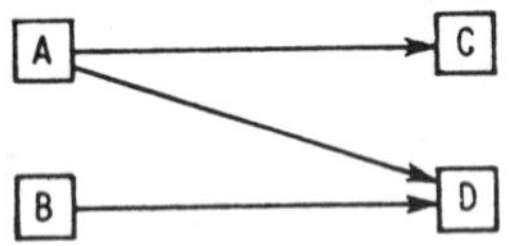
Activity K depends on Activity A; Activity L depends on Activities A and B; Activity M depends on Activities A, B and C	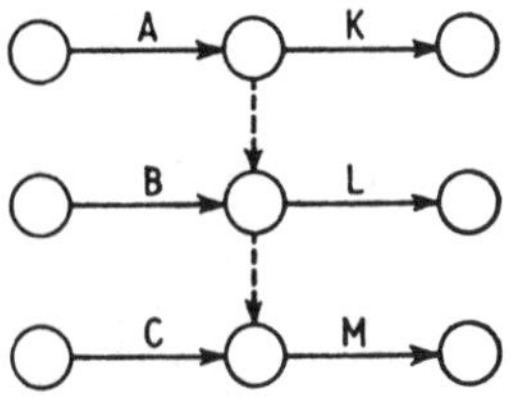	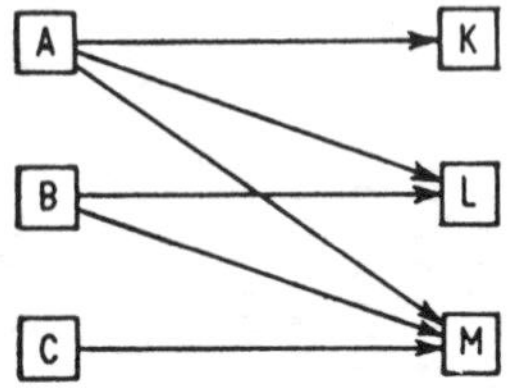

Fig. 30.16

SITUATION	C.P.A.	A-o-N.
Activity B, which must follow Activity A, may not start until D units of time have elapsed after the completion of A.	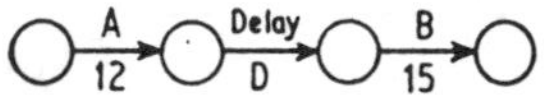	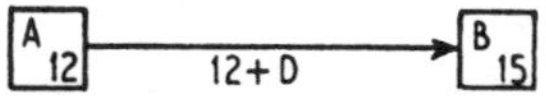
Activity B must not start until at least R units of time have elapsed after the start of activity A.	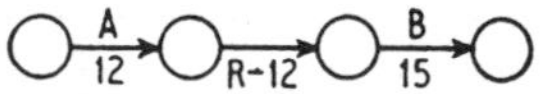	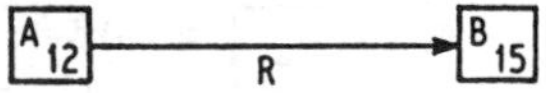
The interval between the completion of A and the start of B must not exceed X. *Note*: This is Roy's 'Negative Constraint.'	NOT POSSIBLE	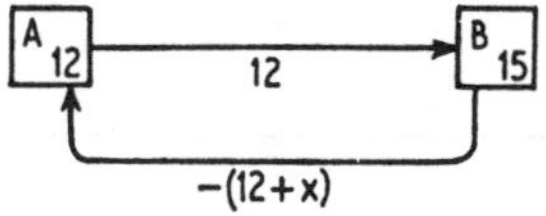
Activity A and Activity W are both opening activities; Activity A may start at the beginning of the project; Activity W must not start until time T has elapsed after the start of the project.	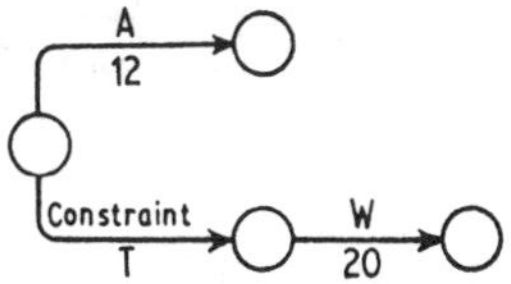	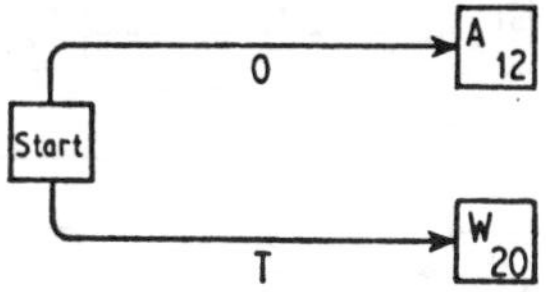

Fig. 30.16 (cont'd)

SITUATION	C.P.A.	A-o-N.
Activity B can start immediately Activity A is complete.	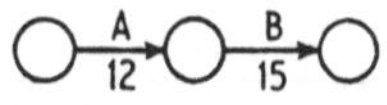 A 12, B 15	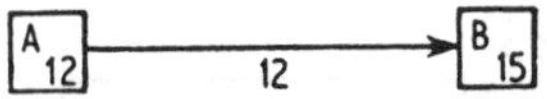 A 12 → 12 → B 15
Activity B can start immediately Activity A is complete and Activity C can start when part p of Activity A is complete.	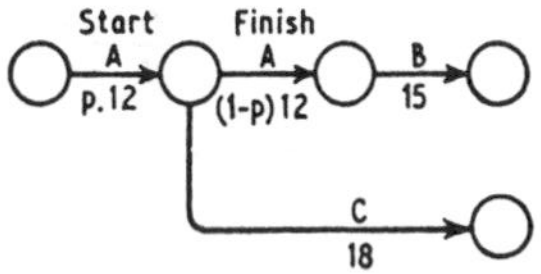 Start A $p.12$, Continue–Finish A $(1-p)12$, B 15, C 18	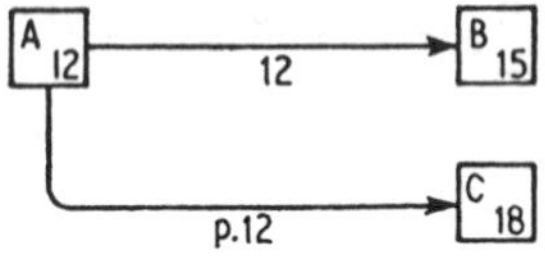 A 12 → 12 → B 15; A → $p.12$ → C 18
Activity B can start when part p of Activity A is complete; Activity C can start when part r of Activity B is complete; Activity B requires at least s.15 time to finish after the completion of A, and C requires at least v.18 to finish after the completion of B.	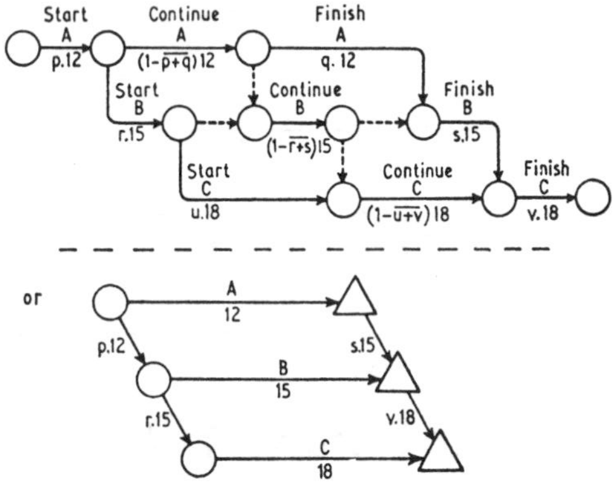 Start A $p.12$; Continue A $(1-\overline{p+q})12$; Finish A $q.12$; Start B $r.15$; Continue B $(1-\overline{r+s})15$; Finish B $s.15$; Start C $u.18$; Continue C $(1-\overline{u+v})18$; Finish C $v.18$	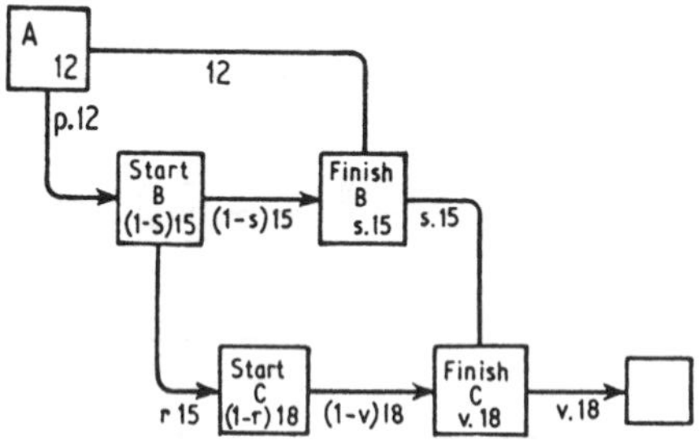 A 12 → $p.12$ → Start B $(1-s)15$; Start B $(1-s)15$ → 12 → Finish B $s.15$; Start B → $r.15$ → Start C $(1-r)18$; Start C $(1-r)18$ → $(1-v)18$ → Finish C $v.18$; Finish B $s.15$ → Finish C $v.18$

or

A 12 → $p.12$ → B 15; B → $r.15$ → C 18; B $s.15$; C $v.18$

Fig. 30.16 (cont'd)

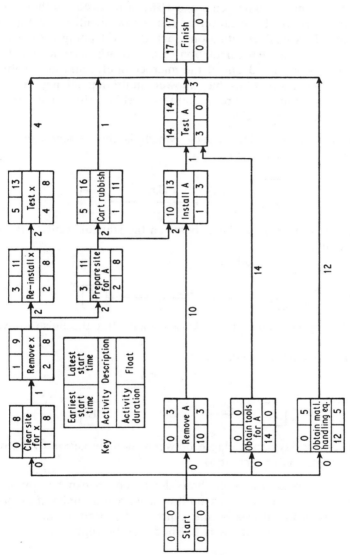

Fig. 30.17 Activity-on-node representation of Fig. 30.11

Multi-dependency A-on-N networking

As discussed above, the arrow used in A-on-N networking shows only one dependency, namely the interval between the start of one arrow and the start of the next. Some years ago IBM introduced another variation of A-on-N whereby the location of the arrow signifies the top of the dependency. This enables situations such as overlapping activities to be easily drawn, but manual calculation of a network becomes much more tedious. However, the advent of the microcomputer and its capability of handling complex situations has allowed multi-dependency A-on-N to become a very straightforward method of working. Essentially, there are three different dependencies:

1. The start-to-start dependency, which is the dependency used in single dependency A-on-N:

Here, at least β days must elapse between the start of Activity B and the start of Activity A.

2. Finish-to-start dependency.

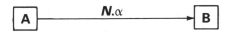

Activity B may not start until at least α days after the finish of Activity A.

3. Finish-to-finish dependency.

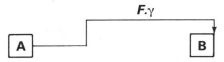

Here, at least γ days must elapse between the completion of Activity A and the completion of Activity B.

In an overlapping situation, these dependencies can be combined so that if Activity B may not start until at least α time units after the start of Activity A, while at least γ time units are required for the completion of Activity B after Activity A is finished, can be represented by:

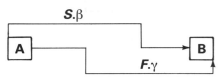

The computer and networking

It would be an act of extreme foolishness for any person to write his/her own CPA program. There are very many highly versatile and simple programs which are available from both software and hardware houses and it is difficult to imagine a situation where one of these would not be acceptable. Anybody needing a program is advised to consult the manufacturer of the microcomputer which is being used and ask for advice of compatible program.

Recommended reading

Battersby, A., *Network Analysis for Planning and Scheduling*, Macmillan, 1972.
   Clear and stimulating but now dated.
British Standards Institution; *Glossary of Terms Used in Project Network Techniques* (BS 4335).
   Very useful. Aims to standardize the terminology and symbols used in PNT.
   Much information on PNT can be obtained from microcomputer software houses. Two companies which have been extremely helpful are:

Claremont Controls Ltd.,	and	Abtex Software Ltd.,
Albert House,		11, Campus Road,
Rothbury,		Listerhills Science Park,
Morpeth, Northumberland,		Bradford,
England, NE6 57S		England,
		BD7 1HR.
(the 'Harnet' system)		(the 'Pertmaster' system)

Lockyer, K. G., *Critical Path Analysis and Other Project Network Techniques*, Pitman, 1984.
   Probably the most comprehensive and up-to-date book on CPA published in the UK. Contains examples for the reader to work through. A solutions manual is available.
Woodgate, H. S., *Planning by Network*, Business Books, 1977.
   Comprehensive. Discusses A o A, A o N, multidependency A o N, resource allocation and cost control.

31 Line of balance

Historically, line of balance (L-o-B) was developed before critical path analysis (CPA), and the two approaches are often considered to be separate but related techniques. Both are applied to 'jobs' which are made up of a number of activities with complex interdependencies. However, it will be seen that if the original time-scaled stage-time diagram is abandoned, then L-o-B can be viewed as a quite conventional CPA system applied to a single-batch situation.

Where L-o-B can be used

Just as CPA is used to schedule and control a single job or project, L-o-B can be used to schedule and control a single batch (of the same job). The following requirements need to be satisfied:

(*a*) there must be identifiable stages in production at which managerial control can be exerted;
(*b*) the manufacturing times between these stages must be known;
(*c*) a delivery schedule must be available;
(*d*) resources can be varied as required.

While it is possible to use L-o-B to control a number of separate batches, just as it is possible to use CPA to control a number of separate projects, the computational difficulties become great. It is, therefore, usual to use L-o-B in single-batch situations where the batch concerned is of some considerable importance to the organization. An estate of houses, a batch of computers, a batch of guided weapons, are examples of the type of work likely to be appropriate to L-o-B control.

L-o-B: an example

The application of L-o-B will be illustrated by the following simplified example.

A sailing dinghy is manufactured as follows: The hull is bought in, materials to manufacture the interior fittings are purchased, these fittings are then made, and then fitted into the hull to make the basic shell. Materials to construct the mast, rigging and so on are purchased, this manufacture carried out, and then the mast assembled with the basic shell. Material for the sails is bought, the sails made, and fitted to the shell and mast to complete the manufacture of the dinghy. The final assembly stage can be considered to include the act of delivering the product to the customer.

The delivery schedule is as follows, with the first delivery in the week ending 1 January:

Week number	1	2	3	4	5	6	7	8	9	10	11	12	13
Quantity		2	4	8	12	10	18	20	22	18	10	8	2	2

Total = 136

Step 1. Construct a CPA diagram to show the logic and timing of the production. It will usually be found most convenient to start to draw this from the end (in this case, final assembly of the dinghy), and work towards the various opening activities. The network need not be closed at the start—multiple starts are quite permissible and useful here—and nodes need not necessarily be identified, although for convenience here, letters are used. Duration times are those required for unit production: these times are maintained constant during production by variation of resources. The CPA diagram is shown in Fig. 31.1.

Step 2. Carry out a reverse forward pass from time 0 at the final event (K), that is, assign to the final node a time 0, and then successively add duration times for each activity in order. This will give the set of figures marked against each node, 2 at J, 4 at I, 7 at H, and so on.

Node times. While node times represent the latest possible finishing times for the various activities, it is probably more useful to consider these times in relation to the quantities which would pass through the head nodes at any given time. Consider, for example, the activity 'Buy materials for interior fittings'. Each kit of materials purchased and received will subsequently require three weeks to be made into the fittings, three weeks to be fitted into the hull to form the basic shell, two weeks to have the mast and rigging installed, and two weeks to fix the sails and complete the dinghy:

$$3 \quad + \quad 3 \quad + \quad 2 \quad + \quad 2 \quad = 10$$

3	+	3	+	2	+	2	= 10
(make fittings)		(basic shell)		(shell + mast)		(complete dinghy)	

If the completion of the dinghy includes delivery to the customer, then the cumulative sets of materials purchased and received which should

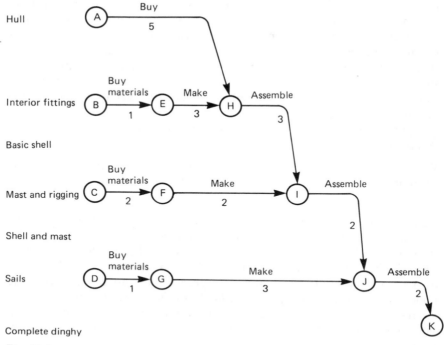

Hull

Interior fittings

Basic shell

Mast and rigging

Shell and mast

Sails

Complete dinghy

Fig. 31.1

'pass through' node E by time t is the cumulative quantity which should pass through node K (i.e. be delivered) by time $t + 10$. For example, two weeks after the start of delivery of complete dinghies to the customer, the total number of kits of materials for interior fittings purchased and received is equal to the cumulative number which should be delivered by week $10 + 2 =$ week 12, that is 134. This node time obtained by the reverse forward pass is called elsewhere the 'equivalent week number' for all the activities entering the node being considered.

Step 3. Rank the activities in descending order of equivalent week number. This ranking gives the activity number—sometimes in L-o-B called the stage:

Activity	Equivalent week number	Activity number
Buy materials: interior fittings	10	1
Buy hull	7	2
Make interior fittings	7	3
Buy materials: mast and rigging	6	4
Buy materials: sails	5	5

Activity	Equivalent week number	Activity number
Assemble basic shell	4	6
Make mast and rigging	4	7
Make sails	2	8
Assemble shell and mast	2	9
Complete assembly of dinghy	0	10

This effectively provides the L-o-B diagram shown in Fig. 31.3.

This can be built up by adding the activities in decreasing activity number, using Fig. 31.2 to give the logical relationships.

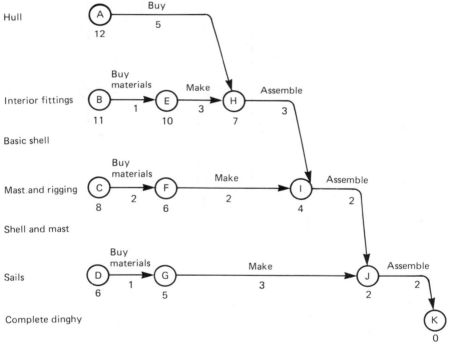

Fig. 31.2

Step 4. Prepare a calendar and accumulated delivery quantity table:

Date	Week number	Quantity	Cumulative quantity
9 October	−12		
16 October	−11		
23 October	−10		
30 October	− 9		
6 November	− 8		

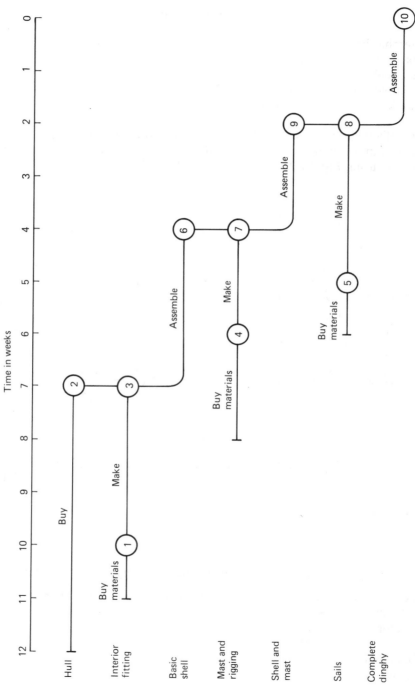

Fig. 31.3

Date	Week number	Quantity	Cumulative quantity
13 November	− 7		
20 November	− 6		
27 November	− 5		
4 December	− 4		
11 December	− 3		
18 December	− 2		
25 December	− 1		
1 January	1	2	2
8 January	2	4	6
15 January	3	8	14
22 January	4	12	26
29 January	5	10	36
5 February	6	18	54
12 February	7	20	74
19 February	8	22	96
26 February	9	18	114
5 March	10	10	124
12 March	11	8	132
19 March	12	2	134
26 March	13	2	136

Step 5. From the above two tables, deduce the quantity of each activity which should be completed by any particular date. For example:

It is now 8 January. How many of each activity should be completed? Consider 'Make mast and rigging'. It is week 2.

The quantity through 'Make mast and rigging' is equal to the quantity which can pass through the final stage in four weeks' time, that is, in week $2 + 4 = 6$. From the table above, this is a total of 54 units. Similarly for all activities:

	Volume of work completed is equivalent to volume delivered at week	Total units
Buy materials: interior fittings	$2 + 10 = 12$	134
Buy hull	$2 + 7 = 9$	114
Make interior fittings	$2 + 7 = 9$	114
Buy materials: mast and rigging	$2 + 6 = 8$	96
Buy materials: sails	$2 + 5 = 7$	74
Assemble basic shell	$2 + 4 = 6$	54
Make mast and rigging	$2 + 4 = 6$	54
Make sails	$2 + 2 = 4$	26
Assemble shell and mast	$2 + 2 = 4$	26
Complete assembly of dinghy	$2 + 0 = 2$	6

This can be represented by the traditional L-o-B chart (Fig. 31.4).

A complete table for the whole 'life' of the batch can be drawn up if desired, and this is shown in Fig. 31.5. The S's in the table indicate the latest dates by which the various chains of activities should *start*,

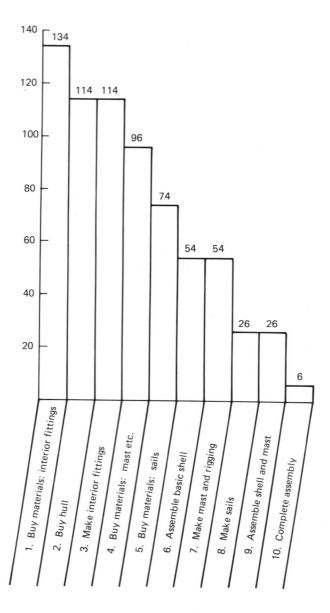

Fig. 31.4

this date being derived from the equivalent week numbers from the opening activities. The C's in the table show that the work must be *continued*.

		Buy materials: interior fittings	Buy hull	Make interior fittings	Buy materials: mast etc.	Buy materials: sales	Assemble basic shell	Make mast and rigging	Make sails	Assemble shell and mast	Complete assembly
−12	9 Oct		S								
−11	16 Oct	S	C								
−10	23 Oct	2	C	S							
−9	30 Oct	6	C	C							
−8	6 Nov	14	C	C	S						
−7	13 Nov	26	2	2	C		S				
−6	20 Nov	36	6	6	2	S	C	S			
−5	27 Nov	54	14	14	6	2	C	C	S		
−4	4 Dec	74	26	26	14	6	2	2	C	S	
−3	11 Dec	96	36	36	26	14	6	6	C	C	
−2	18 Dec	114	54	54	36	26	14	14	2	2	S
−1	25 Dec	124	74	74	54	36	26	26	6	6	C
1	1 Jan	132	96	96	74	54	36	36	14	14	2
2	8 Jan	134	114	114	96	74	54	54	26	26	6
3	15 Jan	136	124	124	114	96	74	74	36	36	14
4	22 Jan		132	132	124	114	96	96	54	54	26
5	29 Jan		134	134	132	124	114	114	74	74	36
6	5 Feb		136	136	134	132	124	124	96	96	54
7	12 Feb				136	134	132	132	114	114	74
8	19 Feb					136	134	134	124	124	96
9	26 Feb						136	136	132	132	114
10	5 Mar								134	134	124
11	12 Mar								136	136	132
12	19 Mar										134
13	26 Mar										136

Fig. 31.5

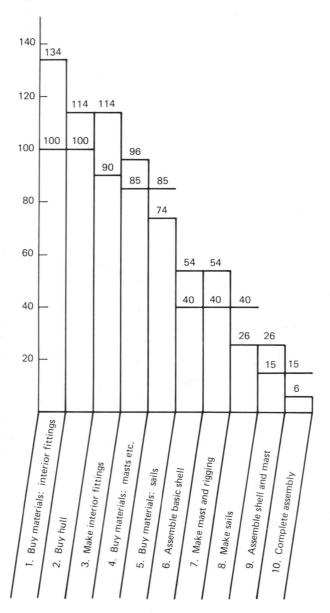

Fig. 31.6

		Buy materials : interior fittings	Buy hull	Make interior fittings	Buy materials : mast etc.	Buy materials : sails	Assemble basic shell	Make mast and rigging	Make sails	Assemble shell and mast	Complete assembly
−12	9 Oct		S								
−11	16 Oct	S	C								
−10	23 Oct	2	C	S							
−9	30 Oct	6	C	C							
−8	6 Nov	14	C	C	S						
−7	13 Nov	26	2	2	C		S				
−6	20 Nov	36	6	6	2	S	C	S			
−5	27 Nov	54	14	14	6	2	C	C	S		
−4	4 Dec	74	26	26	14	6	2	2	C	S	
−3	11 Dec	96	36	36	26	14	6	6	C	C	
−2	18 Dec	114	54	54	36	26	14	14	2	2	S
−1	25 Dec	124	74	74	54	36	26	26	6	6	C
1	1 Jan	132	96	96	74	54	36	36	14	14	2
2	8 Jan	134	114	114	96	74	54	54	26	26	6
3	15 Jan	136	124	124	114	96	74	74	36	36	14	←
4	22 Jan		132	132	124	114	96	96	54	54	26
5	29 Jan		134	134	132	124	114	114	74	74	36
6	5 Feb		136	136	134	132	124	124	96	96	54
7	12 Feb				136	134	132	132	114	114	74
8	19 Feb					136	134	134	124	124	96
9	26 Feb						136	136	132	132	114
10	5 Mar								134	134	124
11	12 Mar								136	136	132
12	19 Mar										134
13	26 Mar										136

Fig. 31.7

Step 6. Record the actual progress upon either the L-o-B chart or the 'life' table. For example, if at 8 January the achieved and planned results are:

	Achieved	Planned
1. Buy materials: interior fittings	100	134
2. Buy hull	100	114
3. Make interior fittings	90	114
4. Buy materials: mast and rigging	85	96
5. Buy materials: sails	85	74
6. Assemble basic shell	40	54
7. Make mast and rigging	40	54
8. Make sails	40	26
9. Assemble shell and mast	15	26
10. Complete assembly of dinghy	15	6

The chart is shown in Fig. 31.6 and the 'life' table in Fig. 31.7.

Despite the over-fulfilment of the delivery schedule (15 delivered and only 6 required), it can be seen that a 'choking-off' of production will occur in weeks to come due to under-fulfilment of some activities, and equally important there is some over-investment in work-in-progress on other activities. It may therefore be possible to transfer resources from the 'rich' activities to the 'poor' ones while preserving the delivery schedule: decisions here can only be taken in the light of local knowledge, and will require reference to both the CPA diagram and the progress results.

Recommended reading

See *Recommended reading* for Chapter 30, in particular Lockyer, K. G. and BS 4335

32 Linear programming (LP)

This is a powerful technique which can be used in a wide variety of situations in a number of different functional areas, including marketing, finance, distribution, in addition to production/operations management. A broad framework is one in which the manager is faced with decisions relating to the extent to which different activities are to be carried out. However, there are normally restrictions on the total extent to which these activities can be undertaken since, for example, they might be competing for limited resources. Overall it is necessary to establish the *actual extent* to which each activity is undertaken, while staying within the restrictions identified, and providing the most 'benefit'. The decisions are represented by variables, the restrictions by equations. If these relationships are linear, e.g. one unit generates £200 profit means three units generate £600 profit, then the resulting decision-making problem can be represented as a *linear programme*.

LP: an example

A small multi-purpose plant is used to manufacture in batches two different herbicides: mosnok and daiseytox. These use different quantities of two active ingredients: CPA and DCP, produced by other plants within the group. There is a limit on the availability of this CPA and DCP. Moreover, the marketing section have established that there are both minimum and maximum numbers of batches of the herbicides required each week. The basic data is shown in Table 32.1.

The plant currently operates a full three shifts per day for six days per week ($6 \times 24 = 144$ hours).

The plant manager wants to know the number of batches of each herbicide to produce in order to maximize the total profit, while staying within the restrictions on availability of active ingredient and so on.

If x_1 and x_2 represent the numbers of batches of mosnok and daiseytox produced each week, the limitations imposed by the minimum acceptable quantities and maximum required quantities can be expressed as:

Table 32.1

	Ingredients per batch (kg) CPA DCP	Minimum no. of batches per week	Maximum no. of batches per week	Hours per batch	Profit per batch (£000's)
Mosnok	10 10	1	9	12	12
Daiseytox	5 17	1	9	12	8
kgs available per week	100 170				

$$x_1 \geqslant 1, \; x_1 \leqslant 9$$
$$x_2 \geqslant 1, \; x_2 \leqslant 9$$

Since there are only two variables, this situation can be presented graphically. The straight lines $x_1 = 1$, $x_1 = 9$, $x_2 = 1$, $x_2 = 9$ are shown in Fig. 32.1; the area which they enclose shows the points which satisfy the minimum and maximum requirements. However, it is also necessary to take account of the other restrictions:

availability of CPA: $10x_1 + 5x_2 \leqslant 100$
availability of DCP: $10x_1 + 17x_2 \leqslant 170$
plant availability: $12x_1 + 12x_2 \leqslant 144$

The straight lines which come from these inequalities can be added to the graph drawn earlier, giving the feasible region of possible solutions shown in Fig. 32.2.

The full problem can now be stated as:

Maximize $12x_1 + 8x_2$
subject to $x_1 \qquad\qquad \geqslant 1$
$\qquad\qquad\qquad x_2 \geqslant 1$
$\qquad\qquad x_1 \qquad\qquad \leqslant 9$
$\qquad\qquad\qquad x_2 \leqslant 9$
$\qquad\qquad 10x_1 + 5x_2 \leqslant 100$
$\qquad\qquad 10x_1 + 17x_2 \leqslant 170$
$\qquad\qquad 12x_1 + 12x_2 \leqslant 144$

Examining the objective function (as maximize $12x_1 + 8x_2$ is called), if the line $12x_1 + 8x_2 = 96$ is added to the graph, all points along this line correspond to solutions which give a profit 96. For this reason, this is sometimes called an isoprofit line. The line $12x_1 + 8x_2 = 120$ is parallel to this first line, further from the origin, and corresponding to a larger profit. To find the point corresponding to the solution with the *maximum* profit, it is necessary to 'push' these isoprofit lines out as far as possible, until the edge of the feasible region is reached. This is shown in Fig. 32.3.

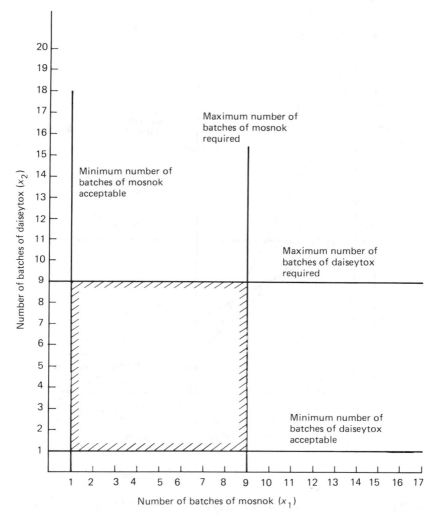

Fig. 32.1

The solution appears to lie at $x_1 = 8$, $x_2 = 4$. It can be seen that this lies at the intersection of the constraints corresponding to availability of CPA, and plant availability, consequently the value can be confirmed by solving the simultaneous equations:

$$10x_1 + 5x_2 = 100 \atop 12x_1 + 12x_2 = 144 \}$$

The profit is 128. There is unused DCP, since the point does not lie on the line $10x_1 + 17x_2 = 170$.

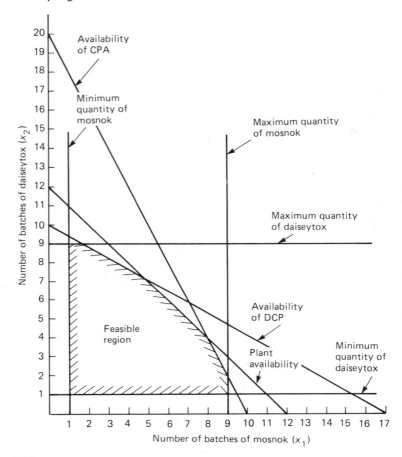

Fig. 32.2

If the profit on each batch of daiseytox is increased to 12, the objective becomes:

$$12x_1 + 12x_2$$

As these new isoprofit lines are 'pushed' out, instead of reaching a corner of the feasible region, they reach one complete side, that part bounded by the plant availability constraint. This means that all points on this side give the same maximum profit, known as alternative optimal solutions.

The R & D section develop a third herbicide which the plant can produce: cloverkil. An estimated minimum of two batches per week will be required, with a maximum of seven batches per week. Each batch

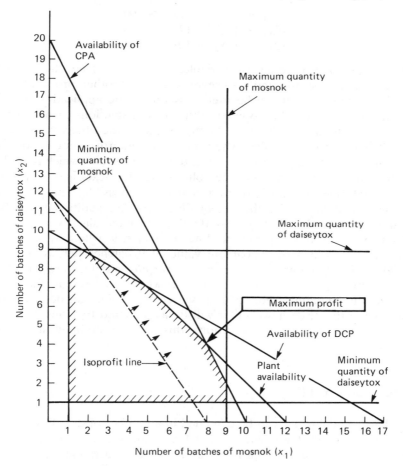

Fig. 32.3

requires 9 kg of CPA, 12 kg of DCP and 10 hours of plant time. The profit per batch is 10. If x_3 represents the number of batches of cloverkil produced per week, then this revised problem can be formulated as follows:

$$
\begin{array}{lccccl}
\text{Maximize} & 12x_1 & + 8x_2 & + 10x_3 & & \\
\text{subject to} & x_1 & & & \geqslant & 1 \\
& & x_2 & & \geqslant & 1 \\
& & & x_3 & \geqslant & 2 \\
& x_1 & & & \leqslant & 9 \\
& & x_2 & & \leqslant & 9 \\
& & & x_3 & \leqslant & 7
\end{array}
$$

$$10x_1 + 5x_2 + 9x_3 \leqslant 100$$
$$10x_1 + 17x_2 + 12x_3 \leqslant 170$$
$$12x_1 + 12x_2 + 10x_3 \leqslant 144$$

Clearly, since more than two variables are now involved, the graphical method cannot be adopted. However, there is another procedure, the *simplex method*, which can be used. Essentially the application of a set of rules results in the development of a series of solutions each satisfying the constraints, and each with a 'better' value of the objective function. This *iterative process* finishes when no further improvement is possible. The simplex method is the name given to this set of rules which is applied to the data to proceed from one solution to the next, and a criterion which establishes that no further improvement is possible. This procedure handles equalities rather than inequalities, so that additional variables need to be introduced. For 'less than' constraints, slack variables are added so, for example, $x_1 \leqslant 9$ becomes $x_1 + s_1 = 9$, where S_1 represents the extent to which the maximum value of 9 batches per week is not achieved. For 'greater than' constraints, surplus variables are added so, for example, $x_1 \geqslant 1$ becomes $x_1 - t_1 = 1$, where t_1 represents the extent to which the minimum value of 1 is over-achieved. Further details of this are beyond this text; however, it will be appreciated that this is a more than suitable computer application—this will be outlined in a later section.

Extensions of LP

The basic model of LP can be extended in a number of directions. In the previous example it was chance that the result was a whole number of batches of each product each week. However, fractional values could have been interpreted: $x_2 = 3\frac{1}{3}$, manufacture 10 batches of daiseytox every 3 weeks. However, this type of interpretation is not always possible. If the decisions are related to the numbers of different types of machine to be purchased, then clearly to talk of purchasing $3\frac{1}{3}$ machines is a nonsense. The basic LP solution procedure can be extended to the situation where the variables can only take whole number values: this is known as *integer programming*.

Frequently the constant values within the LP are not known with certainty, and the decision-maker would like to know the effect of changes in these values. For example, overtime could be worked on Sunday and increase the plant availability; however, will the extra profit cover the additional cost of this overtime? It is possible to increase the profit on one of the products, but will this justify an increase in the quantity produced? These and other 'what if' questions can be answered using *sensitivity analysis*. Indeed, it has been argued that this analysis is more use to the decision-maker than the simple solution to the problem.

Other extensions include handling known forms of uncertainty, more than one objective, non-linearities. Details of these and other extensions can be found in most texts on mathematical programming, the name given to all these techniques.

LP and the computer

In practice, the vast majority of applications of LP rely on the use of a computer for the solution. Most computers support at least one LP package. Many of these can also handle the extensions outlined in the previous section. They automatically generate and interpret the slack and surplus variables required by the simplex procedure. The larger packages can deal with virtually any number of constraints and variables.

Frequently, considerable time can be spent setting up the formulation of the problem. The data comes from a variety of sources for the constraints and objective: selling prices, different elements of costs and so on, requiring various calculations before forming the equations. Equally, having solved the LP, time is needed to interpret the solution in the context of the practical problem. Two computer programs, often supplied with LP packages, the matrix generator and report writer, can help with this. This use is shown in Fig. 32.4.

Application of LP in POM

The successful use of LP comes not so much from the solution to the

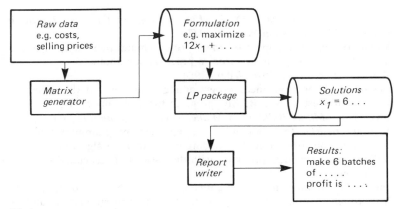

Fig. 32.4

problem, but more from the ability of the decision-maker to formulate the problem as an LP in the first place. Problems arising in a variety of situations have been formulated to exploit the LP solution procedures. Some of these are outlined below:

1. *Product-mix problems.* The example in the earlier section was typical of this type.

2. *Blending problems.* For example, to make an animal feedstuff with specific nutritive qualities, various combinations of basic food stocks may be used. This blending problem is to produce a solution at minimum cost.

3. *Cutting problems.* From a single product, for example, a reel of transformer steel, a number of products may be made by cutting the product. It is desirable to choose the combination which will generate the minimum waste.

4. *Transportation problems.* For example, a number of factories produce products which are supplied to a number of warehouses. The unit cost of each factory supplying each warehouse is given. The objective is to establish the quantity each factory should supply to each warehouse in order to minimize the total cost, while neither exceeding the production of the factories nor the requirements of the warehouses. The special structure of this formulation allows a simpler method than the simplex procedure to be used in the solution.

5. *Assignment problems.* Where a number of resources have to be assigned to a number of tasks, each resource being indivisible and capable of only undertaking one task, each task requiring only the whole of one resource, an assignment LP routine can be used. This is the simplest of the LP routines.

Recommended reading

Hughes, A. J., and Grawiog, D. E., *Linear Programming: An Emphasis on Decision Making*, Addison Wesley, 1973.

    A comprehensive treatment of linear programming, plus many of the extensions, with plenty of examples, from a practical standpoint.

Whitaker, D., *OR on a Micro*, Wiley, 1984.

    Includes a chapter on linear programming, and some of the special cases, together with a listing of a BASIC program for problem solving.

Williams, H. P., *Model Building in Mathematical Programming*, Wiley, 1985.

    A comprehensive text, not only covering linear programming but many of its extensions, but from a model building rather than an algorithmic approach, including twenty practical problems with discussions of associated formulations and solutions.

Zoutendijk, G., *Mathematical Programming Methods*, North-Holland, 1976.

    A thorough coverage of the algorithms for linear programming, and associated models.

33 Purchasing

The importance and objectives of purchasing

There are few organizations which are totally self-contained to the extent that their products and services are generated at one location from basic materials. Some materials or services are usually purchased from outside sources. The primary objective of purchasing is to obtain the correct equipment, materials, supplies and services in the right quantity, of the right quality, from the right origin, at the right time and cost. It has, however, a number of other duties, acting as the organization's 'window-on-the-world', providing information on any new products, processes, materials and services. Purchasing should also advise on probable prices, deliveries and performance of products under consideration by the research, design and development functions.

Since the 'total' cost of bought-in material may form a very large proportion of the final selling price of the organization's products or services, purchasing is an extremely important specialized function which should never be under-estimated. While the value of purchases varies from industry to industry, it averages 65 per cent of the turnover of all industries. Let us examine briefly the effects of good purchasing management on the profitability of a 'typical' manufacturing or service company with a turnover of £1,000,000 per annum and a profit of 10 per cent; the purchases account for £650,000 per annum. If a saving of 5 per cent can be achieved on the costs associated with purchasing by good management—price control, quality assurance, good transport methods, control of storage and stock holding, etc.—then the increase in profits will amount to £32,500, i.e. new profits of £132,500 or 13.3 per cent. If the same profit target of £132,500 is required, but no savings in purchasing are achieved, then the sales must rise to £1,325,000, an increase of 32.5 per cent. Such an increase in sales volume is often accompanied by either additional expenditure on sales and marketing effort or a cut in selling price, so the relationship is often not linear anyway.

Alternative means of generating savings or additional profits, such as increases in productivity, are often slow to be realized and the 'profits' may have to be shared. Savings in purchasing costs show immediately in the profit margin.

Although purchasing is clearly an important area of managerial activity, it is often neglected by both manufacturing and service industries. The separation of purchasing from selling has, however, been removed in many large retail organizations, which have recognized that the purchaser must be responsible for the whole 'product line'—its selection, quality, specification, delivery, price, acceptability and reliability. If any part of this chain is wrong, the purchasing function must resolve the problem. This concept is clearly very appropriate in retailing where transformation activities on the product itself, between purchase and sale, are small or zero, but it shows the need to include market information in the buying decision processes in all other industries.

The organization of purchasing

The inputs to purchasing appear from various sources, depending on the nature of the operation, but they include:

(*a*) *design*—from the concept to the product or service;

(*b*) *research and development*—of the processes used and the outputs produced;

(*c*) *production or operations*—detailed requirements of the transformation process, including data on waste, efficiencies and conformance with existing or planned facilities;

(*d*) *distribution*—either by the supplier or the customer, e.g. in retailing;

(*e*) *marketing*—future demands, feedback on quality, competitors and any other issue which affects purchasing;

(*f*) *finance*—terms of payment, creditors, invoice verification and payment, auditing of procedures, etc.;

(*g*) *legal services*—drawing-up and agreeing of contracts;

(*h*) *general management*—make or buy decisions.

The purchasing function, like any other in an organization, is ineffective if it exists in isolation. There is no ideal structure for the purchasing activity, since each organization will create unique demands, but there are basically two forms of orientation:

(*a*) centralization;

(*b*) decentralization.

Centralization and localization of purchasing

Within a single location, it is now generally accepted that all purchasing should be carried out by one department. This avoids uneconomical small quantities, irritation of the vendors at having several contacts with the company, and the carrying out of a specialized function by non-specialists. In organizations with a number of sites, or with a number of autonomous divisions within the same site, the situation is not so straight-forward. Buying can, under these circumstances, either be carried out at one central location for all units, however widely separated geographically, or by local buying departments.

Advantages of centralization
The advantages of centralized buying are:

1. A *consistent* buying policy.
2. *Maximum* purchasing power when conducting negotiations with vendors.
3. *Uniform* purchasing records and organization.

Advantages of decentralized buying
The advantages of decentralized buying are:

1. *Greater flexibility:* the centralized buyer for a number of sites or divisions will find it difficult to react rapidly to changes in the requirements of individual users.
2. *Close liaison:* a local buyer will be in closer contact with his/her own units and will be able to give greater assistance on the 'window-on-the-world' duties.
3. *Responsibility:* the senior executive who has control of purchasing for a location can be held responsible for the purchase of goods, and the site remains autonomous in this respect.

As is common with most organizational problems, the most usual situation, in widely spread organizations or groups of companies, is a compromise where both centralized and decentralized buying departments exist together. Each site or division has a separate purchasing department, while a centralized purchasing director or manager has the responsibility for co-ordinating the activities and directing the policies of the local buyers.

The responsibility for purchasing

The organizational location of the buyer will vary from one organization to another, but the most commonly found executives to whom the buyer is responsible are:

1. *The accountant.* It is argued that the buyer is spending the organization's money and, since the control of money is the responsibility of

the accountant, then the buyer should report to the accountant. This arrangement will work best when the range of purchases is small and the source of supply limited as, for example, the polythene tubing used in polythene bag manufacture. In a company making complex equipment, particularly on a batch production basis, this location is probably too remote from the point of production to be effective.

2. *The managing director* or the *senior executive*. Where considerable quantities of material or services are being purchased, particularly of an expensive nature, it is often desirable for purchase negotiations to be carried out at as high a level as possible, since favourable terms can often only be negotiated directly with the managing directors of supplying companies. For this reason many managing directors undertake the purchasing function themselves, or delegate it to some person directly responsible to them.

3. *The production manager* or the *production controller*. In many manufacturing or service situations, the need for resources to be flexible will often dictate that the buyer be part of the production manager's staff, either directly responsible to the production manager or to the production controller, possibly as head of the material control section, where he/she will undertake duties which include purchasing.

Make or buy decisions

The make or buy decision refers to the problem encountered by an organization when deciding whether a product or service should be purchased from outside sources or generated internally. The majority of make or buy decisions are made on the basis of price, but this is only one of a number of criteria which must be evaluated in this strategic decision. Other key points which must have influence are:

(*a*) quality and how it is controlled;
(*b*) continuity of supply;
(*c*) technological and commercial knowledge and experience required.

The economics of production or operations probably comes last in this list which places operational conditions higher than financial ones. Moreover, consideration of the 'non-cost' factors encourages longer-term contracts with suppliers to aid the achievement of production and quality levels and encourage investment in appropriate resources and new ideas. This results in excellent, mutually beneficial customer–supplier relationships developed over long periods, based on trust and the achievement of common objectives. The constant re-analysis of the make or buy decision in search of short-term advantage can destroy the relationship needed for long-term supply contracts having mutual profitability as their basic objectives. This does not say that the decision should be once and for all, for it clearly requires some periodic re-analysis to take into account changes in business and environmental conditions, and technology.

Most make or buy decisions are very complex, time-consuming and affect many parts of an organization. Senior management involvement is required in a number of the stages of this strategic decision. Problems may well be experienced in calculating accurate costs, and finding information on quality, supply and reliability, and technical know-how requirements, for each side of the equation.

Information inputs are required from both inside and outside the purchasing function, which clearly has a vital role to play. Informal and formal involvement of technical, financial (accounts) and production or operations control will always be necessary, together with a systematic approach based on careful weighing of the key factors—it is unlikely that one single factor, such as price, will be so conclusive as to dictate the obvious path to be taken.

The purchasing system

The control of purchasing should be set out in a written 'purchasing manual' which:

1. Assigns responsibilities for and within the purchasing function.
2. Defines the manner in which suppliers are selected to ensure that they are continually capable of supplying the requirements in terms of material and services.
3. Indicate the appropriate purchasing documentation—written orders, specifications and certificates of conformity—required in any modern purchasing activity.

The purchase order

The purchase order is a contractual document which may well bind the originating organization to considerable expenditure. It is most important, therefore, that it should be clear and unambiguous. The following statements:

'Price to be agreed'
'Delivery as soon as possible'
'Of good quality'
'Of normal commercial quality'
'As previously supplied'
'As discussed with your Mr Jones'

and others of a similar nature should never be used, since they are too loose to be useful and can cause considerable difficulties later when delivery occurs of a quality other than that required, or at a date later than useful.

The purchase order should carry at least the following information:

1. Name and address of originating organization.
2. Name and address of receiving company.
3. Identifying number.
4. Quantity of produce or amount of service required.
5. A full description of the type, style, grade or other means of precise identification of the product or service.
6. The applicable issue of the product or service specification and any other relevant technical data (a reference to a published, current specification may be used).
7. Reference to any certification of conformity to requirements, which must accompany the delivered product.
8. Price agreed between purchaser and vendor.
9. Delivery agreed between purchaser and vendor.
10. Cost allocation—this for internal use.
11. Delivery instructions.
12. Buyer's signature and standing in the organization.
13. Purchaser's conditions of business.

The authority to sign purchase orders is usually restricted to one or two persons within the organization, and limitations may be imposed as to the amount of expenditure which may be incurred by a signatory: for example, some companies have a rule that orders of value greater than a certain amount must be sanctioned by the board.

Receiving inspection

Inspection on receipt of goods or services may be an essential component of the system of purchasing. The amount and extent of inspection performed on receipt varies, however, with the effectiveness of the suppliers' delivery and quality systems. It must be recognized that the conformance quality of supplied material or services can be controlled only at the point of their production. Inspection at receipt for acceptance or rejection is an inefficient and wasteful device to be replaced, as soon as possible, by the use of receiving inspection to check that the necessary systems and procedures, used by the supplier to control quality, are in fact working effectively.

Futures

In some cases, orders at an agreed price are placed *now* for delivery *in the future*, the price being paid when the goods are delivered. This form of trading is most commonly met with in the commodity markets where foodstuffs and raw materials change hands. The advantage to the purchaser is the ensuring of supply of a vital product at a known price, while the vendor guarantees a sale, again at a known price. If either party forecasts the movement of the market incorrectly, then there will be a loss, but in exchange for some security. Buying futures differs from speculative buying in that both goods/services and money change hands *in the future*.

Duties of a purchasing department

The usual duties that are assigned to a purchasing department are:

1. *Finding and approving suppliers*. In this context, suppliers must be taken to include both those who supply goods and those who supply services. This should be done not only by discussions with representatives and examination of catalogues and samples, but also by visits to the suppliers' premises. The technical approval of the vendor's product is normally the responsibility of the quality or design departments, but the buyer should be confident that the source of supply is stable, reliable and able to fulfil the demands made upon it. Visits to suppliers will not only help to give this assurance but will also allow the buyer to meet, in a direct manner, those people with whom he/she will be dealing and build up a spirit of goodwill between the two parties. Used with discretion, this goodwill can be of great value in times of difficulty.

Purchasing managers should try wherever possible to assign quantitative values to the factors which are desirable in a supplier. There are a number of schemes such as *vendor rating* which is discussed later.

2. *Purchasing at least total cost to the company*. While the quality and quantity of goods or services may be specified elsewhere, the buyer must purchase these at the most advantageous terms. He must be prepared to assist in or lead all discussion on order quantities, and give advice on the imponderables—like anticipated service from the supplier—which can affect decisions on the choice of materials.

Wherever possible, price should be fixed by competitive tender, if possible by comparison with a target purchase price. It has been pointed out earlier that the lowest purchase price may not necessarily be that which is least costly to the purchasing company, since it may attract other costs (rectification, sorting, progressing . . .) which increases the *total* cost of the purchased item. *Any unexpectedly low price should be treated with caution*.

A buyer should obtain a list of satisfactory suppliers and should send out as many inquiries as convenient, requesting information on quality, delivery and price; these inquiries must be marked clearly FOR

QUOTATION ONLY. Quotations should be examined for such items as delivery charges, discount structure (e.g. discounts for prompt payment), supplementary charges and any restrictions. The use of the learning curve as a negotiating tool is advocated by some, while the practice of incorporating a buyer into a value analysis team is well established and very useful.

3. *Ensuring delivery of goods and services at the right time*. This will involve contacting suppliers before the due dates and seeking assurances that these dates will be maintained. A formal 'progress' system should be set up to do this, and a convenient method is to log all delivery requirements in diary form, raising an inquiry say two weeks before the due date, following this up by a final inquiry just before the due date to confirm. It must be realized that deliveries which are too *early* may form a source of embarrassment, not only because payment may be demanded early, but because excessive space might be occupied. In some large organizations the delivery date and, indeed, time of day may require to be specified to avoid congestion. It is not unknown for goods delivered early to be refused or delayed entry.

When progressing an order, care must be taken to avoid chasing that which has, in fact, already been supplied. This can only be done by maintaining a close liaison with the receiving department. A copy of the appropriate receipt documentation is usefully sent to the buying department to be recorded against the orders.

4. *Warning all concerned if deliveries are not going to be met*. If, as a result of the progressing action mentioned above, it is evident that a delivery date is not going to be met, the appropriate departments *must* be informed in order that work can, if necessary, be re-scheduled.

5. *Verifying invoices* presented by suppliers. This task is sometimes carried out by the buying department, sometimes by the receiving department. It is necessary to check that the prices quoted on an invoice agree with those negotiated, and this can be done by a direct comparison with the purchase order if the price is quoted there. The absence of prices from purchase orders is to be avoided, since it restricts the task of verification of invoices to the buying department.

A further and more real need for verification of invoices arises from the problem of incorrect quantities invoiced, perhaps caused by the return of defective material to the supplier. To help resolve this problem, a note of every 'rejection' by the receiving department should be passed to the buying department. The recording of these reject notes will also help to build up a picture of the reliability of the supplier, and this may well affect the placing of future orders.

Note: the cost of verifying invoices can be extremely high, and in the case of low value invoices, quite unjustified. It is as well to consider whether invoices below a fixed figure need to be verified.

6. *Organizing all discussions with suppliers*, both actual and potential. It will be found that departments, such as the design department will need to meet suppliers and discuss problems with them and, while in many cases the only persons competent to carry out technical discussions with suppliers are within the technical departments, these discussions should never take place without the knowledge of the buying department and probably never in the absence of a representative of that department. This will avoid arrangements on delivery and price being made which do not accord with the company's buying policy. In some organizations, a firm rule is laid down that all correspondence with suppliers must be signed by a buyer, even if it originated elsewhere. This may appear restrictive, but it can save much misunderstanding later on, often at a time when the technical departments have relinquished all interest in the purchase.

7. *Speculative buying* is sometimes a duty of the buying department, and implies the purchase of goods not from reasons of immediate need but because it appears that market conditions are particularly favourable. Thus, it may seem to the buyer, from his intimate knowledge of the market, that a particular commodity is likely to become difficult to obtain or that its price is likely to rise sharply. Buying in the first case will guard against a hold-up, while in the second case it may permit material bought cheaply to be resold at a profit. Speculative buying is both difficult and potentially dangerous, and can result in a company carrying stocks which are difficult to clear.

8. *Advising on prices* for materials or services to be used in new or modified designs. This activity can be of substantial value since it may help to decide major policy questions—for example, the feasibility of meeting a marketing requirement on price, or the likely cost of re-equipping a unit.

9. *Acting as a 'window-on-the-world'*. The buyer's job brings continual contact with outside organizations, and this can prove a valuable channel of communication whereby news of novel processes, materials, services and equipments are brought to the notice of departments most concerned with these matters. In like manner, the buyer is often well placed to search out information, and experience of fending off persistent salesmen can avoid considerable waste of time.

1. Finding and approving suppliers
2. Purchasing at least total cost
3. Ensuring delivery at the right time
4. Warning of delays
5. Verifying invoices
6. Organizing all discussions with suppliers
7. Speculative buying
8. Advising on prices
9. Acting as a 'window-on-the-world'

Duties of a buying department

Vendor rating

Vendor rating schemes are designed to assist the purchasing department to select the most appropriate supplier. Inevitably, some sort of ranking must always have been made, but the schemes should attempt to formalize the ranking technique and bring some objectivity to it. Basically, all schemes require that some quantitative data is obtained for each supplier on factors such as:

1. Quality.
2. Delivery.
3. Cost.
4. Service and reliability.

The importance of each of the above is not necessarily the same: for example, for many classes of goods, quality will be of much greater importance than cost. To account for these differences, the above factors may be weighted: for a hypothetical case, the weightings might be:

Factor	Weight
Quality	8
Delivery	6
Cost	4
Service and reliability	2

Suppliers are then 'scored' for these factors, each score being multiplied by the appropriate weight to give the final factor score. In the crudest possible scoring system, the buyer may make a subjective assessment on a 1–5 scale, 5 being the 'excellent' score. 1 being the 'poor' score. The result might then appear as follows:

Supplier A

Factor	*Weight*	*Score*	*Weighted score*
Quality	8	4	32
Delivery	6	4	24
Cost	4	5	20
Service and reliability	2	3	6
		Total	82

Factor	Weight	Possible Supplier A		B		C		D	
Quality	8	4	32	3	24	5	40	2	16
Delivery	6	4	24	5	30	2	12	3	18
Cost	4	5	20	2	8	2	8	5	20
Service	2	3	6	5	10	1	2	2	4
Totals			82		72		62		58

Fig. 33.1

For a range of possible suppliers, this could be combined into a matrix as in Fig. 33.1.

Subjective scoring should, of course, be replaced by some objective method if possible. For example, the 'quality' score may be derived from a periodic assessment of the supplier's quality management system; the 'delivery' score from the number of late deliveries; the 'cost' score from ratio of the price quoted by a supplier to the target purchase price or the lowest obtainable price; and the 'service and reliability' score from a measurement of the number of 'progressing' calls which have to be made.

The buyer, having placed a purchase order with an approved supplier, is dependent upon that supplier to fulfil the delivery promises. While 'penalty' and 'break' clauses can be written into an order, they are often difficult to enforce, and by the time that it is known that the delivery will be late, it is often too late to renegotiate the order with a new supplier.

Just-in-time (JIT) purchasing

Purchasing is an important feature of just-in-time (JIT) methods of inventory control. The development of long-term relationships with a few suppliers, rather than short-term ones with many, leads to the concept of *co-producers* in networks of trust providing dependable quality and delivery of goods and services. Each organization in the chain of supply is encouraged to extend JIT methods to its suppliers.

The requirements of JIT mean that suppliers are usually located near to the purchaser's premises, delivering small quantities, often several times per day, to match the usage rate. Paperwork is kept to a minimum and standard quantities in standard containers are usual. The requirement for suppliers to be located near to the buying organization, which places those at some distance at a competitive disadvantage, causes lead times to be shorter and deliveries to be more reliable.

It can be argued that JIT purchasing and delivery is suitable mainly for assembly line operations, and less so for certain process industries, but the reduction in the inventory and transport costs that it brings should encourage innovations to bring about its widespread adoption. Those committed to open competition and finding the lowest price will find most difficulty, as will those countries which, for geographical reasons, suffer greater transport distances between customer and suppliers. Nevertheless, there must be a recognition of the need to develop closer relationships and to begin the dialogue—the sharing of information and problems—which leads to the product or service of the right quality being delivered in the right quantity at the right time.

Recommended reading

Baily, Peter and Farmer, David, *Purchasing—Principles and Management*, 5th edn, Pitman, 1986.

This edition has been fully updated and substantially rewritten to meet the needs of modern management. It is a clearly written practical guide, and contains a number of very useful references and suggestions for further reading.

Farmer, David (Ed.), *Purchasing Management Handbook*, Gower, 1985.

A comprehensive work which should be in the hands of all those involved in the purchasing function.

Heinritz, Stuart F. and Farrell, Paul V., *Purchasing: Principles and Application*, Prentice-Hall, 1986.

An interesting book aimed at the generalist and offering an overview with useful practical guidance.

Heinritz, Stuart F., Farrell, Paul V. and Smith, C. L., *Purchasing, Principles and Application*, 7th edn, Prentice Hall, 1986.

An excellent, wide-ranging American book. Well referenced. With case studies.

Leenders, Michael R., *Purchasing and Materials Management*, 8th edn, Irwin, 1985.

Remains the standard US text on this subject.

Section VI **The people**

34 Personnel administration

Personnel management can be considered to consist of two parts: one, the supervisory management exerted by the departmental head and his superiors in day-to-day relationships—the leadership exerted by the supervisor; and the other the direction of the conditions of work of the employee. This chapter will be concerned only with the second aspect, which for convenience will be called *personnel administration*.

Personnel administration is generally accepted to cover the following activities:

1. Employment and manpower planning.
2. Education, training and development.
3. Industrial relations.
4. Welfare.
5. Remuneration.
6. Health and safety.

None of these can be said to be more important than others, although some are more neglected. It should be noted that, in general, the personnel administrator acts in an advisory capacity: as Pigors and Myers point out '. . . the responsibility for achieving results with members of his work group belongs to the manager, not to the personnel administrator'. This should not be taken to imply that the personnel function is any less important than any of the other support functions: indeed, there is no doubt that with the considerable growth in legislation and intervention by outside bodies, over the last decades the tasks of the personnel department have become extremely complex. Furthermore, behavioural scientists are daily revealing information concerning the nature of man and this, allied to the complexity of the task, requires that the personnel function can only be satisfactorily carried out by trained executives of a very high calibre.

Need for a personnel policy

Accepting that personnel administration is an important feature of managerial activity, then, as in all other substantial matters, decisions should be made on the basis of a declared policy, not in an arbitrary manner. The importance of this cannot be over-emphasized: a location where anomalies or distinctions exist will eventually develop internal stresses which can eventually seriously upset behaviour. Unless a policy has been carefully considered, anomalies will be extremely difficult to avoid. Equally, no organization can develop robustly unless the implications of technological and sociological developments and changes have been incorporated into its personnel policy. If the policy has been made public, then the translation of that policy into action is simplified, although it must be realized that the implementing of a personnel policy is made much more difficult if other aspects of management are weak. Goodwill and loyalty can and should be used to overcome difficulties, but they cannot be expected to make up for managerial inefficiencies.

The personnel manager must be actively involved in drawing up and determining this policy. He should be able, by training and inclination, to ensure that the needs of the employees *as people* should carry as much weight as the needs of the company *as a corporation*. As discussed elsewhere in a quite different context, '. . . all needs are utilitarian to their possessors', and the personnel officer must advise not only on matters such as the number of employees, their recruitment, selection, training and remuneration, but must also be in a position to comment upon human reactions to proposed action.

Employment

This aspect of personnel work covers the obtaining and selecting—in conjunction with departmental supervisors—of new staff, their introduction to the company, and the checking of working conditions to ensure compliance with statutory rules and orders, local by-laws, trade union agreements and any other appropriate regulations. It is interesting to consider that in many companies where the purchase of a piece of plant worth £50,000 will be the subject of much deliberation at board level, the recruitment of a new employee will be done on the basis of a five-minute interview, yet the cost of bringing the new employee to a fully useful working condition will be many times greater than the cost of the piece of plant. It is difficult to see why it should be considered that the choice of a new employee—possibly the most complex and unpredictable of organisms—is very much simpler than the choice of a new inert assembly of metal.

The personnel officer should try to ensure that:

1. The need for a new employee has been established.
2. The job has been adequately defined—here he can assist by

analysing in appropriate detail the *needs* of the job, and setting them down in a comprehensible manner.

3. Appropriate action is taken to locate likely staff. This may involve the use of Job Centres, of advertising or direct 'head-hunting', or of identifying appropriate internal staff. Properly kept records will show which channels are most effective in any particular circumstances.

4. Useful methods of selecting particular candidates are used. The range of tools here is very wide, from simple five-minute interviews to 'stress' interviews, from simple aptitude tests to complex psychological investigations. All of these, even the apparently simple interview, require skill in use, and the trained personnel officer should be able to advise on the technique to be used and assist in the actual performance of the selection method. However, again to quote Pigors and Myers, '. . . the work of the employment department . . . is a supplement to the judgement of line officials and not a substitute for it'.

5. Once an employee is engaged, he/she should be introduced to the work ('inducted') in such a manner that he/she understands clearly what is required, and what he/she can require of the organization.

6. When an employee leaves, the reasons for departure are investigated, not with a view to harassing the individual, but in order to resolve any problems. The costs of hiring are substantial, and if labour turnover can be reduced, real savings can be made.

Education, training and management development

All assets waste if untended, and this is probably more true of the human assets of a company than any of the assets usually recorded on a balance sheet. Undoubtedly, there are everywhere human abilities which are untapped, and it is these which in the final analysis determine the success or failure of an enterprise. In a very dramatic way, professional football teams show how human development can be turned to financial benefit: a young player can be 'bought' for £100 and after appropriate training be 'sold' for £1,000,000 or more.

Throughout industry there is a continual need to educate and train, not only 'on the bench' but at all levels. 'Sitting next to Nelly' is an inefficient way of learning, the student acquiring the bad habits along with the good. A positive training programme, based upon an analysis both of the needs of the job and of the individual, should be drawn up and implemented. Such programmes should encompass not only a training in manipulative skills but also in academic *and supervisory* skills, where appropriate. While a leader may be born, by training he/she can be made more useful more rapidly. Moreover, if a potential supervisor can be withdrawn from immediate tasks for a training period, he/she can find time to think of the difficulties *and responsibilities* of the new post. This is as true at the production manager's level as at the chargehand level. Too often a supervisor finds himself submerged in day-to-day problems without being able to consider more general problems, and if a training period does no more than allow a 'standing back' it will serve a very useful purpose, although it can often serve as a very positive motivating device. It should also be noted that in the UK *training in safety* is required by law: 'employers are to prepare written company safety policies and make them known'.

Not only should training be carried on *inside* the company, but the broader extra-mural training available at technical colleges, polytechnics and universities must be encouraged. Evening classes are extremely cheap, and part-time day classes scarcely more expensive. Many companies allow time off, with payment of fees and book allowances for such courses, believing that the long-term return will be substantial. External courses do have the added advantage over internal courses of allowing students from different companies and industries to exchange ideas—a most salutary experience when it is found that very few problems are special to any one factory. Considerable assistance, both financial and advisory, can be obtained from the appropriate Industry Training Boards.

Industrial relations

The relationships between employer and employee are difficult and delicate, frequently being dependent upon subtle intangibles and the ethos of the company. Too often companies seek to simplify this situation by appointing an industrial relations officer and expecting him/her to solve all problems. In truth, this relationship is not one which can be avoided. Good industrial relations stem from good personnel policies, and these *must be known and used by all managers at all levels*.

One author recalls a company where security of employment was extremely poor—as the founder of the company, a dynamic and forceful entrepreneur, would cheerfully and brutally dismiss 'offending' employees at all levels. This behaviour steadily hardened itself into a 'hire and fire' policy, as managers modelled themselves on the founder. The costs of this behaviour were substantial, and in an attempt to reduce them, personnel officers were regularly employed—and as regularly were lost, as they tried to operate a personnel policy in conflict with this extant policy. Quality in industrial relations is like quality in the product: '. . . everybody's business'.

The above having been said, it must also be recognized that the increasing intervention of the state in matters concerning employment, and the growth of the trade unions have made it necessary that at least one executive within the organization should specialize in industrial relations. The executive must be capable of representing the management of the company at any meetings which might take place with either trade unions, works committees, shop stewards committees or other negotiating bodies. This requires a thorough knowledge of all relevant agreements and local customs, and is not a matter which can be easily undertaken, since in some industries the various agreements are most complex and require great study. The situation in a multi-trades factory where a number of trade unions are involved is even more complex. In the United Kingdom the Department of Employment can help greatly in quoting the relevant agreements and advising on local customs.

Probably the most important feature of this work is that the personnel officer shall be *seen* to be scrupulously fair. He must present the company's point of view clearly and dispassionately and must not take issue on personal points. Goodwill in industrial negotiations is essential, and any suspicion of underhandedness will result in a loss of confidence which will increase immeasurably the difficulties of later negotiations. Clearly, the company's policy on industrial relations must be part of the overall personnel policy, and as such known to all.

Health and safety

There are a large number of statutory requirements concerning health and safety which must be observed, and these must be familiar to the personnel department who should bring to the notice of appropriate executives any breaches of these requirements. Good personnel records can be invaluable: poor 'sickness' figures may be an indication of dissatisfaction with work or the workplace.

Safety of the employee is not only a statutory requirement, it is a human obligation. Unfortunately, bad safety habits can spring up very easily and it is necessary to observe very closely all potentially dangerous activities. A climate of safety-consciousness must be built up by constant encouragement and propaganda, and in many organizations a special safety officer is appointed whose sole responsibility is the safety of the employees. This function, if carried out thoroughly, can result in a prevention of lost time due to accidents and an avoidance of unnecessary suffering and hardship. Without adequate managerial backing, however, the safety officer will have great difficulty in performing the job and managements must realize that safety pays, if for no other reason than that industrial injuries lose more working time than any other cause. This matter is of such importance that it is discussed later in a separate chapter.

Welfare

Under the general heading of welfare work in industry, the personnel officer will usually help in organizing any special sickness benefit schemes, social and recreational facilities, and personal assistance to staff. The attention given to this aspect depends greatly upon company policy, but it can be said that comparatively small expenditures in this field can produce substantial returns in staff loyalty and goodwill. Any personal assistance given, however, should be consistent: help given to one should not be arbitrarily withheld from others. Thus a small loan to one employee which is withheld from another can result in rancour far greater than that arising from the loss of the loan itself. Care must therefore be taken in considering the long-term result of any welfare assistance, and it is important to avoid creating precedents which later would become embarrassing to follow.

The provision of a canteen or restaurant can also be considered under this heading. In a small or medium-sized factory, the time spent by staff on running a canteen can often be substantial, and the accountant, for example, can find an unreasonable volume of the work in his office occupied by purely catering problems, while the production manager will find himself embarrassed by having to provide staff to make up for canteen staff who are suddenly absent. For this reason it is becoming usual to find specialist caterers engaged to provide a canteen service. This removes entirely from the operating personnel the problems of catering, and can be most satisfactory provided a wise choice of caterer is made. An elected canteen committee, where grievances can be aired, is a useful safety valve, particularly if the discussions can rise above the 'shortage of sugar' type of complaint.

Remuneration

Decisions on wages and salary structures are the responsibility of the board of directors. However, it is in this area of personnel management that the personnel manager must play a leading part in preparing the facts upon which any decisions are based. Fundamentally, the problems can be considered to be four in number: (1) the setting up of a logical structure appropriate to the company, the technology and the environment; (2) the placing of employees within the structure; (3) the use of an incentive scheme; (4) the use of 'side' benefits, the provision of a company car, and private health schemes being two common additions to the salary 'package'. Of these, the first two will be considered in this section, the third being discussed in the next chapter (Chapter 35). The fourth feature of a salary package is, as yet, too company-specific to be sensibly discussed here. It is, however, now generally agreed that in considering remuneration it is the total package which must be identified. It must be emphasized that the personnel department can act only in an *advisory* capacity on these matters, but if it has built up sufficient goodwill it will be better placed than any other department to be of assistance.

Wage and salary structures

Within any one homogeneous department, it is relatively simple to set up an acceptable structure, but when comparisons are made between departments the problem becomes much more difficult. How, for example, should the wages of a senior laboratory assistant compare with those of a shorthand typist? Should a line inspector draw more pay than a stock control clerk? To try to achieve some parity between the pay of workers in dissimilar occupations within the same organization it is necessary to refer all jobs to a common base, that is, to place all jobs in a recognized and agreed order of value to the company. Once this has been done, this scale of values can be used as a basis upon which to build a wage structure. Whether, in fact, the scale of values is acceptable to the employer and the employee is a matter for local discussion. At least, the setting up of such a scale can help clarify managerial ideas on the relative worth of various tasks.

Job evaluation, grading or ranking

The setting of tasks in a scale of values is known as job evaluation, grading or ranking, and while it appears to the authors that job ranking is the best description, since it promises no more than the setting of various jobs in some sort of order, the term job evaluation is most commonly used, and consequently will be employed here. There are a large number of methods of job evaluation, and the choice of one or other must depend upon local circumstances. Reference should be made to the study and report entitled *Job Evaluation*, published by the International Labour Office.

In general, as a first step, all the jobs to be evaluated are considered and a list drawn up of the characteristics of the work which are considered to be important. These characteristics may vary between different types of work, but should be the same for similar occupations (that is, for jobs within a 'job-cluster'). It is probably unwise to list too many characteristics or the analysis will become unwieldy. The National Electrical Manufacturers Association (NEMA) in the United States recognizes four main headings which will cover the majority of occu-

pations, namely SKILL, EFFORT, RESPONSIBILITY and WORKING CONDITIONS.
These main headings can then be subdivided into minor or derived
characteristics according to the job-cluster concerned. For example,
clerical work might be considered under the following headings:

Skill	1. Mental
	2. Manipulative
Effort	1. Mental
	2. Physical
Responsibility	1. Financial
	2. For subordinates
	3. Personal
Working conditions	1. Surroundings
	2. Monotony
	3. Distractions

While in the same organization the analysis for a worker in a productive
department might be:

Skill	1. Experience
	2. Manipulative
	3. Versatility
Effort	1. Physical
	2. Aural
Responsibility	1. Quality of product
	2. Safety of equipment
Working conditions	1. Surroundings
	2. Noise

For each group of jobs these characteristics are drawn up. The total
value of the characteristics is then divided between the various constituents: characteristics of little importance are assigned low values, and
those of greater importance high values, so that for the two cases above
the values assigned might be as shown below.

Using these scales, a small committee, often of management and
workers, will meet representatives of the various departments, explain
the scales and the general idea to them, and invite them to assist in
defining and grading the various tasks. These gradings must, of course,
apply to the jobs, not to the individuals doing them, so that it is a
comparison between, say, a copy typist, a telephonist, a stock records
clerk and a wages clerk, not between Miss A, Mr B, Mrs C and Mr D.
The gradings throughout a department must be carried out by the same
group of people in order that consistency is preserved, and it is useful

Clerical			Production		
Skill—		30	Skill—		20
Mental	15		Experience	5	
Manipulative	15		Manipulative	5	
			Versatility	10	
Effort—		30	Effort—		40
Mental	20		Physical	30	
Physical	10		Aural	10	
Responsibility—		30	Responsibility—		20
Financial	10		Quality of product	10	
Subordinates	5		Safety of equipment	10	
Personal	15				
Working conditions—		10	Working conditions—		20
Surroundings	2		Surroundings	5	
Monotony	3		Noise	15	
Distractions	5				
Total		100	Total		100

to rate each characteristic of all jobs at once, rather than rate all the characteristics of each job at once. It is also desirable to include among the raters representatives of the persons doing the various jobs in order that the less obvious features are not overlooked.

From this a series of definitions, along with a classification in order of value of the various jobs in a department, will be produced. This is done for all departments, and the various departmental classification integrated, usually by finding tasks of comparable value in each department. For example, an analysis may produce ranking as follows:

Dept. A		Dept. B	
Job 1	90	Job 1	80
Job 2	80	Job 2	60
Job 3	75	Job 3	50
Job 4	70	Job 4	40
Job 5	60	Job 5	30
Job 6	30	Job 6	10
Job 7	20		

and discussion may reveal that workers are often transferred from Job 1 of department A to Job 5 of department B without loss of efficiency or value. Jobs A.1 and B.5 are thus equated and an integrated table produced:

Job B.1	80
B.2	60
B.3	50
B.4	40
B.5 and A.1	30
A.2	27
A.3	25
A.4	23
A.5	20
B.6 and A.6	10
A.7	7

This table will then enable comparisons to be made between the values of the various jobs, which in turn could assist in setting up a wage structure. One useful approach would be to investigate local customs, national agreements, employment advertisements and any other source of information, and obtain rates of pay for comparable jobs wherever possible. These can then be graphically represented, relating pay and ranking, the best fitting curve being drawn through the various points obtained and a wages scale produced (see Fig. 34.1) which might read:

Job	Rank	Hourly rate (p)
B.1	80	100
B.2	60	92
B.3	50	87
B.4	40	80
B.5 and A.1	30	70
A.2	27	65
A.3	25	61
A.4	23	59
A.5	20	54
B.6 and A.6	10	36
A.7	7	30

This wage scale would thus form the basis of a wages structure—maximum increments at any point might be fixed at 10 per cent greater than basic wage, and these two scales (the basic and the maximum) could define the limits between which rates could be fixed for various tasks.

Job evaluation as outlined above will be useful not only as a method of setting equitable wage rates but also as a means for identifying and defining jobs, thus simplifying the employment, movement and promotion of staff. It is not, as stated above, a method of examining the relative effectiveness of various individuals and placing them within the structure: this is done by a merit rating of the individuals within a department.

The above refers to job evaluation for 'direct operations'. Schemes are

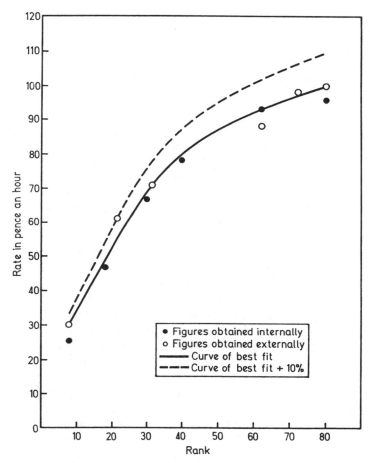

Fig. 34.1 Relation between rank and rate

available for setting up managerial job evaluations, for example the Hays/MSL scheme.

Merit rating

As with job evaluation, a careful study of the job is required, laying down the qualities required of the individuals expected to carry out the job concerned. These should cover only those characteristics which are likely to be of importance to carrying out the job; thus, in a work study engineer, 'tact' is a very necessary quality, but in a research physicist it may be of little significance. A typical group of qualities for a development engineer might be:

1. Technical qualification.
2. Technical ability.
3. Application to the task in hand.
4. Originality of thought.
5. Co-operativeness.
6. Timekeeping.
7. Length of service with the company.

All members of the company who are development engineers are then compared with each other for the above qualities, and ranked in order of ability. The sum of the rankings would then give a measure of the value of each engineer compared with his immediate colleagues. The value of all qualities is not necessarily the same: 'timekeeping' might be assumed (in the case of development engineers) to have only one-quarter the importance of 'originality of thought' and its contribution to the total would be so placed.

Ranking (or rating) is best carried out by at least two people with whom the group come into close contact. These rate all individuals separately and independently and then come together with a third person—for example, a personnel officer—to discuss the ratings and hence produce a consolidated rating. The method of rating is controversial: numerical systems (for example 1–10) are appealing, but it is the authors' experience that raters are loath to use either end of the scale, so that in fact a 1–10 scale becomes a 3–8 scale. A better way probably is by definition, e.g. outstanding, excellent, very good, good, very fair, fair, poor, bad, very bad. The rater then ticks the appropriate description, and at the joint discussion the descriptions are translated into numerical terms. In order to achieve consistency, one quality should be rated at a time for all staff being considered by any rater.

Merit ratings should be carried out at least quarterly, and the results made known to the persons concerned. This will have the effect of informing all staff of their progress, and letting them know where they are failing and where they are most successful. The quarterly assessment will prevent any distortion occurring due to the exceptional happening; for example, if rating was carried out once only, and that just before pay increments were decided, a particularly serious mistake might colour the whole rating, giving an unreasonably poor result.

Recommended reading

Pigors P. and Myers, C. A., *Personnel Administration and Point of View and a Method*, 9th edn, McGraw-Hill, New York, 1981.
    The 'Bible' on personnel administration. Reflecting US practice and thought its subject matter reaches far wider than the material of this chapter.

Molander, C. (Ed.), *Personnel Management: a Practical Introduction*, Chartwell-Bratt (Publishing and Training) Ltd, Kent, 1987.

Eight personnel management specialists came together to produce this readable, valuable book.

Field, D., *Inside Employment Law*, Pan, 1982.

A short sweep through a wide range of topics—contract of employment: payment of wages: equality of work: health and safety: redundancy: trade unions: collective bargaining. Enables the P/OM manager to talk sensibly to the expert. Easy reading.

Lorrington, D. and Chapman, J., *Personnel Administration*, Prentice-Hall, London, 1983.

Written by two people with dissimilar backgrounds, one in industrial relations, the other in organizational behaviour. Presents an overview of personnel management in the British situation.

35 Payment by results (PBR)

One of the most common methods of attempting to increase effectiveness is by the setting up of a payment by results (PBR) financial incentive, or bonus, scheme whereby the earnings of a person or group depend upon the results achieved. There is an increasing body of thought which holds that such schemes are not in themselves desirable and that any benefits which may appear to be derived arise, in fact, from the improvements in managerial methods necessary to run a PBR scheme. However, this matter is not in any way resolved, and PBR schemes are found very commonly through industry, both service and manufacturing.

Non-financial incentives

Within every organization there must be present a number of non-financial incentives, for example: loyalty to the company or to the supervisor, pride in the product or service, desire for praise or recognition, or a personal pride in the ability to carry out a task better than anybody else. Such 'emotional' incentives can act very forcibly, and a good leader or manager will always make the maximum possible use of them. Without such appeals, any organization will lose 'life', the atmosphere will become oppressive, and work will become nothing but drudgery.

Some companies, however, offer tangible benefits as rewards for increases in effectiveness. Among these are:

1. Extra holidays.
2. Greater security.
3. Improved status.
4. Special working conditions.

The use of such incentives requires particular care on the part of the management to avoid any appearance of partiality, and it is often difficult to operate a comprehensive non-financial incentive scheme. The results are probably more long-term than the results of financial bonus schemes, and for this reason both types of scheme are often worked side-by-side.

Financial incentives

It is the financial or wage incentive that is most commonly thought of when PBR schemes are discussed. In these the earnings are related to effort, and such schemes are common at all levels. A managing director's earnings can include a portion dependent upon the turnover of the company, a salesman can earn commission—a bonus on the orders he takes—and an operator can be paid on piece-work. In this chapter, only those wage incentives which can be applied to direct labour will be discussed.

Installation of a PBR scheme

The installation of a PBR scheme must be the culmination of a great deal of preliminary work, all of which should be normal in a well-run organization. No scheme must be regarded as a substitute for good management, nor must it be considered the basis upon which good management is built. An insecurely founded scheme which is later withdrawn will create such persistent ill-will that subsequent well-conceived plans will have little chance of success.

The following must be investigated and put into operation before any incentive scheme is installed:

1. *Work measurement.* Consistency in reward is essential. To achieve this, all rewards should be based upon some objective measure of the work content of the job. There is a temptation, particularly when under pressure, for rewards to be based upon the selling price. This will not only give rise to inconsistencies, one job 'paying' more than another of equal difficulty; it will also prevent selling prices being altered without a great deal of difficulty. Only when selling price *accurately* reflects the work content should it be used as a basis for an incentive scheme, and the setting of the selling price itself must then require accurate work measurement. Furthermore, if selling price determines reward, then high-priced jobs may be made or sold to the detriment of other lower-priced but possibly more important jobs. Any work measurement programme will provide both the measurements and/or definition of the task measured. As a result, any subsequent discussions on rewards can refer back to the original conditions which applied at the time of setting the reward and so enable worthwhile comparisons to be made. In some organizations it may be necessary to obtain trade union agreement to carry out a work measurement programme, and this agreement may include a statement of the measurement technique which will be used. Increasingly, one of the PMTS methods is employed in these circumstances, although in low-

volume situations PMTS may be too expensive and some other indirect work measurement method—see Chapter 18—may have to be used. Training shop stewards or other union officials in whichever method is to be employed will remove much of the suspicion often felt towards work measurement in general.

2. *Effective production control.* Under any circumstances the results of ineffectual production control are serious. Under a PBR scheme, the idle time due to absence of material, of drawings, of plant capacity, of tools, of test equipment, will result not only in frustration by the management but in loss of earnings by the operators which can lead to considerable ill-will and a high labour turnover. If the loss of earnings is made up by means of lieu bonuses (that is, bonuses paid for idle time in lieu of the bonuses which would have resulted if the operator had been working) the result will be an increased overhead burden to be borne by the work which is done and an inducement to create idle time.

3. *Effective quality control.* A reward is normally only paid for satisfactory work, defective work being returned for correction before any payment is made. It is therefore necessary that an acceptable quality control system is in being, one that is impersonal enough to be free from any suggestion of bias. The usual practice is for reward to be paid only on those items passed at the inspection stage, and many bonus cards have a space 'Quantity passed by inspection . . .' on them from which particulars the bonus can be calculated.

4. *Sound wages structure.* To try to use a PBR scheme as a means of 'correcting' an unjust wage structure is to court disaster. Not only will the basic inequity remain, the obvious bias in the PBR scheme will create considerable distress.

5. *Training of wages staff.* Whatever type of scheme is used, it will inevitably increase the burden upon the administrative staff, and in particular upon the wages department. A very thorough training in the scheme must be given to the wages staff, who will need to be able to:

(*a*) carry out all the calculations; and
(*b*) appreciate all the details of permissible allowances.

Should this not be done, and should the scheme run into administrative difficulties at its inception, it may be discredited and fail. A 'dry run' whereby reward calculations are made and circulated for several weeks before any reward payments are made will often help to resolve any difficulties here.

6. *Modification to payroll program.* Where the payroll is prepared by computer, the installation of a financial incentive scheme will obviously require the amending of the program.

7. *Consultation with employees.* Before any PBR scheme is installed, it is essential that those most directly concerned—those who are going

to be paid under the scheme—should be consulted and any proposed scheme thoroughly explained, discussed and, if necessary, modified. This is not merely common courtesy; it prevents any misunderstandings and ill-feeling later on. It is better to postpone the installation of a scheme if discussions have either not been held or have not reached agreement. Forcing a PBR scheme through against opposition will eventually lead to innumerable difficulties.

---

1. Work measurement	4. Wages structure
2. Production control	5. Wages staff
3. Quality control	6. Amend payroll program
7. Employee consultation	

Points to be considered before installing a PBR scheme

Safeguards in PBR schemes

To prevent any unfairness, *or suspicion of unfairness*, to either the employer or the employee, it is usual to write into a PBR scheme a number of safeguarding clauses. These include:

1. *Payment for idle or extra time.* If an employee on a PBR scheme is idle, the opportunity is lost to earn a reward and this may substantially affect the wage packet. It is usually accepted as a principle that an operator will not suffer financial loss for reasons attributable to managerial weaknesses, and that idle time due to an individual's fault is borne by the individual. Thus, should an employee be idle because of, say, lack of material due to bad buying, then a lieu bonus would be paid. On the other hand, if the idleness was due to inefficient work on the part of one individual, only 'time' rate—basic hourly rate—would be used to calculate wages.

If this payment or non-payment for idle or extra time is accepted, then it is necessary for all such time to be recorded, and causes assigned to it. This is often done by setting up an idle-time code, listing the usual sources of idle time and booking time against that code. This time is usually verified by some responsible person, and the act of providing an idle and extra-time analysis will then give useful information upon which other managerial decisions can be based.

2. *Payment for holidays.* When an employee is entitled to a paid holiday, the question of the basis for payment must be resolved. Two alternatives are available: either the payment be at 'day rate' or 'basic rate', or some 'lieu' reward must be made. Generally, the second alternative is adopted, and careful consideration must be given to the method

of deriving this lieu reward. Consultation with employees is invaluable here.

3. *Payment for incomplete work*. Payment is often required to be made for work which is not complete at the end of the wage period. If a reward is paid weekly, and the pay week ends on a Friday, there may be work partly completed at the end of Friday. In short time-cycle jobs this is of minor consequence, since any loss at the end of one week will be offset by an equivalent gain at the beginning of the next. Moreover, for a task lasting 10 minutes, the error in excluding it from a 40-hour week is insignificant. In the case of a long time-cycle job, a different situation is created when a task is unfinished at the end of a period, or when a part-finished job is handed over from one person to another, for example, during annual holidays or when somebody leaves. Some technique is required whereby payment can be made for a partly completed job. This is extremely difficult, and the most usual solution is for an independent person to assess the percentage of work complete, any errors resulting being borne by the management. Some companies operate a 'loan' system, whereby part payments are paid as the job progresses, a reconciliation taking place during the concluding stages of the job.

4. *Ability to change a reward when in error*. Lack of decision in this problem has wrecked many PBR systems. A reward which allows an abnormally high wage (a 'loose' rate) to be earned will result in a restriction of output to a level which will provide what is considered by those immediately concerned to be a 'fair' wage, while a reward which is unachievable (a 'tight' reward) results in frustration. Work measurement will tend to prevent this, but there will be inevitable errors, particularly at the outset of any scheme. Safeguards should therefore be set up which will enable rewards to be adjusted, and a common technique is for all rewards to be accepted as provisional for the first jobs or the first weeks. During this time they can be adjusted without consultation, but thereafter the reward is considered 'established' and can be altered only if there is a change in materials or methods. Fear of reward-changing is ever present and must be avoided.

5. *Defective work*. If work is defective it is not usual for a reward to be made for it, although in some group schemes an allowance is made for the correction of defective work. Safeguards are necessary to ensure that a worker does not achieve high rewards by poor workmanship, and the quantity 'passed by quality control' is usually the quantity for which reward is paid. Should the defects arise through causes other than those under the worker's control—for example, poor material or faulty equipment—a lieu reward is often paid.

6. *Guaranteed week*. It is usual to guarantee to each person covered by a wage incentive scheme a minimum weekly sum of money as wages,

whatever the circumstances. This is known as the *guaranteed week* and is extremely common both in the UK and the rest of the world.

1. Idle time?	4. Error in reward?
2. Holiday pay?	5. Defective work?
3. Incomplete work?	6. Guaranteed week?

Questions to be resolved in a PBR scheme

Characteristics of apparently effective incentive schemes

As mentioned above, there is much debate on the total effectiveness of *any* PBR scheme and to try to list the characteristics of an effective scheme is to accept the view that such schemes can be effective, a matter about which there is some doubt. However, where schemes are apparently running satisfactorily, there are a number of conditions which appear to have been fulfilled:

1. *Intelligibility*. Some schemes are ingenious to the point of obscurity. Should those concerned not understand how the scheme operates, there will be a persistent fear of 'sharp practice' or fraud. 'Justice must not merely be done, it must be seen to be done.'

2. *Administrative simplicity*. To operate a confused or 'clever' scheme can be very costly indeed, and in one company in which one author was employed he remembers with recurrent dismay that he would spend every Friday afternoon checking operators' queries on the reward scheme. The scheme was such that it was barely intelligible, and administratively extremely difficult, so that a query would involve not only tedious calculations, but also cross-referencing to several other departments.

3. *Direct*. The scheme should directly relate effort and reward.

4. *Speedy*. Payment should be made as rapidly as possible after it is earned: some delay is inevitable, but this should be kept as short as possible. The holding up of reward is a considerable source of mistrust.

5. *Adequate*. The reward given shall be sufficiently great to give stimulus, particularly in these days of high income tax. It is often recommended that a 133 performance should earn a reward of one-third of the basic rate of pay.

6. *Equitable*. Rewards between individuals should be equitable. A potent source of mistrust is the belief that one individual is earning much more than another, that one gets all the 'easy' jobs and another all the 'tight' ones. Often this mistrust is unjustified, and one author recalls that in one company all rewards were calculated, entered into a single book, and this book circulated. This allowed queries to be dealt with but, just

as important, it enabled everybody to see the earnings of all his/her colleagues.

1. Intelligible	4. Speedy
2. Administratively simple	5. Adequate
3. Direct	6. Equitable

Characteristics of apparently effective incentive schemes

Wage drift and PBR schemes

A PBR scheme involves the setting of rewards at a level acceptable to both the company and the employees. Usually such schemes involve the equation:

Total wage = Basic wage + Reward

Once the level of reward has been decided, usually in a form such as:

Reward = $x\%$ of basic wage for such-and-such an effort

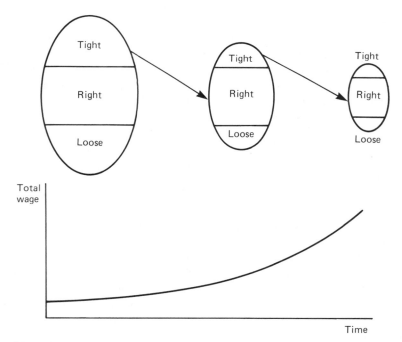

Fig. 35.1 The mechanics of wage drift

it is then necessary to assign values to tasks which will generate the reward when the effort is applied. Inevitably, since the assessment of effort is difficult, errors in reward-setting will result. *On an average*, the overall level of rewards will be correct, but some will be too low ('tight'), some will be correct ('right') and some will be too high ('loose').

Clearly those people whose rewards are 'right' or 'loose' will be satisfied, but those whose rewards are 'tight' will complain. Management will then be likely to respond by resetting the 'tight' tasks, with the inevitable result that some then remain 'tight' (possibly less so) while others become 'right' or 'loose'. The effect will then be that *on an average* the overall level of rewards will have *risen*, so that the *total wage* package will be higher than initially anticipated. This is one cause of wage drift, a cause which is very difficult to check. See Fig. 35.1.

Types of incentive scheme

There are very many different types of incentive scheme, and the most suitable depends upon many local factors, for example: tradition, type of work, time-cycle and so on. One decision has to be taken at the outset, however: that is, whether a scheme shall apply to an individual or a group. Where the output of any one person depends immediately upon the effort of another, as in a flow line, then a bonus can be calculated only on the output of the group of people concerned. On the other hand, group schemes are sometimes installed even when individual output can be measured. Such a group scheme has the direct advantage of administrative simplicity and the indirect advantage, often not fully appreciated, that the group can exert considerable pressure upon its less satisfactory members, even expelling those who are 'passengers'. From the management's point of view, in a group scheme it is not possible to derive any figures illustrating the effectiveness of either an individual or a method. This is a substantial loss, and must be well considered before installing a group PBR scheme.

The benefit to management in operating a financial incentive scheme derives, of course, from the fact that unit contribution remains effectively constant whatever the quantity produced, so that the greater the quantity produced, the greater the total contribution. In general, all financial incentive schemes operate in the same way: a 'norm' or 'standard' task is derived, desirably by work measurement, and the individual is given an incentive to achieve this norm. This is done by setting an *allowed time* for a task which is *greater* than the *standard time* by an amount known as the *policy allowance*. A *reward, bonus* or *premium* is then paid, the size of which depends upon the *time saved*, that is, the difference between the allowed time and the *time taken*. Thus:

Time allowed   = Standard time + Policy allowance
Reward   ∝ Time allowed − Time taken
                  or writing
Time saved   = Time allowed − Time taken
Reward   ∝ Time saved

The difference between various schemes lies in the way in which the bonus is calculated from the time saved, and very many ingenious formulae are available, some simple, some extremely complex, and some where the bonus calculation changes with the level of output. As illustration, the most common method is discussed below.

Piece-work

The most common, and in many ways the most satisfactory, PBR system is straight piece-work, where a price is assigned to each piece (or item), and the wage paid calculated by multiplying the price by the quantity produced. This can be either a *money* piece-work (in which case each unit has a price of so much) or a *time* piece-work (in which case each unit has an 'allowed time'). The difference between the two approaches is probably best illustrated by an example.

Assume a worker has a guaranteed rate of 350p an hour for a 40-hour week (that is, a guaranteed wage of £140 a week). Under a monetary system, he may have a price of 49p an article, and in a 40-hour week he may produce 400 articles. He is then paid 400 × 49p for that week—that is, £196. Under a time system for the same article he is allowed a time of 8.4 minutes each and, producing the same quantity, he earns 400 × 8.4 minutes' pay, that is 56 hours' pay at 350p an hour, which is again £196. In both cases the 'bonus' (i.e. the difference between basic pay and earned pay) is the same, namely £196 − £140 = £50. The *money* rate has the advantages of administrative simplicity, clarity and a constant direct labour cost, whatever the guaranteed wage paid to the individual, although when inflation is significant it is necessary to re-calculate piece-work prices to allow total wages to keep pace. This can be a very difficult and time-consuming task, particularly if some of the 'prices' are viewed with suspicion. On the other hand, the *time* rate will allow savings to be made if an individual of lower guaranteed wage than originally planned is employed on the job. It also allows changes in basic rate to be made without re-calculating the piece-work price, thus avoiding the effects of inflation.

In both cases above, the time taken for the job is the same (namely, 6 minutes each) and if the total earnings are those which it had been expected that the operator would earn, then this time of 6 minutes would be the 'expected time', which coincides with the 'standard time'. Production control calculations must be based on this expected time *and not on the allowed time*. The allowed time is obtained from the standard time by the addition of a policy factor derived from a managerial decision of the amount of bonus which it is expected that a normal operator will earn. In the case of the example above, it was anticipated that an operator would earn 2.4 minutes every 6 minutes—a bonus of 40 per cent. If the operator had been earning only 'straight time'—that is, earning exactly £140—he would have been said to earn *day rate*. Had he earned twice that amount (i.e. £280) he would have been said to earn *double time*, so that the earnings under piece-work are linear or 'straight', that is, they increase in direct proportion to the amount of work done once day rate has been passed.

For piece-work by time, the earnings can be written:

Wage   = Time allowed × Rate
    = (Time taken + Time saved) Rate
    = Time taken × Rate + Time saved × Rate

and the bonus (or premium) can be considered to be:

Bonus = Time saved × Rate

Halsey-Weir and Rowan schemes

Many other PBR schemes appear in the literature, and one of the authors once listed 72 different schemes. Two frequently mentioned schemes are the Halsey-Weir and the Rowan schemes. If:

Time taken   = T_T
Time allowed = T_A
Time saved   = T_S
Basic rate of pay = R

then total earnings for the same period of time are:

Piece-work: $T_T \times R \ + \ T_S R$
Halsey-Weir: $T_T \times R \ + \ p.T_S R$
    (p is a fraction, usually $\frac{1}{2}$)
Rowan: $T_T \times R \ + \ \dfrac{T_T}{T_A}.T_S R$

If earnings start at the same output, then the operation of three schemes is as shown in Figs 35.2 and 35.3.

Measured day work

In the above, and related, schemes, the operator's earnings will vary with output. It may well be that this results in a deliberate control of effort

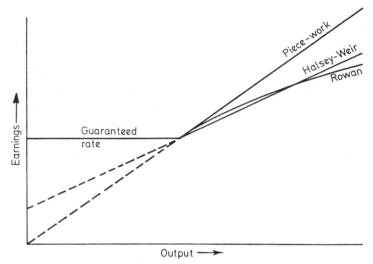

Fig. 35.2 Operator's earnings under piece-work, Halsey-Weir and Rowan schemes, all with guaranteed rate

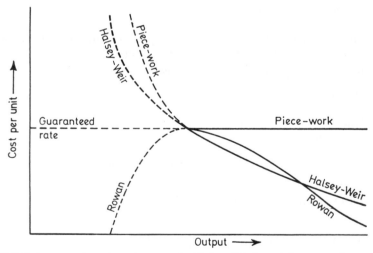

Fig. 35.3 Labour cost under piece-work, Halsey-Weir and Rowan schemes, all with guaranteed rate

in order that the wage packet is kept constant, and that changes in method are opposed or, if operator-devised, concealed. To overcome these and other problems, a measured day work (MDW), high day rate or controlled day work system is sometimes advocated. In this, a 'norm' of work is established, and if operators achieve *or exceed* this norm for an extended period of time, then an increase in pay is automatically awarded. For example, a norm may be set which requires a continuous effort rating of 125 and, if this is achieved, then an increase of perhaps 30 per cent above the previous basic pay is awarded.

The benefits claimed for this system are:

(*a*) stabilized wages;
(*b*) improved employer/employee and employee/employee relationships;
(*c*) administrative simplicity;
(*d*) less opposition to methods improvement.

It must be made clear, however, that MDW does not reduce the need for managerial efficiency in general and work study in particular.

Group bonus schemes

Any of the above can be adapted to use as group schemes, and there are also a number of special group bonus schemes, among them the Priestman scheme, the Scanlon plan and various 'value-added' schemes.

The Priestman scheme
In this scheme all employees are paid a guaranteed basic wage. A figure for total output is then fixed (and agreed) and if the output from the factory exceeds the target by, say, x per cent, then all wages are increased by x per cent. The problem which arises in this system is in fixing the measure of output. In a single-product factory this is quite straightforward, but in a multi-product factory difficulties arise which are often resolved by assigning a 'points' value to each product, and calculating output and targets in terms of the total number of points produced.

The Scanlon plan
Here again, all employees receive a guaranteed basic wage, but the bonus received is calculated from the effective reduction in total labour cost. Some measure—often the ratio of labour cost to total sales value—is adopted as an index of total labour effectiveness. Any reduction in this index (whether from a reduction in labour cost or an increase in sales value) results in an increase in pay, usually for all employees. In some cases, directors and commission-earning salesmen are excluded from participation in the bonus. For example, if a 'norm' of 38 per cent for labour cost/total sales value is adopted, and total sales were £100,000, a labour cost of £38,000 would have been considered normal. If, in fact, the labour cost was £34,000, the difference (= £4,000) would be shared among the employees as bonus. In some schemes the whole of this 'saving' is used as bonus, in others only part of it—75/25 being not uncommon.

The advantages of this plan are claimed to be that there is very much more worker participation and interest in methods of increasing productivity. Since improvements can come from any source; it is suggested that problems are seen as *joint* problems, and joint efforts are made to solve them. The Scanlon plan first appeared to have been formalized in the US just previous to the Second World War, and as yet there is too little experience with the plan outside the US to judge of its value in different employer/employee climates.

Value-added schemes
Value-added is usually defined by: value-added = income − expenditure on materials and services. This measure, either by itself or as a ratio with other key figures, may be used as the basis of a bonus scheme. One common ratio which is used is:

$$\frac{\text{Value added}}{\text{Wages} + \text{Salaries}}$$

When this ratio increases over a previously agreed norm, a bonus is paid to all employees.

Supervisory bonus schemes

The use of bonus schemes for supervisory staff is even more contentious than the use of such schemes for direct labour, as it is often argued that supervisors should not require the spur of a wages incentive. However, many schemes are in current use, some of an extremely complex nature. The simplest and most direct is a bonus which is directly proportional to the algebraic sum of the bonus earnings of the staff under the supervisor's control. This will induce the supervisor to attempt to see that all his staff are trained to such a pitch that they all earn substantial bonuses. It may have the disadvantages, if safeguards are not imposed, that the supervisor may sacrifice quality for output, that he might raise lieu bonuses too easily, or that he might give direct assistance to an operator to produce more, thus neglecting other supervisory duties. It is probably best to see that supervisory bonus does not form too great a proportion of his wages.

Profit-sharing and co-partnership schemes

Other attempts at 'overall' bonus schemes are those known as *profit-sharing* or *co-partnership* schemes. While these are extremely varied, they all have the basic form of a bonus being declared out of profits. This bonus is divided among the employees—if in cash, then the scheme is a *profit-sharing* one; if in the form of shares, then it is a *partnership* scheme. It will be observed that the Scanlon plan is, under this definition, a form of profit-sharing scheme. In the UK, profit-sharing may have a tax advantage to the employer and to the employee over more direct financial incentive schemes. Co-partnership has the advantage to the company of not significantly affecting cash flow.

Advantages of a wage incentive scheme

The most usually quoted advantage of a wage incentive scheme is that it increases productivity. This may well be so, particularly if it is a well-designed scheme, although a badly conceived, badly executed one will have the reverse effect. There is, no doubt, however, that the increases in productivity can be achieved by other means, principally those of good leadership. There are two other important advantages which accrue and which are rarely appreciated, namely: that an incentive scheme will provide a ready measure of the effectiveness of a department, and that control is easier.

An incentive as a yardstick

A well-designed incentive scheme will be such that the bonus paid will be related to overhead recovery. This is not to suggest that bonus is paid only when all the overheads are recovered: political consideration may dictate that bonus is paid at a lower level than this. Nevertheless, it can be calculated at what bonus level an individual or a department fully recovers the appropriate overheads. In a stable organization then—that is, one where a budget is being maintained—any department or individual earning above the minimum bonus level can be considered, without any further calculation, to be efficient within the requirements of the organization.

The earning of bonus can also be used as a simple test of efficiency without any considerations of overhead recovery. Even if the bonus scheme is not correctly founded, and the rates used are in error, the amount of bonus earned is an indication of the efficiency of the operator *within the framework in which he is working*. Variations in bonus earnings will similarly indicate variations in efficiency, thus providing an objective measure of progress.

An incentive scheme as an aid to control

Any production, budget or cost control scheme will depend eventually upon the accurate recording of time. Performance, lost time, labour content, will all require to be expressed in hours of work. Without a bonus scheme it will be found that time recording is slipshod, being regarded as an unimportant task. Once a bonus scheme is in operation, however, it is found that the operator will co-operate very actively in recording, since even without the financial advantage of good bonus, performance is a matter of prestige. Furthermore, social pressure is exerted on indirect staff in order to ensure that, for example, material is issued rapidly from stores, or goods are passed through inspection as soon as possible.

Productivity agreements

While productivity agreements are not necessarily financial incentive schemes—although they may include them—they are designed to serve the same purpose, namely, increasing productivity. Generally, they involve company-wide agreements in which outmoded working practices are replaced by more effective methods, in return for improvements in pay or conditions. In this way, long-established manning and demarcation traditions have been overthrown, and simpler and more effective structures have been instituted. Inherently the establishing of such an agreement will involve a very considerable investigation into the factors affecting productivity and lengthy discussions with employees at all levels, the whole process being known as 'productivity bargaining'. When the results of the first agreement of this type were published in 1963, they appeared to be so striking that it was felt that the productivity agreement was the long-sought-after panacea which would cure all the ills of British industry. However, this view has been somewhat modified with the passage of time.

Recommended reading

Bowey, A. (Ed.), *Handbook of Salary and Wage Systems*, Gower, 1982.
    An extremely valuable collection of chapters written by leading authorities, both industrial and academic, on all aspects of payment systems.
Husband, T. and Schofield, A., *Wage and Salary Audit*, Gower, 1977.
    Useful, practical and down to earth.
White, M., *Payment Systems in Britain*, Gower, 1981.
    The findings of a study on current payment systems for manual workers. A large interview programme enables the author to make useful comments on existing practices.

36 Health and safety

Accidents

Every year hundreds of fatalities occur and many thousands of injuries are suffered by men and women as a direct result of accidents at work. Others suffer impairment brought about by health hazards with which they work. Clearly, there are humanitarian, legal and economic grounds for providing a safe place and system of work. To honour these obligations, it is necessary to implement an active programme of accident prevention. The preparation of a properly thought out health and safety policy, together with continuous monitoring, can do much to reduce, if not eliminate, injuries and damage to health.

In order to formulate such policies and programmes it is necessary to define the word *accident*. Let us consider a case of four men tripping over the same obstacle. The first man trips and recovers his balance, the second falls and dirties his trousers, the third cuts his knee, the fourth fractures his skull on an adjacent table. Although the results differ widely and only two of the four men are hurt, these are identical accidents. It is the accident itself—the tripping—not the consequence of the accident which determines the need for investigation and corrective action.

A working definition of an accident then is:

> *An accident*
> is any unplanned, uncontrolled, unwanted, or undesirable
> event, or sudden mishap which interrupts an activity or
> function.

From this definition it should be clear that injury to people or damage to property is not an accident, but evidence to show that an accident has occurred. When considering some of the very large disasters resulting from industrial accidents, particularly those in the world's chemical industries, it is difficult to avoid the emotion which demands retribution and corrective action. However, it must be recognized that similar *accidents* are happening all over the world every day, fortuitously without the same consequences. The call for investigative and preventative programmes in these cases is often less audible, but the need for their avoidance is just as important.

Everyone, from the senior executive to the youngest and newest entrants in the organization, has a part to play in creating and maintaining healthy and safe working conditions which have the principal objective of avoiding accidents, the consequences of which are pure chance. To achieve this, an effective safety policy must ensure that, just as with quality, 'everyone's concern' does not become 'nobody's business'.

The effects of accidents

The effects of the most publicized industrial accidents are clear for all to see, but they may be classified for any accident under the headings:

I	*njury*—including disability, pain and suffering, etc.
D	*amage*—to equipment, buildings, markets, etc.
L	*oss*—of life, of earnings, of output, of 'image', of time, of profit.
E	*motion*—following injury, pain, death, etc.

The mnemonic constructed from the first letters of these headings may be used to emphasize that the inevitable discussion of the *effects* of accidents may be IDLE gossip in the business of accident *prevention*.

There are many statistics produced concerning the number of people who experience time off work, the number of deaths, or the value of lost production due to accidents at work. It is not proposed to repeat those here, but an interesting concept is Heinrich's pyramid of potential for accidents, which is derived from data on 'serious' and 'minor' injuries reported:

1	Serious injuries
30	Minor injuries
300	'Near misses'
?	Potential accidents

The potential for accidents which extrapolates from the known effects must be a concern for the POM function, and lead to an effective accident prevention programme being an essential part of its responsibilities.

The causes of accidents

Accidents don't just happen, they're caused is an often used cliche which must be taken seriously if accidents are to be prevented. The use of excuses such as 'it was just a unique combination of circumstances', 'a risk we had to take', 'the result of human error', 'an unavoidable danger' as definitions of causes of accidents actually hinders their avoidance. What is required is a clear definition of an accident cause:

> *An accident cause*
> is an uncontrolled hazard, without which there could
> be no accident.

It is possible to classify accident causes under the headings:

P	*lant*, e.g. a faulty stairway, electrical hazards.
E	*quipment*, e.g. a defective guard, incorrect equipment.
E	*nvironment*, e.g. high noise, insufficient light.
P	*eople*, e.g. careless, untrained, over-stressed.
S	*ystems* of work, e.g. poor procedures, bad housekeeping.

The mnemonic derived from the first letters of these headings may help to concentrate effort into finding the accident causes, which requires careful PEEPS at the workplace, training, systems of work, etc. The idea that a human being may present an 'uncontrolled hazard' may be foreign to some, but the responsibilities of the production or operations manager for training, supervision and motivation in safety consciousness cannot be abdicated.

Responsibilities and organization for safety

The establishment of positive safety policy objectives within an organiz- ation must be accompanied by the clear allocation of responsibilities within the management structure. It is generally accepted that the primary operational responsibility for ensuring safe working must rest with line management, and in particular there are two key areas which require attention:

1. *Senior executive level.* Direct responsibility for the general manage- ment of safety and health matters should be included in the duties of one of the senior executives in the same way that a director may be allocated overall responsibility for production, quality or marketing. In other words, safety and health should be treated like any other major mana- gerial function, with a clear line of responsibility and command running up to an accountable individual at the top of the organization.

2. *First-line supervision level.* The supervisor is 'on the spot' and in a position to know whether or not safety arrangements are working in prac- tice, and his/her influence can be dramatic. The promotion of health and safety at work is first and foremost a matter of efficient management.

As with other areas such as quality and productivity, real progress in safety is impossible without the full co-operation and commitment of all employees. If they are to accept their full share of responsibility, however, they must be able to participate fully in the making and monitoring of arrangements for safety and health at their place of work. The appointment of safety representatives and committees is one way of increasing involvement and commitment. Some organizations have arrangements whereby all employees in a particular unit meet periodically for discussions about safety. This 'total involvement' approach stresses the need for the participation of every individual employee.

The safety adviser

Many organizations have realized the importance of the contribution which a qualified health and safety adviser can make to accident prevention. Smaller organizations may well feel that the cost of employing a full-time safety adviser is not justified, other than in certain very high-risk areas. In these cases, a member of the management team should be appointed to operate on a part-time basis, performing the safety advisory function in addition to his/her other duties. To obtain the best results from a safety adviser, he/she should be given sufficient authority to take necessary action to secure the implementation of the organization's safety policy, and must have the personality to be able to communicate the message to his/her colleagues or employees. Occasionally the safety adviser may require some guidance and help on specific technical safety matters.

The role of the safety adviser is to give advice to management on the:

(*a*) establishment and review of *safety regulations* to meet the organization's requirements;

(*b*) relevant *statutory/legislative requirements*;

(*c*) *safety programmes* necessary;

(*d*) existence of the correct *safety elements* in all job instructions;

(*e*) *safety content* necessary in all training;

(*f*) regular *inspection* of safety and housekeeping standards in all work areas.

Safety planning

Systematic planning is a basic requirement for health and safety in all workplaces. For a safety plan to be effective, it must be part of a continuous review process which has as its objective zero accidents, through a strategy of never-ending improvement. The overall plan should include the basic elements set out in Fig. 36.1.

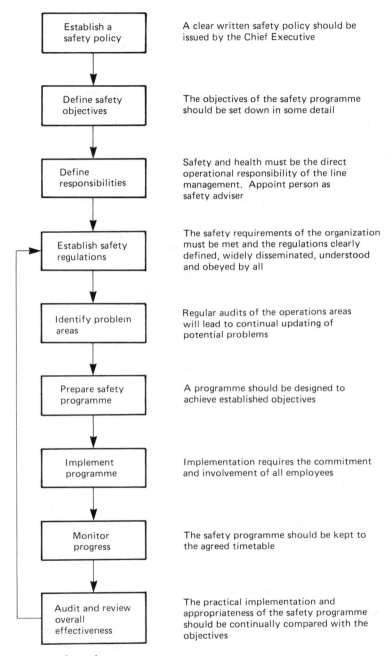

Establish a safety policy	A clear written safety policy should be issued by the Chief Executive
Define safety objectives	The objectives of the safety programme should be set down in some detail
Define responsibilities	Safety and health must be the direct operational responsibility of the line management. Appoint person as safety adviser
Establish safety regulations	The safety requirements of the organization must be met and the regulations clearly defined, widely disseminated, understood and obeyed by all
Identify problem areas	Regular audits of the operations areas will lead to continual updating of potential problems
Prepare safety programme	A programme should be designed to achieve established objectives
Implement programme	Implementation requires the commitment and involvement of all employees
Monitor progress	The safety programme should be kept to the agreed timetable
Audit and review overall effectiveness	The practical implementation and appropriateness of the safety programme should be continually compared with the objectives

Fig. 36.1 A safety plan

Some of the main points in the planning of safety are:

Plant: the design, layout and inspection of plant and equipment, including heating, lighting, storage, disposal of waste.

Processes: the design and monitoring of processes to reduce to a minimum the possibility of malfunction. Processes with high fire, toxic or explosion risks should be separated from less hazardous ones.

Workplace: the establishment and maintenance of clean and orderly places of work, with clearly defined access ways and fire exits.

Facilities: the provision and maintenance of adequate first-aid and medical facilities, and clean and hygienic wash and eating areas.

Procedures: the preparation and practice of major emergency and first-aid procedures in the event of a serious hazard situation. These should be in the form of general plans and guides, rather than tremendous detail, but they should include specific managers' duties. Establishment of close liaison with the emergency services is essential here.

Training: the provision of effective training for fire-fighting, rescue and first-aid crews.

Protection: the provision of such protective clothing and equipment as may be necessary in the light of the processes operated. It is worth remembering, however, that priority should be given to prevention over protection.

The accident prevention programme

Accident prevention is the process of removing or controlling accident causes. There are three major elements in the accident prevention process:

Workplace inspection
Accident or incident investigation and follow-up
Safety training

The first two have the same objectives: to find, record and report *possible* accident causes, and to recommend future corrective action.

Workplace inspections

There are basically six methods in general use:

1. *Safety audits and reviews* which subject each area of an organization's activity to a systematic critical examination. Every component of the total system is included, e.g. safety policy, attitudes, training, process, design features, plant construction and layout, operating procedures, emergency plans. Audits and reviews, as in the field of accountancy, aim

to disclose the strengths and weaknesses and the main areas of vulnerability or risk.

2. *Safety survey* which is a detailed, in-depth examination of a narrower field of activity, e.g. major key areas revealed by safety audits, individual plants, procedures or specific problems common to an organization as a whole.

3. *Safety inspection* which takes the form of a routine scheduled inspection of a unit or department. The inspection should check maintenance standards, employee involvement, working practices, and that work is carried out in accordance with the procedures, etc.

4. *Safety tour* which is an unscheduled examination of a work area to ensure that, for example, the standards of housekeeping are acceptable, obvious hazards are removed, and that in general safety standards are observed.

5. *Safety sampling* which measures by random sampling, similar to activity sampling, the accident potential by counting safety defects. Trained observers perform short tours of specific locations by prescribed routes and record the number of defects seen. The results may be used to portray trends in the safety situation.

6. *Hazard and operability studies* (HAZOP) which are the application of a formal, critical examination to the process and technological intentions of new or existing facilities, or to assess the hazard potential of maloperation or malfunction of equipment and the consequential effects on the facility as a whole. There are similarities between HAZOP and FMECA studies (see Chapter 9).

The design of a workplace inspection system, combining all these elements, is represented in Fig. 36.2.

Accident or incident investigations and follow-up

The investigation of accidents and near accidents can provide valuable accident prevention information. The method is based on:

Collecting data and information relating to the accident or incident.
Checking the validity of the evidence.
Selecting evidence relevant to the investigation aims.
Analysing the evidence without making assumptions or jumping to conclusions.

The results of the analysis are then used to:

Decide the most likely cause(s) of the accident or incident.
Notify immediately the person(s) able to take corrective action.
Record the findings and outcomes.
Report them to everyone concerned, to prevent a recurrence.

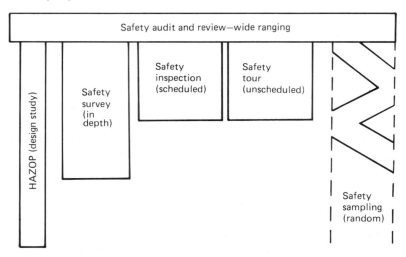

Fig. 36.2 A workplace inspection system

The investigation should not become an inquisition to apportion blame, but focus on the positive preventative aspects:

System type	Overall aim	General effects
Investigation	To prevent a similar accident	*Positive*: identification notification correction
Inquisition	To identify responsibility	*Negative*: blame claims defence

Types of follow-up to accidents and their effects

It is hoped that accidents are not normally investigated so frequently that the required skills are developed by experience, nor are these skills easily learned in a classroom. One suggested way to overcome this problem is the development of a programmed sequence of questions which form the skeleton of an accident investigation questionnaire. This can be set out using the PEEPS method to include:

Plant/Equipment — description, condition, guards, hazards, controls, access, etc.
Environment — climatic, fumes, vapour, space, humidity, noise, etc.

People   — duties, information, supervision, instruction, training, protection, etc.
Systems   — procedures, instructions, monitoring, hazard warning, permits to enter, etc.

Safety training

It is generally believed that training is an important factor in improving safety performance. For training to be effective, however, it must be planned in a systematic and objective manner. Safety training must be continuous to meet not only changes in technology, but also changes in the environment in which an organization operates, the structure of the organization and, perhaps most of all, the people involved.

Safety training activities can be considered in the form of a cycle (see Fig. 36.3), the elements of which are:

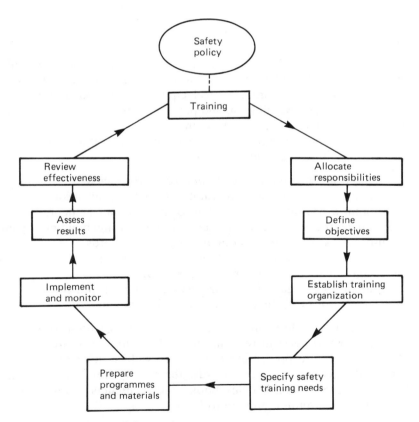

Fig. 36.3 The safety training cycle

Ensure training is part of safety policy
Allocate responsibilities for safety training
Define training objectives
Establish training organization
Specify safety training needs
Prepare training programmes and materials
Implement and monitor training
Assess the results
Review the overall effectiveness

The review process is essential for, even if the overall safety policy remains constant, there is a need to ensure that new safety training objectives are set, either to promote work changes or to raise the standards already achieved. The training organization should be similarly reviewed in the interests of continuous improvement.

Fire

Fires, like accidents, are rarely experienced by most individuals, but if a fire does occur it is likely to affect directly large numbers of people. The main causes of fire are electrical equipment, smoking, gas equipment, gas cutting and welding, oil and petrol equipment, rubbish burning, blowlamps and spontaneous combustion.

Organizing to prevent fire is, of course, the responsibility of management, and the following guidelines are useful:

1. Set up a fire prevention policy *and regularly review it.*
2. Establish clear lines of responsibilities for fire prevention.
3. Appoint a fire officer responsible to the top management.
4. Estimate the possible effects of a fire in losing buildings, plant, work-in-progress, workers, customers, plans and records.
5. Identify the fire risks, considering sources of ignition, combustible material and means whereby fire could spread.
6. Estimate the magnitudes of the risks to establish priorities.
7. Set up a fire protection drill for each department.

As with general safety, there is a wealth of information available at little or no cost to assist in reducing the risk of fire. Each fire authority in the UK has a fire prevention officer who will be delighted to advise on any matter concerning fire hazards; the Fire Prevention Association (FPA) and HMSO publish many books and pamphlets dealing with all aspects of fire prevention and control.

Health and safety at work legislation

Health and safety legislation pervades most industrialized countries. The example of UK legislation will be used in this text, but similar approaches may be found in other countries. The aim of the 'Health and Safety at Work etc. Act 1974 is to provide the legislative framework to promote, stimulate and encourage safety awareness, effective safety organization and performance, and high standards of health and safety at work. It does this by various schemes designed to suit the particular industry or organization and by the accumulation of influences and pressures, operating at many different levels, in a variety of ways and from a number of directions. The Act's provisions do not supersede any of that large body of legislation generally referred to as the Factories Acts, but it produces a framework within which these and other Acts operate. Any summary of such a complex document must be inadequate, and the Act itself should be consulted where a detailed understanding is required.

Throughout the Act the phrase 'so far as is reasonably practicable' is used frequently to condition statements and provisions. The purpose of this is to recognize that technology is advancing and that which is 'reasonably practicable' in 1990 may be trivial in the year 2000. Thus, an organization's attitude to health and safety at work must be continually changing to take cognizance of changing capabilities.

The philosophy of the Act is embodied in three clauses:

1. It is the duty of every employer to ensure the health and safety at work of all employees.
2. It is the duty of every employer and every self-employed person to conduct his undertaking in such a way as to ensure that persons not in his employment . . . are not exposed to risks to their health and safety.
3. It is the duty of every employee while at work to take reasonable care for the health and safety of himself (herself) and of other persons . . . and to co-operate with his (her) employer on matters concerning safety.

To give substance to these matters, an employer is required specifically:

1. To prepare and distribute to all employees a written statement of general policy with respect to the health and safety at work of all employees, and of the means whereby this policy is to be carried out (where five or more people are employed). An example of an acceptable policy is given in the box below.
2. Provide and maintain plant, systems, methods and places of work that are safe and without risks to health.

3. Make arrangements for ensuring safety and absence of risks to health in connection with the use, handling, storage and transport of articles and substances.

4. Provide information, instruction, supervision and training to ensure health and safety at work of all employees.

5. Provide and maintain means of access and egress which are safe and without risks.

6. Consult with employees' representatives and committees on matters concerning health and safety. Regulations and codes of practice now exist concerning the appointment of safety representatives.

7. Establish safety committees if requested by safety representatives.

8. Ensure that information is given on safe use, instructions and hazards to all non-employees who may use plant and substances.

The Act concludes with a list of *criminal* offences which arise from failure to discharge any of the duties arising from it, or from contravention of sections of the Act or the requirements of an Inspector arising from the Act. The penalties include both fines and terms in prison and are clearly designed to make all at work take the Act very seriously indeed.

Company safety policy

The company's policy is to give the greatest importance to the safety of its employees. It is considered that this is a senior management responsibility which ranks with marketing, sales, design, production and accounting.

In the design, purchase, construction, operation and maintenance of all plant, equipment and facilities, it is the duty of management to do everything possible to prevent personal injuries.

It is also the duty of every employee to exercise personal responsibility and to do everything possible to prevent injury to themselves and others.

A typical company safety policy

Recommended reading

A large number of useful Government publications are obtainable from the Health and Safety Executive (HSE). These set out facts and figures, and give guidance on how specific health and safety issues may be tackled.

Chandler, P., *An A-Z of Employment and Safety Law*, Kogan Page, 1981.

An encyclopaedic text which contains much detailed information. The emphasis is on the practical application of the law, and the book summarizes the duties and obligations of employers and employees.

Dalton, A. J. P., *Health and Safety at Work for Industrial Managers and Supervisors*, Cassell, 1982.

Possibly the most useful short text on the subject currently available. Well written with exercises in most chapters and suggested answers at the end of the book. Very usefully referenced. Thoroughly recommended.

Grimaldi, John and Simons, Rollin H., *Safety Management*, 4th edn, Irwin, 1984.

A handbook and a mine of useful information.

Pantry, Sheila, Edit. *Health and Safety: A Guide to Sources of Information*, Capital Planning Info, 1985.

Useful for the health and safety officer.

Ritson, John, *Health and Safety at Work Act*, Ravenswood Publications, 1983.

A down-to-earth practical guide to the health and safety legislation in the UK.

Appendices

Appendix 1
A–B–C analysis

One of the most useful analyses which can be carried out on a set of data is the *A–B–C*, or *Pareto* analysis. The way in which this is done is best shown by means of an example. The income and the contribution from the products sold by an organization are (in appropriate monetary units):

Product	Income	Contribution	Product	Income	Contribution
T214	102	−11	N204	57	17
N305	4	0	S271	35	10
T114	63	2	T274	20	6
F257	245	42	A079	0	0
P244	217	59	F103	9	3
H121	23	5	W151	42	13
N211	105	24	P215	90	29
B100	43	10	S173	27	9
P218	0	0	H227	62	21
B237	42	10	B166	188	64
A186	519	131	A153	62	21
H132	41	11	N190	59	20
A138	24	7	P191	6	2
B172	0	0	H247	382	133
S284	23	7	A126	6	2
W197	24	7	P229	413	147
A056	0	0	T155	335	121
S107	31	9	F253	19	7
			Totals	3,318	938

Thus, product T214 produces a total income of £102, and a contribution of −£11, N305 a total income of £4 and a contribution of £0, and so on.

Two analyses are possible: income against product range, and contribution against product range. Both are carried out in the same way, and the income against product range analysis will be described in detail.

Step 1. Rank the products in order of descending income (as in Table 1). (*Note* if the data originates from a set of cards, it is most convenient to 'shuffle' them into the appropriate ranking. Where there is a large number of items, the sorting is best carried out by computer.)

Table 1 Product-income ranking (1)

Rank	Product	Income
1	A186	519
2	P229	413
3	H247	382
4	T155	335
5	F257	245
6	P244	217
7	B166	188
8	N211	105
9	T214	102
10	P215	90
11	T114	63
12	A153	62
13	H227	62
14	N190	59
15	N204	57
16	B100	43
17	B237	42
18	W151	42
19	H132	41
20	S271	35
21	S107	31
22	S173	27
23	A138	24
24	W197	24
25	H121	23
26	S284	23
27	T274	20
28	F253	19
29	F103	9
30	A126	6
31	P191	6
32	N305	4
33	B172	0
34	A079	0
35	P218	0
36	A056	0
	Total	3,318

Step 2. Accumulate the individual incomes (as in Table 2).

Table 2 Product-income ranking (2)

Rank	Product	Income	Accumulated income
1	A186	519	519
2	P229	413	932
3	H247	382	1,314
4	T155	335	1,649
5	F257	245	1,894
6	P244	217	2,111
7	B166	188	2,299
8	N211	105	2,404
9	T214	102	2,506
10	P215	90	2,596
11	T114	63	2,659
12	A153	62	2,721
13	H227	62	2,783
14	N190	59	2,842
15	N204	57	2,899
16	B100	43	2,942
17	B237	42	2,984
18	W151	42	3,026
19	H132	41	3,067
20	S271	35	3,102
21	S107	31	3,133
22	S173	27	3,160
23	A138	24	3,184
24	W197	24	3,208
25	H121	23	3,231
26	S284	23	3,254
27	T274	20	3,274
28	F253	19	3,293
29	F103	9	3,302
30	A126	6	3,308
31	P191	6	3,314
32	N305	4	3,318
33	B172	0	3,318
34	A079	0	3,318
35	P218	0	3,318
36	A056	0	3,318
	Total	3,318	

Step 3. Divide the total number of items into convenient groups (in the example used, these are groups of 3) and calculate the accumulated percentage of the total range of products represented by each group, and

the accumulated percentage of total income represented by each group. The result is shown in Table 3.

Table 3 Product-income ranking (3)

Percentage of range	Rank	Product	Income	Accumulated income	Percentage of income
	1	A816	519	519	
	2	P229	413	932	
8.3	3	H247	382	1,314	39.6
	4	T155	335	1,649	
	5	F257	245	1,894	
16.6	6	P244	217	2,111	63.5
	7	B166	188	2,299	
	8	N211	105	2,404	
25.0	9	T214	102	2,506	75.4
	10	P215	90	2,596	
	11	T114	63	2,659	
33.3	12	A153	62	2,721	81.5
	13	H227	62	2,783	
	14	N190	59	2,842	
41.6	15	N204	57	2,899	87.2
	16	B100	43	2,942	
	17	B237	42	2,984	
50.0	18	W151	42	3,026	90.5
	19	N132	41	3,067	
	20	S271	35	3,102	
58.3	21	S107	31	3,133	94.3
	22	S173	27	3,160	
	23	A138	24	3,184	
66.6	24	W197	24	3,208	97.5
	25	H121	23	3,231	
	26	S284	23	3,254	
75.0	27	T274	20	3,274	98.5
	28	F253	19	3,293	
	29	F103	9	3,302	
83.3	30	A126	6	3,308	99.0
	31	P191	6	3,314	
	32	N305	4	3,318	
91.6	33	B172	0	3,318	99.5
	34	A079	0	3,318	
	35	P218	0	3,318	
100.0	36	A056	0	3,318	100

This table is one form of A–B–C analysis, but it is more usual to represent it graphically (see Fig. 1). Table 4 and Fig. 2 show the corresponding product range/contribution analysis.

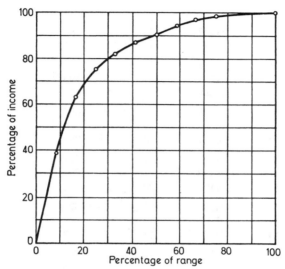

Fig. 1 Range v. income

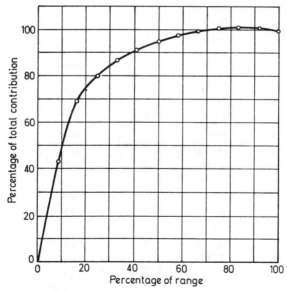

Fig. 2 Range v. contribution

Table 4 Product-contribution analysis

Percentage of range	Rank	Product	Contribution	Accumulated contribution	Percentage of total contribution
	1	P229	147	147	
	2	H247	133	280	
8.3	3	A186	131	411	43.8
	4	T155	121	532	
	5	B166	64	596	
16.6	6	P244	59	655	69.7
	7	F257	42	697	
	8	P215	29	726	
25.0	9	N211	24	750	80.0
	10	H227	21	771	
	11	A153	21	792	
33.3	12	N190	20	812	86.5
	13	N204	17	829	
	14	W151	13	842	
41.6	15	H132	11	853	91.0
	16	B100	10	863	
	17	S271	10	873	
	18	B237	10	883	
50.0	19	S173	9	872	94.0
	20	S107	9	901	
58.3	21	S284	7	908	96.7
	22	A138	7	915	
	23	W197	7	922	
66.6	24	F253	7	929	98.8
	25	T274	6	935	
	26	H121	5	940	
75.0	27	F103	3	943	100.5
	28	P191	2	945	
	29	A126	2	947	
83.3	30	T114	2	949	101
	31	N305	0	949	
	32	P218	0	949	
91.6	33	B172	0	949	101
	34	A056	0	949	
	35	A079	0	949	
100.0	36	T214	−11	938	100
		Total	938	938	100

The result shown by Table 3 and Fig. 1, that a large proportion of income is represented by a small proportion of range, is quite usual. Frequently, an 80/20 relationship is found, 80 per cent of one result being represented by only 20 per cent of the possible causes, and some writers refer to an '80/20 law'. Claims for such generality are probably too strong, but there is no doubt that it is extremely common to find a pattern of results similar to Figs 1 and 2.

Deductions from an A–B–C analysis

Having carried out an A–B–C analysis, it is tempting to draw too many deductions from it. For example, Fig. 1 could suggest that all products from B100 onwards should be discontinued as the income they produce is trivial. This need not necessarily be justified, as some of the products may not have acquired any maturity in the market. Similarly, a high income item may produce a very low contribution, and there may be a good case for discontinuing this item. The A–B–C analysis will help to put problems into perspective: it is a tool to *assist* decision-making, not a 'go-no-go' gauge in itself.

When an A–B–C analysis can be useful

1. *Production control.* In a factory making large numbers of batches, an A–B–C analysis will often reveal that detailed control of a few works orders will control the bulk of the workload of the factory.
2. *Material control.* Analysis of annual usage commonly shows a concentration of value in a comparatively small number of items, so that if there are 10,000 items in stock at any one time, control of 20 per cent of these will effect control of 80 per cent of annual spending. This leads to a stock classification system whereby the first 'slice' is closely controlled, the next 'slice' (say from 20 per cent to 50 per cent of the ranked items) is controlled with less precision, and the remaining 'slice' (from 50 per cent to 100 per cent of the ranked items) is controlled very loosely. These three 'slices' are often known as A items, B items and C items, and it is in the field of material control that the term A–B–C analysis was first used.
3. *Quality control.* Assigning defectives to causes frequently demonstrates that the bulk of them originate from very few causes.
4. *Variety reduction.* This has already been discussed.
5. *Maintenance.* Calculation of time lost due to breakdown against assignable causes often assists in planning a maintenance programme.

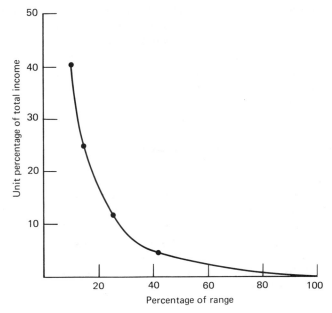

Fig. 3 Range v. unit income

An alternative A–B–C display

It is sometimes useful to display results in a different manner. After step 1, where the items are ranked, the *individual* value of each item is calculated *as a percentage of the total*. Thus, item A186, which is rank 1, provides 519 units to a total of 3,318 units, that is 15.6 per cent. This is done for each item, or group of items—see step 3—and the resulting curve will be as Fig. 3.

Recommended reading

Juran, J. M., *Managerial Breakthrough*, McGraw-Hill, 1965.
   Though over 20 years old, this book is well worth reading. Dr Juran shows how an A–B–C (Pareto) analysis can be applied to a wide variety of managerial problems.

Appendix 2
Activity sampling—number of observations required

N random observations of the proportionate occurrence of a statistic form a sample, size N, of mean proportionate occurrence π drawn from a population with a true proportionate occurrence P and a standard error:

$$\text{S.E.} = \sqrt{\frac{P(1 - P)}{N}}$$

In repeated sampling:

67% of the values of π lie between $P \pm 1$ S.E.
95% of the values of π lie between $P \pm 2$ S.E.
99.7% of the values of π lie between $P \pm 3$ S.E.

The inaccuracy resulting from taking π as an estimate of P may be expressed as L and for the 95 per cent (confidence) limits:

$$L \leqslant 2 \text{ S.E.}$$

that is:

$$L \leqslant 2 \sqrt{\frac{P(1 - P)}{N}}$$

Thus, the number of observations N necessary to achieve an accuracy L at the 95 per cent confidence level is:

$$N \leqslant \frac{4P(1 - P)}{L^2} \qquad \text{where } P \text{ and } L \text{ are expressed as proportions}$$

or:

$$N \leqslant \frac{4P(100 - P)}{L^2} \qquad \text{where } P \text{ and } L \text{ are expressed as percentages}$$

If $P = 20$ per cent and $L = 3$ per cent (that is, the value of P lies between 17 and 23 per cent), then:

$$N = \frac{4 \times 20 \ (100 - 20)}{3 \times 3} = 711$$

Some typical values for this calculation are shown in the following table:

		\multicolumn{9}{c}{Percentage occurrence P}
		10	15	20	25	30	35	40	45	50
L = Acceptable percentage accuracy	1	3,600	5,100	6,400	7,500	8,400	9,100	9,600	9,900	10,000
	2	900	1,275	1,600	1,875	2,100	2,275	2,400	2,475	2,500
	3	400	567	711	833	933	1,011	1,066	1,100	1,111
	4	225	319	400	469	525	569	600	618	625
	5	144	204	256	300	336	364	384	396	400
	6	100	142	178	208	233	252	267	275	278
	7	73	104	130	153	171	186	196	202	204
	8	56	80	100	117	131	142	150	155	156
	9	44	63	79	93	104	112	119	122	123
	10	36	51	64	75	84	91	96	99	100

This calculation expresses the accuracy in absolute terms. It may be more convenient to express the accuracy in relative terms: as a proportion l of the proportion occurrence P.

This means $L = lP$ where l is the relative accuracy, so:

$$L = lP = 2 \sqrt{\frac{P(1 - P)}{N}}$$

$$l^2 P^2 = \frac{4P(1 - P)}{N}$$

or

$$N = \frac{4P(1 - P)}{l^2 P^2} = \frac{4(1 - P)}{l^2 P}$$

where P and l are expressed as proportions.

Alternatively,

$$N = \frac{4(100 - P) \times 100^2}{l^2 P}$$

where P and l are expressed as percentages.

Suppose a factor occurs 25 per cent of the time ($P = 0.25$), and a relative accuracy in P of 10 per cent ($l = 0.10$) is acceptable (that is it lies between $25 \pm 0.1 \times 25$ or 22.5 to 27.5 per cent), then the number of observations required:

$$N = \frac{4 \times (1 - 0.25)}{(0.1)^2 \, 0.25} = 1,200$$

or

$$N = \frac{4 \times (100 - 25) \times 100^2}{(10)^2 \times 25} = 1,200$$

Appendix 3
Derivation of an exponentially weighted moving average

Forecast for week N

$$= \text{weighted average } M_{N-1}$$

i.e. $\quad F_N = M_{N-1}$

$$= \alpha_1 A_{N-1} + \alpha_2 A_{N-2} + \ldots \alpha_{N-1} A_1$$

where $\quad A_t = $ Actual value at time t

and $\quad \alpha_t = $ weighting factor

The weighting is chosen so that:

$$\frac{\alpha_2}{\alpha_1} = \frac{\alpha_3}{\alpha_2} = \frac{\alpha_4}{\alpha_3} = \ldots \text{ constant } r$$

where $r < 1$.

So:

$$a_2 = r\alpha_1$$
$$\alpha_3 = r\alpha_2 = r^2\alpha_1$$
$$\alpha_4 = r\alpha_3 = r^3\alpha_1$$

The weights, therefore, form an exponential series diminishing in size as the actual values become older.

To obtain a true average:

$$\alpha_1 + \alpha_2 + \alpha_3 + \ldots = 1$$

then:

$$\alpha_1 + r\alpha_1 + r^2\alpha_1 + r^3\alpha_1 + \ldots = 1$$

i.e. $\quad \alpha_1 (1 + r + r^2 + r^3 + \ldots = 1$

i.e. $\quad \alpha_1 \left(1 + \sum_1^\infty r^t\right) = 1$

i.e. $\quad \alpha_1 \left(1 + \frac{r}{1-r}\right) = 1$

i.e. $\quad \dfrac{\alpha_1}{1-r} = 1$

and

$$r = 1 - \alpha_1$$

Now:

$$
\begin{aligned}
F_N &= \alpha_1 A_{N-1} + r\alpha_1 A_{N-2} + r^2\alpha_1 A_{N-3} + \ldots \\
&= \alpha_1 A_{N-1} + r(\alpha_1 A_{N-2} + r\alpha_1 A_{N-3} + \ldots) \\
&= \alpha_1 A_{N-1} + rF_{N-1} \\
&= \alpha_1 A_{N-1} + (1 - \alpha_1)F_{N-1} \\
&= F_{N-1} + \alpha_1(A_{N-1} - F_{N-1})
\end{aligned}
$$

Appendix 4
The learning curve

It is well established that the time taken for an individual to carry out a task will depend upon, among other factors, the experience of the operator, and that speed of performance and number of repetitions are related by a curve of the general shape of Fig. 1.

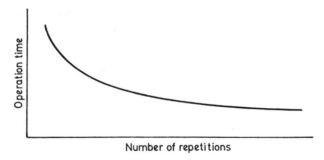

Fig. 1 Learning curve

This curve is the *learning curve* of the operator for a particular task, and some observers claim to have detected noticeable learning even for short-cycle tasks after 1,000 or more repetitions. The slope of the curve at any point would seem to depend upon intelligence, motivation and age.

Organizations, which are groups of individuals, seem also to exhibit the same learning characteristics *but in a more predictable form*. The first observations of this phenomenon were by T. P. Wright in the US aircraft industry, and his findings have been repeated by many later workers. The learning curve for an organization is given by Wright's Law:

For any operation which is repeated, the mean time for the operation will decrease by a fixed fraction as the number of repetitions double.

Wright found that the reduction fraction was 0.8, so that an operation obeying Wright's Law would have the following time characteristics:

Time for first operation			100
Mean time for first two operations	= 100	× 0.8 =	80
Mean time for first four operations	= 80	× 0.8 =	64
Mean time for first eight operations	= 64	× 0.8 =	51.2
Mean time for first sixteen operations	= 51.2	× 0.8 =	40.96

and so on, giving the curve of Fig. 2, which is plotted on normal cartesian co-ordinates, or Fig. 3, which is plotted on log-log co-ordinates.

Later work in fields other than the aircraft industry suggests that the fraction is not necessarily 0.8 and that its value depends upon the

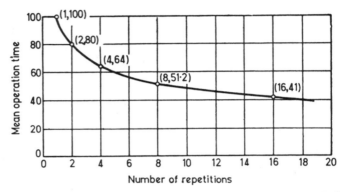

Fig. 2 Learning curve obeying Wright's Law (reduction fraction 0.8) (linear scales)

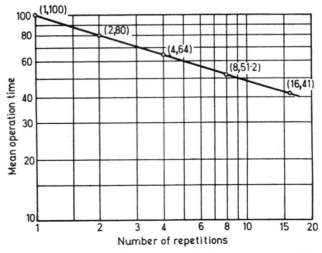

Fig. 3 Learning curve obeying Wright's Law (reduction fraction 0.8) (logarithmic scales)

proportion of labour which is man-controlled. The following figures were given by Herschmann:

% of labour which is man-controlled	Reduction fraction
75	80
50	85
25	90

Appearance of the learning curve

The process of learning by an organization is no more automatic than the process of learning by an individual and, as with an individual, the most important factor appears to be motivation, which arises from a belief that something can be learnt and that it is desirable that it should be learnt. An organization which believes that it has no need or no room to improve is unlikely to demonstrate any marked learning.

Apart from this apathy, there are other factors which will depress learning:

(*a*) Lack of continuity. If a process is repeated, and then stopped, and then restarted after a time break, the mean time will increase immediately after the time break.

(*b*) Restrictions to output. Some circumstances can give rise to deliberate restrictions in output—for example, the operation of some incentive schemes, the existence of 'cost-plus' pricing, the belief or knowledge that work is coming to an end.

Desire to improve
Ability to improve
Absence of time breaks
Absence of restricting factors

Factors affecting learning in an organization

Recommended reading

Note: The learning curve: the author knows of no significant work currently in print which deals exclusively with this topic.

Bestwick, P. F. and Lockyer, K. G., *Quantitative Production Management*, Pitman Books, London 1982.

Chapter 19 discusses this topic.

Appendix 5
Representative examination questions

Unlike the practice in previous editions, the sources of questions have not been identified. There are reasons for this:

1. The authors have found that questions are quite widely used and that identification of source is difficult.

2. Many questions have had to be modified in order to provide sensible figures—inflation made the original figures appear nonsense.

3. Some questions which are still useful—a good examination question, like a good joke, never dies—were derived from institutions which no longer exist.

We would, nevertheless, like to thank all the authors of questions and hope that they will appreciate and accept our reasons.

Chapter 1 The production/operations function within the corporation

1. Define 'operations'.
How will the actions of the marketing department affect the behaviour of the operational department?

2. What is to be sold is strictly the affair of marketing, while how it is to be produced is strictly the affair of operations.'
Comment.

3. Operations management is necessarily a complex task. Suggest ways in which it can be simplified.

4. Discuss the definition: 'Operations management is the management of the transformation process.'

5. Sketch a framework for auditing the operations function.

Chapter 2 Planning

1. Why is good market research an essential basis for good operations management?

2. 'From: The Marketing Manager
   To: The Operations Manager

One of my reps. tells me that he can get an order—which could lead to substantial annual orders—for a product which would nicely fill up the spare capacity which you were telling me about. Moreover, the quality required is inferior to our present range so that you could transfer over any less satisfactory resources on to this job. Of course the profit margin is not so great as we would normally expect, but since your resources are not fully occupied it would, nevertheless, be an increase in total profit. As the volumes both immediate and potential are substantial I shall take no action until I hear from you. Details of the product are being passed to you by my rep. John Smith.'

As an operations manager, what would be your response?

3. Discuss the proposition 'All objectives must be considered and optimized simultaneously'. Illustrate your answer with examples of your own choice.

4. 'Change is now the norm.' Discuss this statement with particular reference to the operational aspects of an organization.

5. Preparing procedural manuals for, say, quality assurance, material control, credit checking is a bureaucratic waste of time. Discuss.

Chapter 3 Control

1. All successful management control systems appear to have a number of features in common. List and discuss these features.

2. Show the similarities between 'production control' and 'quality control'.

3. What are the advantages of an explicitly designed control system over simple annual reports of performance.

4. Discuss the proposition 'Control is only possible if choice of action is present'.

5. 'It is always desirable to measure as precisely as possible.' Discuss.

Chapter 4 Budgets and budgetary control

1. What is meant by the 'break-even' point? An organization whose fixed costs are £5,625,000 sells a single product for £31.25 each. The unit material cost is £9.375, while the other costs, assumed to be wholly variable, are £10.625 a unit. Graphically or otherwise, determine:

(*a*) the break-even point;

(*b*) the volume sold which will produce a profit of 10 per cent on the selling price;

(*c*) the effect on the break-even point of a reduction in material cost of 10 per cent.

2. What are the objectives which would influence you in setting up a system of budgetary control? Write short notes about the activities for which you would budget.

3. Marginal costing allied to the employment of the break-even chart has particular value in the jobbing environment.

(*a*) Give reasons why this should be the case.

(*b*) Outline, for this situation, the method of using (i) marginal costing techniques; (ii) break-even charts and profit analysis; (iii) budgetary planning and control with four-weekly reporting and analysis.

4. Outline the scope and limitation of controlling a manufacturing concern through its budget.

5. What is budgetary control? Show as fully as possible how this technique is used by management to control expense, and draw up a typical expense budget for a department in your own works.

Chapter 5   Classification and coding

1. Define:

(*a*) classification;

(*b*) coding

Construct a simple classification and coding system for any group of articles or activities with which you are familiar.

2. 'We know all the parts we have in store and as a small undertaking we don't want the bother of giving code numbers to everything.' Discuss.

3. Discuss the premise 'The efficiency of a designer can be increased by a good coding system'.

4. What is a 'field' in a classification system?

5. Discuss the desirable characteristics of a good coding system.

Chapter 6   Control of variety

1. Discuss the useful scope of standardization (*a*) of products, (*b*) of operating methods and (*c*) of management techniques, making some reference to the possible methods of achieving such standardization.

2. Of what significance is standardization and simplification to:

(*a*) operations manager;
(*b*) marketing manager;
(*c*) consumer?

3. (a) Explain how a company should undertake a comprehensive variety reduction exercise and describe the benefits which such an exercise might yield.

(*b*) Table 1 gives sales and cost data for a range of products. Which products should be considered as possible lines to discontinue?

Table 1

Product	Selling price (£)	Sales volume	Material cost (£)	Labour cost (£)	Overhead (£)
1	100	100	20	20	50
2	50	20	10	10	26
3	71	40	30	20	36
4	3	900	1	4	2
5	27	400	5	5	14
6	61	50	12	10	30
7	22	40	4	2	10
8	16	30	3	1	10
9	107	20	22	20	80
10	20	100	4	2	10

4. From the operation manager's point of view, what benefits accrue from carrying out a variety reduction programme?

Discuss some ways in which such a programme may be carried out.

5. The agenda of the board of directors of a travel company contains an item 'that this company shall seek to double the number of package holidays offered within the next two years'. As an operations director, what would be your response?

6. The 'Credit' department of a large company involved in hiring equipment to a wide range of companies has a credit system whereby customers can submit queries to the department. The rental fee is not normally paid until the query has been resolved. This affects the cash flow of the company in addition to the costs associated with dealing with the query. In some cases, the invoice will be adjusted or a credit note issued; in other cases, no adjustment is needed. Typical examples in this latter class are (*d*) the customer's misunderstanding of the agreement. (*b*) the customer's misreading of the invoice itself, (*c*) transfer of the equipment to another site, resulting in the invoice being wrongly addressed.

Each query is given a code number identifying the type of query, the code numbers running from 01–17. 5,561 queries were received over a 3-month period, these being distributed amongst the codes as follows:

Nature of query	Credit code	Queries
Duplicated charges	01	274
Incorrect sales/rental tariff used	02	309
Trade-in credit to customers changing from competitor's product	03	1
Quality dispute—service	04	19
Quality dispute—machines	05	4
Incorrect invoice/credit note/invoice calculation	06	452
Incorrect allowance/discount	07	218
No proof of indebtedness to company	08	11
Non-cost adjustments (i.e. no credit given)	09	3,460
Machine discontinuation	10	304
Misrepresentation—waive minimum billing	11	11
Misrepresentation—non-standard terms	12	204
Delivery dispute—machines	13	117
Delivery dispute—consumables	14	10
Incorrect meter reading	15	138
Debt not worth pursuing	16	12
VAT adjustment	17	19

You are asked to look at ways of reducing the staff within the credit department. What initial action would you take? What additional benefits may accrue from the exercise?

Chapter 7 Control of value

1. Discuss the techniques associated with value analysis. Illustrate your answer with examples.
2. Discuss the use of value analysis in a non-manufacturing situation such as a bank.
3. What is value analysis? How is it carried out, and how should the recommendations resulting from value analysis be presented to management?
4. Describe the methods of value analysis and discuss the structure of a value analysis team.
5. Comment on the phrase seen in an advertisement: 'Price £15 . . . today's value £20.'

Chapter 8 Quality

1. Quality cannot be 'inspected' or checked into a service, nor can it be advertised in. Explain this statement with respect to the services offered by an hotel.

2. Explain the role played by the managing director of a manufacturing company in its quality assurance activities. What organizational features should exist for promoting and controlling quality?

3. Describe the various components of 'total quality related costs' and explain how they are inter-related. Discuss what action management may take to reduce these costs.

4. Quality is often said to be everyone's business, but what are the elements of an effective quality management system, and what are its detailed information requirements?

5. Explain the principles and operation of quality circles. How can they help an organization such as a bank to improve its overall efficiency?

Chapter 9 Reliability

1. Explain what is meant by the reliability of a product. Indicate what influence the designer may have on reliability.

2. Discuss the various types and causes of failure and explain how 'failure mode, effect and criticality analysis' (FMECA) can be used to reduce the frequency of its occurrence.

3. Bruddersford Breweries have recently introduced a new 'party dispenser' pack, which basically consists of a re-fillable spherical container mounted in a cylindrical jacket. It is fitted with taps for filling and dispensing, and with a 'pressure' cartridge. The original batch, assembled for the test market, met with such a favourable response that the company was encouraged to start large-scale production for the national market. The quality of the product, as monitored during production and by final inspection, seemed satisfactory. However, customers soon complained of various malfunctions, such as leaks, loss of pressure, etc. How would you institute a reliability management programme to cure the problems and prevent their recurrence?

4. Oakman and Lockland Ltd operate a preventative maintenance programme in their polishing shop. Each machine is overhauled at six-monthly intervals. One set of items—the polishing brushes—are routinely replaced at this time, irrespective of their condition. An experiment has been carried out recently in which the performance of a batch of one hundred brushes was monitored. These brushes were only replaced at the overhaul if they were thought to be unsatisfactory.

Brushes failing between overhauls are replaced immediately. The table below shows the number of brushes replaced each month. Draw the 'bath-tub' curve and explain how it could be used to design a maintenance policy for the brushes. What additional information might be required?

Months in service	1	2	3	4	5	6	7	8	9	10	11	12	13	14	15	16	17	18
Number failed in month	2	1	2	2	1	5	0	2	1	2	2	5	2	3	4	4	5	8

5. You have been appointed as a trainee production manager at the Backwoods plant of the Bruddersford Group. Your first assignment is to prepare a report on the 'Polykayoss' plant. One problem is that a key part of a transmission drive appears to be subject to frequent breakdowns with consequential production losses. You are able to find records of time to first breakdown of a batch of thirty components installed a year ago (see table below). Your supervisor is convinced that these failures are 'burn-in' failures. Is he correct?

1 period = 4 weeks   No. of components installed = 30

Period no.	1	2	3	4	5	6	7	8	9	10	11	12	13
Number suffering first breakdown	1	3	5	8	11	14	16	19	22	23	24	26	27

Chapter 10 Design of the product

1. What principles should be considered in creating designs for economic production? To what extent should the operations department be allowed to influence the design of a product?

2. List and explain the need for the information which should be written into a design specification.

3. List the principal stages in the design of a product and suggest a method of organizing the design work, indicating where the responsibility lies at each stage.

4. 'Thinking cannot be timed.' Discuss this remark with particular reference to the design of a product.

5. 'The design department is the cradle of operating costs.' Discuss this statement and suggest the contribution that the design department could make towards minimizing such costs.

Chapter 11 Location and design of the plant

1. A rapidly expanding company, occupying rented premises extending to about 30,000 square feet on an industrial estate, is looking for a new site, about four times this size. List the factors to be considered in finding a suitable location.

2. Explain how various alternative sites, which have been identified by the company in question 1, should be evaluated and a selection made.

3. How may the choice of location affect the activities of a non-manufacturing organization such as a management consultancy?

4. What contribution can the following make to solving a plant location problem:

(*a*) linear programming;
(*b*) a computer?

5. Discuss the factors which must be considered in the design of office premises for the head office of a large building society.

Chapter 12 Layout of the plant

1. A decision has to be made to arrange the layout of a factory, either by grouping similar types of machines together in separate sections or by arranging them in sequence for line production.

Give the factors you would consider in order to arrive at a decision and state the advantages and disadvantages of the sequential method of layout.

2. (a) Discuss the different criteria which could be used to assess the layout of production facilities.

(*b*) List the information you would require to lay out equipment in an empty warehouse which is being converted to a manufacturing workshop.

(*c*) Describe the method of sequence analysis and show how each piece of information obtained would be used to complete the layout. How can a computer help in this process?

3. A Pareto analysis of work flow reveals that, of the total of 50 different items processed, 9 constitute more than three-quarters of the total number of movements. Materials for all jobs are requested from an issuing store and the jobs are finally delivered to a finished goods store. Details of these 9 items are as shown overleaf:

Product type	1	2	3	4	5	6	7	8	9
Volume (*in units*) per unit time	5,000	3,000	7,000	2,000	1,000	4,000	5,000	3,000	800
Units per load moved	100	10	70	10	50	20	250	100	20
Operation no.	*Work centre performing the operation*								
1	A	F	F	A	A	B	D	G	A
2	B	G	G	B	C	C	A	H	B
3	C	H	H	C	B	A	D	K	C
4	D	J	J	D	D	H	C	J	D
5	E	K	G	K	A	J	B	H	E
6	K		K	E	K	K	J	J	F
7	A			C	H	C	K	B	G
8	F			G	J	D	G		H
9					K				J
10									K

The approximate areas of the work centres and stores are:

Work centre	A	B	C	D	E	F	G	H	J	K	Issuing store	Receiving store
Areas (m²)	100	120	80	60	90	60	105	130	100	120	210	250

It is required that all the above be accommodated within the following rectangular plan area:

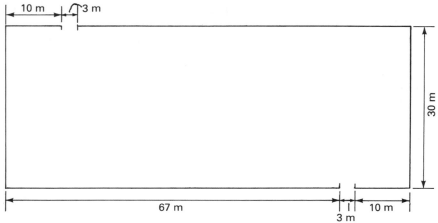

All aisles must be at least 3 metres wide.

(*a*) From the above, deduce the travel chart.

(*b*) From question *a*, deduce the journeys between the chart.

(*c*) Suggest a possible schematic diagram.

(*d*) Draw a scaled plan area diagram showing the location of (i) all work centres, (ii) aisles, (iii) issuing and receiving stores.

4. The process involved in the manufacture of a product is as follows: It starts with the manufacture of four components, A, B, C, D. A, B and C are then used in the manufacture of sub-assembly E, which is then used with component D to make F. G is manufactured from F, and the finished product, H, is manufactured from G. The times for these elements are given below:

Element	A	B	C	D	E	F	G	H
Time (min)	2.3	3.6	4.1	3.1	6.2	1.5	3.2	1.1

Output is set at 50 units per 8-hour day.

Draw the precedence diagram. Determine the minimum number of stages required if flow production methods are to be used. Suggest an allocation of elements to stages and discuss this allocation.

5. A product consisting of 17 work elements is to be produced down a flow production line. The work elements, their standard times and inter-relationships are given in the table below.

Work element	A	B	C	D	E	F	G	H	I	J	K	L	M	N	P	R	S
Work content (sec)	8	4	12	7	10	4	10	8	12	3	6	4	8	2	4	3	5
Preceded by	–	–		A	B,C	C	D,E	F	G,H	I	I	J	K	L	L,M	N	P

The technological zoning constraints are that elements A and E *must not* be carried out at the same work station and elements G and I *must* be carried out at the same work station.

If 120 products are required from the line per hour:

(*a*) Suggest a suitable assembly line allocation of work elements to work stations.

(*b.*) What is the total balance delay and balance loss in the system you have designed?

(*c*) Can the balance delay and balance loss be reduced?

Chapter 13 Equipment selection

1. A small company is considering the purchase of a new lorry. List and discuss the factors which should be considered before making a recommendation, and indicate the components of a specification.

2. Briefly outline the basic principles and comment on the practical application involved in:

(a) payback period method;
(b) accounting rate of return method;
(c) discounted cash flow method of economic evaluation of plant or equipment.

3. A plant engineer was considering the choice of purchasing one of two drilling machines, machine P and machine Q, both technically efficient and of the latest design. They both equally do the job sought in the factory.

Machine P costs £50,000 to purchase, whereas machine Q costs £60,000 to purchase. Machine P is estimated to last 8 years with a salvage value of £10,000 at the end of this period. Machine Q is estimated to last 10 years with a salvage value of also £10,000 at the end of 10 years.

Machine P is estimated to cost £6,000, £3,000 and £2,000 respectively for operating, power and maintenance expenses. Machine Q is estimated to cost £5,000, £2,000 and £1,000 respectively for operating, power and maintenance expenses.

Assuming a current rate of interest or cost of capital at 10 per cent, which machine should the plant engineer choose?

Critically comment on the assumptions made. Would you, as plant engineer, assess the machines solely upon economic or cost considerations?

4. Explain the principles of discounting cash flows. A new photo-copying machine costs £5,400 to buy. The annual running cost and second-hand values vary with age as shown below:

Age (years)	1	2	3	4	5	6	7
Annual running cost (£)	700	780	880	1,000	1,150	1,300	1,500
Second-hand value (£)	4,400	3,600	2,900	2,400	2,000	1,700	1,500

Assuming discounting is not required, find the most economic age for replacement in the following circumstances:

(a) a machine is required for an indefinite future;
(b) the current machine is now three years old and a machine is only required for five more years.

Discuss the theory employed and explain any changes which become necessary if cash flows are to be discounted.

5. Investment decisions for items of capital plant and equipment

require consideration of numerous costs other than that of the item itself. What other costs are involved and how would an operations manager approach the task of selecting and justifying plant for a new project?

Chapter 14 Maintenance of the plant

1. State the objectives of maintenance and explain the various types of maintenance policies available to an organization.

2. State what you understand by the term 'preventative maintenance' as applied to a factory, and describe the features of such a system of maintenance.

3. Present the case for planned maintenance and outline the basic elements of a planned maintenance scheme. How has the approach to maintenance changed over recent times?

4. Show how data on reliability of plant may be used in maintenance decisions, indicating the changes in approach which may be required throughout the life of equipment in use.

5. (*a*) What is meant by replacement theory?

Discuss the main factors that require consideration in developing a replacement policy.

(*b*) A manager finds from past records that the costs per year of running an item of plant whose purchase price is £3,000 are as given below:

Year	1	2	3	4	5	6	7	8
Running costs (£)	500	600	700	900	1,150	1,400	1,700	2,000
Resale price (£)	1,500	750	375	185	100	100	100	100

How often should the plant be replaced?

Chapter 15 Types of production I: job, batch, flow

1. Define and discuss:-

(*a*) job production;
(*b*) batch production;
(*c*) flow production;
(*d*) mass production;
(*e*) group technology.

2. Discuss the kinds of problems likely to be encountered when a new production method involving a number of work stations on a flow line is installed.

3. Explain what you consider to be the main requirements which must

be met to maintain effective flow production in a factory. Discuss in what circumstances you consider that this type of production would be most suitable and what advantage you would expect to obtain from its introduction.

4. What circumstances necessitate the use of batch production methods of manufacture? Describe the characteristics of this method of manufacture and the managerial problems involved.

5. 'Flow production made possible mass transportation and thus changed the world.' Discuss:

(*a*) the factors which brought about flow production; and

(*b*) an alternative means of organizing production, and its claimed advantages over flow production.

Chapter 16 Types of production II: group technology

1. What is meant by a 'cell' in group technology? Assuming that you were in a position to install group technology, what factors would you consider in setting up the first cell?

2. 'Group technology is all very well, but it must result in under-utilization of plant, and this must increase costs.' Discuss.

3. The reduction of set-up times is only one of the benefits of group technology. Discuss some of the others.

4. Discuss the proposition that group technology has a profound influence upon the administrative tasks carried out within a factory.

5. Batch production has traditionally suffered from the disadvantages of relatively long set-up time, high work-in-progress and extensive material movement. How does the adoption of a 'group technology' approach help to tackle these problems?

Why do you feel that group technology has been under-exploited in recent years?

Chapter 17 Work study I: method study

1. 'Work study is seen by the work force as a means whereby management can either get more work done for the same pay or the same work done for less pay.'

Discuss the above statement in the context of what you regard as the correct objectives for work study in production/operations management.

2. 'Work study consists of the two distinct and unrelated techniques of method study and work measurement.'

Discuss.

3. 'The principal objective of work study is to achieve higher productivity.'

Discuss this statement with particular reference to the role played by method study.

4. Explain what you understand by the following in the context of work study:

(*a*) the questioning technique;
(*b*) flow process charts;
(*c*) flow diagrams.

5. (*a*) Many organizations neglect the area of materials handling yet simple guidelines and a structured approach to this can bring real benefits.
Discuss.

(*b*) While work study aims at improving productivity, the environment in which work is carried out can have a significant influence on efficiency.
Discuss.

Chapter 18 Work study II: work measurement

1. (*a*) A job consisting of four work elements is timed and rated through five cycles, the results of which are presented below:

							Element	
Cycle	*1*		*2*		*3*		*4*	
	OT	R	OT	R	OT	R	OT	R
1	1.54	100	3.10	100	2.21	95	4.12	100
2	1.68	90	3.31	95	2.10	100	4.27	95
3	1.41	110	2.91	105	2.07	105	3.90	105
4	1.21	130	2.21	140	1.62	130	3.10	135
5	1.45	105	2.98	105	2.01	105	4.21	95

OT = Observed time (in minutes), R = Rating

What do you understand by observed time and the rating process?

Using figures of your own choice for the various allowances, use the above data to show how the allowed time is calculated, explaining carefully the steps involved.

(*b*) Distinguish between (i) predetermined motion time systems; (ii) analytic estimating; (iii) synthetic timing.

2. 'Work measurement is simply the process by which a task is timed and rate set for the task for use in a payment by results scheme.'
Discuss.

3. (*a*) Compare and contrast direct and indirect methods of work measurement, describing a technique from each approach.

(*b*) Outline *three* reasons why the production/operations manager needs to know the work content of the tasks undertaken by his unit.

4. You are the production manager responsible for a small manufacturing unit. Output for the unit is consistently significantly below target. On your visits to the unit (frequently en route to the canteen) you gain the impression that workers are slacking. When tackled about this, your foreman claims that his men spend much of their time waiting for either raw materials or components from the adjacent unit. The men themselves claim that the machines are old, cannot hold their tolerances and require frequent resetting and repair.

You are determined to investigate the situation in your unit more fully. Explain in detail how you would go about using the various methodologies of work study to help you with this task.

5. Write short notes on the following:

(*a*) the rating process;	(*d*) basic time;
(*b*) observed time;	(*e*) standard time;
(*c*) allowances;	(*f*) allowed time.

Chapter 19 Work study III: non-manufacturing examples

1. You have just been appointed the first O & M officer that a small building society has ever employed. Describe how you would go about selecting your first task for a method study exercise, and how you might go about this exercise.

2. You are the manager of the processing branch of the Western Trust Bank. You are becoming increasingly aware that staff within your branch appear to be 'wasting time'. Frequently, when passing through the work area, going either from your office to the canteen or to your regular daily planning meetings with other managers, you notice groups of staff talking and apparently idle, while others are missing altogether.

When you ask your work area supervisor about this, he claims that the irregular patterns of work flow from the input branch cause the problems. The staff themselves claim that both the terminals and the central processor frequently break down and some of the delay is caused by the switch to the standby system.

Describe how you would go about investigating the situation in your branch in a quantitative manner.

3. Compare and contrast the application of work study techniques in manufacturing and non-manufacturing organizations.

4. (*a*) You are the manager of an insurance office. Explain what benefit

you would expect from carrying out an activity sampling exercise, and describe in detail how you would carry out such an exercise.

(*b*) You have just carried out the preliminary study for an activity sampling exercise. This was based on 40 tours of observations of five clerks. The activity 'productive work' was observed on 139 occasions. Describe two different ways in which the accuracy could be expressed. Calculate these if the preliminary study results are used to estimate the percentage of time spent productively. Assume that 95 per cent confidence in the results is required. Determine the number of tours in the full study if an actual accuracy of 2 per cent in the final productive time percentage is required.

5. It is frequently suggested that activity sampling is simply an investigatory tool which is used primarily in a manufacturing environment to establish areas for further detailed analysis using other appropriate techniques such as method study.

Use figures of your own choice to demonstrate that the above is a false impression and that activity sampling can be used in a much more sophisticated manner.

Chapter 20 Control of quality I

1. How should the principles of quality control be applied in a non-manufacturing unit? Who is responsible for maintaining the quality of the 'output'? What role does 'inspection' play in the system?

2. You have inherited, unexpectedly, a small consultancy business which is both profitable and enjoys a full order book. You wish to be personally involved in this activity where the only areas of immediate concern are the high levels of paperwork errors and re-doing of administrative operations—costing together a sum equivalent to about 15 per cent of the company's total sales.

Discuss your method of progressively picking up, analysing and solving this problem over a target period of 12 months. Illustrate any of the techniques you discuss.

3. (*a*) In quality control, what is meant by a process being 'in control'? When a process is not in control, what possible causes of variation should be considered?

(*b*) Discuss the use of control charts for the control of both process and product variables. Indicate when these charts may not be used for *control* and, under these circumstances, how they may be used.

4. A panel is designed to fit an assembly, the process requiring a length of 100 mm ± 12 mm. An electrically driven saw is used and its output is examined by taking twenty samples of five panels over a period of 8 hours. The results of this investigation are given below in mm:

Sample no.	Panel no. 1	2	3	4	5
1	104	90	90	95	102
2	95	101	94	93	103
3	89	98	93	91	96
4	95	97	105	95	100
5	102	95	100	97	104
6	93	97	102	94	101
7	97	94	93	97	96
8	98	97	96	102	92
9	101	103	92	98	100
10	102	104	106	101	95
11	98	96	104	101	93
12	103	97	98	101	106
13	106	106	108	109	107
14	99	99	105	104	102
15	89	99	92	97	102
16	98	96	99	95	103
17	98	101	102	100	103
18	103	100	99	102	104
19	97	100	98	95	101
20	96	102	97	98	104

Using the appropriate control charts, analyse this data and comment on the state of the process and its capability to meet the requirements. (Hartley's constant $d_n = 2.33$)

5. Two identical reactors are used to produce a high-density polyethylene material. Process capability studies have been carried out by measuring the melt flow index (MFI) of the output. One-gramme samples are taken every 10 minutes and the MFI measured. The data is then grouped successively into fives and the following results have been produced over two shifts:

Sample no.	MFI values Reactor 1 Mean	Range	Reactor 2 Mean	Range
1	138.2	6	136.0	1
2	137.8	5	140.0	1
3	138.8	7	138.6	2
4	137.8	5	138.0	0
5	138.0	6	135.6	1
6	138.4	6	136.0	2
7	137.2	4	135.2	1 *(cont'd next*
8	139.4	8	137.4	1 *page)*

| Sample no. | MFI values | | | |
| | Reactor 1 | | Reactor 2 | |
	Mean	Range	Mean	Range
9	137.4	4	138.4	1
10	137.0	3	140.2	1
11	138.0	5	140.0	0
12	138.6	6	140.4	1
13	139.2	8	139.8	1
14	139.6	8	136.0	1
15	136.4	2	135.6	1
16	136.8	3	136.0	0
17	138.6	6	141.6	1
18	138.6	6	141.2	1
19	137.0	3	139.2	1
20	139.2	7	135.2	2

The requirements for the product are that it should possess a melt flow index of 138 ± 4 units.

Use the appropriate techniques to examine this data and discuss fully the state and capability of the individual reactor processes and any differences between them.

Explain all terms used to demonstrate your understanding of the methods used.

Discuss the implications for action by the process management, fully utilizing your analysis of the data.

Chapter 21 Control of quality II

1. A manufacturer of worsted cloth produces pieces of a constant length. Each piece is examined for defects. The minor defects (contaminating fibres, dirt) are repaired and the major defects (holes, slubs) are identified for the customer by tags attached to the cloth. A record of the number of minor and major defects is kept. The results over a period of one week are shown below.

Sample	1	2	3	4	5	6	7	8	9	10	11	12	13	14
Major defects	1	3	1	4	1	4	5	3	4	2	4	4	5	4
Minor defects	5	3	6	3	5	5	6	5	3	5	3	3	6	5

Discuss two ways in which this data can be presented graphically and how it can be interpreted. Illustrate one of the methods by plotting the results for both the minor and major defects. Draw conclusions from your plots.

2. The following record shows the number of clerical errors found in a sample of 100 documents taken twice per day:

Sample no.	1	2	3	4	5	6	7	8	9	10	11	12	13	14	15
No. of errors	4	2	4	3	2	6	3	1	1	5	4	4	1	2	1

Sample no.	16	17	18	19	20	21	22	23	24	25	26	27	28
No. of errors	4	1	0	3	4	2	1	0	3	2	0	1	3

Sample no.	29	30	31	32	33	34	35	36	37	38	39	40
No. of errors	0	3	0	2	1	1	4	0	2	3	2	1

Set up and plot the appropriate attribute chart and a cusum chart.

3. Identical oil seals were being produced on ten supposedly identical machines and the output was being mixed. However, one of the machines was producing all defectives. The products were packed into cartons of 1,000 seals and at this stage a random sample of 20 seals was taken and examined. The carton was passed if no defectives were found in the sample.

Comment on the operation of this scheme, performing a complete analysis to support your conclusions. Explain all terms used.

Explain how you would attempt to investigate and correct the problem of the faulty machine, indicating any methods, techniques and resources you might enlist for the task.

4. (a) Discuss the purpose of acceptance sampling, including in your answer a diagram showing the main features of an operating characteristic curve.

(b) Explain briefly the following terms which are used in acceptance sampling: (i) producer's risk; (ii) consumer's risk; (iii) acceptable quality level (AQL).

(c) Discuss how the technique of acceptance sampling may be applied in an accountancy function.

5. Batches of 500 electronic components are being inspected before despatch; the AQL is 1 per cent and a single sample plan is required to ensure a consumer's risk of 5 per cent for batches containing 8 per cent defectives. All defectives found during inspection will be replaced with good ones and all batches rejected by the scheme are to be rectified. Design a plan which will *minimize* the total inspection effort.

If the average outgoing quality limit (AOQL) of the scheme must be 1.3 per cent or less, which single sample plan would you use?

Chapter 22 Costing

1. Show how a successful costing procedure can assist an operations manager in controlling his labour costs.

2. (*a*) Historical or standard costing techniques may be used to arrive at the costs of jobs or processes.

Describe the limitations of the purely historical costing approach and how historical costs are used in a standard costing system.

Outline the requirements for establishing a standard costing system.

(*b*) Calculate the wages variance from the following:

> *Product data:*
> Direct labour—20 standard hours per unit of product
> Direct wages—500p per standard hour
> *Cost data:*
> During one month 500 units of the product were produced; 12,000 hours were worked; actual direct labour cost was £65,000

3. Summarize the nature of:

absorption costing, marginal costing and standard costing

If a well-run manufacturing company regularly used all three methods, explain the circumstances in which marginal costings are likely to be more important than absorption costing.

4. Explain in detail the significance of standard costs as compared with actual costs and show how they are applied and what information can be obtained from their application.

5. 'Costing is an instrument of management control.'

'Costing is nothing more than a detailed analysis of expenditure.'

Reconcile these two statements, quoting examples to illustrate the truth of each.

Chapter 23 Programmes—an overview

1. Describe the main functions of production/operations control, and compare and contrast their relative importance with different methods of organizing production/operations.

2. It has been argued that the success of an organization is determined by three factors:

(*a*) the price;
(*b*) the quality;
(*c*) the availability;

of the product or service being provided.

Describe how the production/operations control function contributes to this success.

3. Compare and contrast the production control function in a manufacturing organization of your choice with operations control in a non-manufacturing organization of your choice.

4. You are the production controller for a manufacturer of a standard range of office furniture. This range includes desks, chairs and cabinets. All your orders are for the wholesale market, against specific customer orders.

Describe your principal responsibilities, and outline some of those factors likely to influence the way you discharge your responsibilities.

5. Describe, in general terms, the contribution a microcomputer might make to the production/operations control function, and suggest how this might develop over the next five years.

Chapter 24 Forecasting

1. You are the operations manager of the input section of an international bank. The following table shows the transactions received for processing each week for the last fifteen weeks:

Week	Transactions received	Week	Transactions received
1	1,964	9	1,884
2	1,832	10	2,046
3	1,913	11	1,756
4	1,791	12	1,816
5	1,984	13	1,882
6	1,961	14	1,781
7	1,776	15	1,914
8	1,943		

Show how a five-period moving average could be set up to forecast the transactions which might be received each week. How could the accuracy of these forecasts be measured? What would be the effect of changing to a ten-period moving average?

2. A small company manufactures a product used by the domestic leisure market. As might be expected, the demand for this product is highly seasonal. Describe why this is likely to cause problems for the production controller. Outline how a forecasting technique could be developed to predict the requirements.

3. The usage of a cleaning fluid used for pipelines in a chemical plant is shown below:

Week	Usage (litres)	Week	Usage (litres)
1	5,109	8	5,873
2	6,323	9	6,121
3	4,821	10	5,124
4	5,425	11	5,926
5	4,234	12	4,435
6	5,513	13	5,461
7	4,719	14	4,691

Show how exponential smoothing (with a smoothing constant $\alpha = 0.2$) can be used to forecast the requirement for cleaning fluid each week. How can the accuracy of these forecasts be measured. What would be the effect of changing the smoothing constant to $\alpha = 0.6$?

4. 'The production/operations manager has no use for forecasts. The nature of his responsibilities is such that he can only handle information and data which are certain.'

Discuss.

5. Compare and contrast moving averages and exponential smoothing as forecasting techniques, with particular reference to their use by the production/operations controller.

Chapter 25 Scheduling and loading

1. A printing services section has eight sets of documents to copy/collate and spiral bind. There is only one machine for each of these two processes, and the times required by each set on each machine are given below.

	Process (hours required)	
Document	Copy/collate	Spiral bind
1	8	4
2	6	3
3	5	9
4	11	6
5	3	10
6	7	3
7	10	11
8	2	5

In what order should the documents be worked on if they should be all finished as soon as possible (minimize makespan)? What is this makespan? Is the order unique? Outline the limitations of the method used.

2. (*a*) Describe the contribution work study makes to the production/operations control function.

(*b*) Outline what you understand by and distinguish between the following in the context of production/operations control: (i) job schedule; (ii) production schedule; (iii) load.

3. 'The use of the Japanese developed technique "just-in-time" will solve the problems frequently encountered in scheduling in the UK manufacturing industry.'

Discuss.

4. You are the operations controller at the head office of a building society. All the society's different transactions are processed through the input section, and your responsibility includes the difficult task of scheduling work in this area.

Describe some of the steps you might consider taking to reduce the scale of this scheduling problem.

5. Outline the two fundamental problems in scheduling production, and discuss how they may be overcome.

Chapter 26 Example of schedule preparation

1. Three jobs require processing in a small machine shop with three machines A, B, C. Details are below:

Job	Machine (duration—hours)			Value of job	Required for week no.
	Operation 1	*Operation 2*	*Operation 3*		
1	A(20)	B(40)	C(30)	£4½K	24
2	A(60)	B(10)	C(20)	£6½K	25
3	A(30)	C(90)		£3½K	22

Describe in detail *three* criteria which could be used to determine the order in which the jobs could be scheduled. Use a bar chart to illustrate one of the schedules.

2. You are the production controller for a small manufacturing company using batch production methods. A standard range of products is made for the wholesale market against specific customer orders with specified delivery dates.

Describe your information requirement to plan and control production, indicating the relative importance and explaining how this information will be used.

3. In general terms, scheduling can be carried out either backwards or forwards in time, and to either finite or infinite capacity.

Examine these possible combinations of approach, indicating the advantages and disadvantages of each.

4. A small manufacturing unit has four machines, A, B, C, D, which are used to manufacture a range of four standard hydraulic valves: HVl, HV2A, HV4, HV6HD. The standard times (standard minutes) on the machines for each valve are as follows:

| Valve | Machine—standard time | | | |
	A	B	C	D
HVl	150	80	120	210
HV2A	200	240	140	120
HV4	170	190	210	160
HV6HD	90	120	130	190

Currently, six jobs are waiting to be processed:

Job	Type	Required by end of week
1	10HV1	20
2	30HV2A	18
3	10HV4	17
4	10HV2A	19
5	30HV6HD	21
6	20HV1	22

The valves must be processed first by A, then B, then C and finally by D. All the valves for a particular job must be processed together, with the job only moving to the next machine when processing of all of the valves comprising a job is complete.

Use bar charts to compare the results of scheduling the jobs in order of:

(a) least total processing time;
(b) smallest total slack time.

5. Discuss the use of loading rules to schedule tasks and their relationship to performance measures.

Chapter 27 Data capture and release

1. A factory produces a range of ready-to-wear men's garments using batch production methods.

Outline the responsibilities of the despatch section, together with the information necessary to carry out these responsibilities.

2. 'The responsibility of the progress section is to check that operations are proceeding according to plan. Consequently the existence of such a section is an admission of lack of confidence in the planning function.'

Discuss.

3. The appropriate method for collecting progress data will depend in part on the method of manufacture being used.

Discuss the above statement, comparing the situation when job, batch, flow or group technology methods are being used. Outline some of the other factors which are likely to influence the decision.

4. 'The availability of cheap and widely available computers will resolve the two major problems facing the progress chaser.'

Discuss.

5. 'The progress function is a fundamental part of production control in a manufacturing organization. However, it has no role in a non-manufacturing environment.'

Discuss this statement in the context of an example of a non-manufacturing organization of your choice.

Chapter 28 Materials assessment

1. A small company manufactures the trolleys used for carrying luggage and cases at airports, railway stations and ferry ports. They make two basic sizes, small and large, which are identical in design. This consists of a frame, made from square-section tube, cut and welded with special sockets welded to the bottom corners into which the four wheels are screwed. The handle is of circular-section tube, plastic covered, welded to and part of the frame. A special wire basket (common to both sizes) is bought-in complete and fixed in front of the handle with two special clips. Stock status information is given below:

Item	Current stock	Lead time (week)	Unit of measure
Small trolley	10	2	unit
Large trolley	10	2	unit
Basket	20	2	unit
Basket clips	30	1	pair
Wheel	25	1	unit
Wheel socket	25	2	unit
Square-section tube	30	3	metre
Round-section tube	10	2	metre
Plastic cover	15	3	metre
Large frame	0	1	unit
Small frame	0	1	unit

The large trolley requires 14 metres of square-section tube and 1.5 metres of round section. The corresponding figures for the small trolley are 10 metres and 1 metre respectively. The length of plastic cover required is the same as the round-section tube.

The current requirements are for 100 large trolleys and 150 small trolleys in week 8.

Draw the bill of material for the trolleys. Produce the material requirement plans for all items.

2. (*a*) Write short notes on the following in the context of materials requirements planning (MRP):

(i) bill of materials;
(ii) safety stock;
(iii) master production schedule;
(iv) stock status data;
(v) time phasing.

(*b*) Explain why a company may wish to develop from materials requirements planning (MRP) to manufacturing resource planning (MRP II).

3. Distinguish between dependent demand and independent demand in the context of stock control, and describe methods appropriate for each.

4. The manager of a large insurance office is examining the purchasing policy for stationery. He starts with an envelope which is used extremely frequently—he estimates 10,000 per week—and costs 5p each. He estimates that the cost of placing an order is £50, independent of the order quantity, and that the cost of holding stock is approximately 35 per cent of the average value of the stock held.

Derive the economic order quantity for the envelope, and suggest how frequently it should be ordered.

The supplier offers to reduce the price to $4\frac{1}{2}$p each, if the whole year's requirement is ordered and paid for in advance. Should this offer be accepted?

Clearly outline all the assumptions made in the above analysis, and the consequences if these do not hold.

5. Discuss the contributions that the computer can make to stock management, clearly identifying its scope and its limitations.

Chapter 29 Materials management

1. You have just taken over the responsibility for a stores which is used to hold maintenance materials for the plant and buildings of a large factory complex. There are over 20,000 different items in stock, with no

formal methods currently being used for control. You suspect that the number of items stocked is excessive.

Describe some of the analyses you would carry out, and some of the methods you might use to manage the stores more effectively. Clearly indicate what data you will require.

2. Describe the basic documentation you require to run a materials control system, together with the information requirements.

Outline some of the contingencies which may need to be allowed for within the system.

3. Major difficulties can arise when what is actually in stock does not correspond with what the stock records claim is in stock.

Describe some of these difficulties and outline how this problem can be overcome.

4. You are the storekeeper for a medium-sized pharmaceutical company. Describe your likely responsibilities, paying particular attention to the interfaces with the various other departments.

5. Outline the documentation and information requirements for the storekeeping function and the overlap with the materials control area.

Chapter 30 Critical path analysis

1. Draw and analyse the network for:

	Activity	*Precedes*	*Duration*
Start	A	B, C	4
	E	F, G	3
	B	D	6
	C	H	5
	F	D	10
	G	H	9
Finish	D	—	8
	H	—	7

2. An established company has decided to add a new product to its line. It will buy the product from a manufacturing concern, package it, and sell it to a number of distributors selected on a geographical basis. Market research has been done which has indicated the volume expected and size of sales force required. The following steps are to be planned:

Organize the sales office—hire the sales manager	*5 weeks*
Hire salesmen—the sales manager will recruit and hire the salesmen needed	*4 weeks*
Train salesmen—train the salesmen hired to sell the product to the distributors	*7 weeks*

Select advertising agency—the sales manager will select   *2 weeks*
the agency best suited to promote the new product

Plan advertising campaign—the sales office and the   *4 weeks*
advertising agency will jointly plan the advertising
campaign to introduce the product to the public

Conduct advertising campaign—the advertising agency   *10 weeks*
will conduct a 'watch for' campaign for potential
customers to end at the time distributors receive their
initial stocks

Design package—design the package most likely to   *4 weeks*
'sell', work to be done within the company on the basis
of results of market research

Set-up packaging facilities—prepare to package the   *12 weeks*
products when they are received from the manufacturer

Package initial stocks—package stocks received from   *8 weeks*
the manufacturer

Order stock from manufacturer—order the stock   *13 weeks*
needed from the manufacturer on the basis of the
volume indicated by the market research. The time
given includes the lead time for delivery

Select distributors—the sales manager will select the   *9 weeks*
distributors whom the salesmen will contact to make
sales

Sell to the distributors—take orders for the new   *6 weeks*
product from the distributors with delivery promised for
introduction date. If orders exceed stock, assign stock
on a quota basis

Ship stock to distributors—ship the packaged stock to   *6 weeks*
the distributors as per their orders or quota

Questions:

(*a*) What is the earliest number of weeks in which we can introduce
the product?

(*b*) If we hire trained salesmen and eliminate the training period of 7
weeks, can our product be introduced 7 weeks earlier?

(*c*) How long can we delay in selecting our advertising agency?

(*d*) What is the effect of a delay of (i) 1 week; (ii) 2 weeks; (iii) 3
weeks, in organizing the sales office?

(*e*) If the whole product launch operation is to be completed as rapidly
as possible, what activities *must* have been completed by the end of week
16?

(*f*) What advantage, if any, would accrue if the selection of the advertising agency took place at the same time as the organizing of the sales
office?

3. Draw and analyse the network for:

	Activity	Precedes	Duration
Start	A	D, E	4
	B	F, G	6
	C	G	2
	D	L	3
	E	H	8
	F	H, K	9
	G	L	10
Finish	H	L	6
	K	L	8
	L	—	1

4. Within a small neighbourhood department store there are three sections in the shoe department:

(*a*) men's;
(*b*) women's;
(*c*) children's.

There are three staff:

(*a*) a junior;
(*b*) a management trainee;
(*c*) a manager.

The manager has to have a stock-take and he decides to do it as follows:

(*a*) The junior will remove stock, clean fixtures thoroughly and replace stock conveniently for stock-taking. She is not considered experienced enough to do more than this.
(*b*) The management trainee will then count and record the stock.
(*c*) The manager will sample check the trainee's stock-take.

It is decided to carry out the work section by section, starting with the men's section, following with the women's and finishing with the children's section. How long will this take? Considering only the activities:

Remove and clean men's stock	R_M	2 hours
Remove and clean women's stock	R_W	8 hours
Remove and clean children's stock	R_C	2 hours
Carry out men's stock-check	S_M	4 hours
Carry out women's stock-check	S_W	8 hours
Carry out children's stock-check	S_C	6 hours
Check men's stock-take	C_M	3 hours

Check women's stock-take C_W *8 hours*
Check children's stock-take C_C *2 hours*

(Careful! If using A on A, this requires 4 dummies.)

Chapter 31 Line of balance

1. The delivery schedule of components and the operation programme for the manufacture of these components are given below. Construct the line of balance for week 5. Indicate how you would use the line of balance to analyse production progress in the several different departments involved in the production system.

Week no.	0	1	2	3	4	5	6	7	8	9	10	11	12
Delivery required (units)	0	12	15	12	20	5	10	15	20	27	15	20	17

Fig. 1 Components delivery schedule

Figures in parentheses show the time in days that operations must be completed before delivery (e.g. operation 5 of component 3 must be completed 20 days before the delivery date).

2. Compare and contrast the use of critical path analysis with the use of line of balance.

3. Develop your own example to illustrate the use of line of balance, paying particular attention to the various steps involved in the analysis.

4. Explain what you understand by the following in the context of line of balance:

(*a*) CPA diagram;
(*b*) equivalent week number;
(*c*) line of balance diagram;
(*d*) line of balance chart;
(*e*) life table.

5. Line of balance and critical path analysis are techniques which can be used for planning and controlling manufacture.

Consider each technique in turn, indicating when you would use it, giving reasons for your choice and explaining its contribution to management control.

Chapter 32 Linear programming

1. You are the production director for a company which operates a number of multi-purpose plants at various different geographic locations.

Describe some of the areas where linear programming can help you with your decision-making.

2. The following is a formulation of a product-mix problem facing a production manager:

$$\begin{aligned}
\text{Maximize} \quad & 30x_1 + 10x_2 \\
\text{subject to} \quad & 10x_1 + 5x_2 \leqslant 50 \\
& 8x_1 + 8x_2 \leqslant 64 \\
& 16x_1 + 4x_2 \leqslant 64
\end{aligned}$$

Explain the interpretation of the variables and constraints.

Show how the graphical method can be used to solve the problem.

3. A multi-purpose plant can be used to manufacture two products, A and B, from raw materials, Y and Z. The amounts of raw materials required, plant times and profits per batch are shown below:

Product	Profit per batch	Plant time per batch (hrs)	Units of raw material per batch Y	Z
A	30	5	18	30
B	8	10	12	10

There are 216 units of raw material Y, and 300 units of raw material Z available per week. The plant is available for 150 hours per week.

Formulate, as a linear programme, the problem of establishing how many batches of each product to manufacture each week to give maximum total profit. Use the graphical method to solve this problem.

4. The basic linear programming model has a number of limitations when used to analyse certain production management problems.

Describe some of these limitations and problems, and indicate how the model might be extended.

5. Linear programming has much to offer the production manager as an aid to decision-making.

Discuss.

Chapter 33 Purchasing

1. What are the main objectives of efficient purchasing and what is the scope of the purchasing function within an organization?

2. Describe the work of the purchasing manager in a large hospital, explaining his relationships with other departments and with suppliers.

3. The board of directors of a large manufacturing company is to decide whether to centralize its purchasing activities. Discuss the advantages and disadvantages of such a move. Indicate the range of activities to be carried out by the senior purchasing executive if central-ization goes ahead.

4. Explain how you would set up a system for purchasing. Draw up a list showing clearly all the information needed on a purchase order, justifying each entry.

5. A company is to establish a contract with a car-hire organization. Explain how a choice would be made between several different organ-izations offering this service.

Chapter 34 Personnel administration

1. Discuss the differences between, and the purposes of, job evaluation and merit rating. Describe how a job evaluation may be carried out.

2. 'The personnel manager holds the key to good relationships within a factory.' Examine this statement and state your reasons for agreeing with or dissenting from it.

3. Describe the operation of a scheme of merit rating, applicable to clerical and junior staff workers, with a view to rationalizing their salaries and assessing their worthiness of promotion. Discuss the likely reactions of the employees to such a scheme.

4. State a case justifying the establishment of a personnel department to a director who opposes this action on financial grounds.

5. The years 1945 to the present have seen the steady increase in the status and function of the personnel manager. What are the implications of this development for the operations manager?

Chapter 35 Payment by results

1. State the principles which you consider must be observed when formulating an incentive bonus scheme.

2. 'Time study and incentives are terms which are regarded as synony-

mous in industry.' Discuss this statement, giving your views concerning its validity.

3. What are the advantages of a measured day work system of payment over other systems?

4. Bosses tend to favour piece-work; unions tend to oppose it. Discuss.

5. Show how wage-drift may come about when a PBR scheme is in operation.

Chapter 36 Health and safety

1. Explain what you understand by the following terms in the context of health and safety at work:

(*a*) an accident;
(*b*) an accident cause;
(*c*) an accident prevention programme.

2. Discuss the responsibilities for the safety of employees in a medium-sized engineering manufacturing company. Indicate how you would organize and plan the health and safety programme.

3. Describe how you would set up an accident prevention programme for a potentially dangerous chemical production unit.

4. As the safety officer of a university, what steps would you take to communicate the 'message' of health and safety at work to the staff (academic and non-academic) and students?

5. Discuss the implications of legislation for health and safety, indicating the main components required. Give an outline of the essential contents of a company safety policy.

Appendix 1 A–B–C analysis

1. 'A–B–C (Pareto) analysis is an essential tool for the POM manager.' Discuss, giving five examples of its possible use.

2. The unit for which you are responsible manufactures a range of products including electric toasters. You are very concerned about customer warranty claims on the toasters. The following data relates to claims over the last three months:

Defective area	No. of claims	Repair cost per claim (£)
Handles	121	1.2
Element	1,019	10.5
On/off switch	6,421	0.8
'Ejection' mechanism	219	3.2
Trim—screws, etc.	1,512	0.7
Finish—plastic	104	1.1
Finish—metal	69	1.3
Plug	106	3.1
'Colour' control switch	19	9.8
Cable	82	3.2
Variable thickness mechanism	500	14.6

Show how Pareto analysis can help you in tackling the quality problem.

3. The reasons for attendance at the emergency department of Bruddersford General Hospital were recorded:

Reasons for attendance	Number of patients attending
Arm	22
Ear	4
Eye	16
Foot	20
General body	10
Genitals	1
Hand	42
Head	57
Internal organs	2
Leg	51
Neck	2
Trunk	1
Unknown	13
Whole body	2
TOTAL	259

Carry out a Pareto analysis on these figures and hence deduce where there is most likely need for further resources.

4. The Bruddersford Car Accessory Company carries out an activity sampling exercise whereby the activities of its staff are logged with the following results:

Description of task	Percentage occurrence
Absent from desk (AD)	0.8
Aborted telephone calls (ATC)	1.0
Final filling in of customer information (CI)	4.7
Customer on telephone (CT)	18.7
Looking up directories (DIR)	2.2
Examine desk-maps (EDM)	12.2
Dealing with existing job (EJ)	4.2
Examine wall-maps (EWM)	7.8
Responding to general telephone calls (GTC)	2.2
Internal telephone calls (ITC)	1.4
Other telephone calls (OTC)	0.9
Discussing problems with supervisor (PS)	3.90
Searching database (SDB)	12.4
Sending telex (ST)	3.0
Telephoning agents to carry out work (TA)	5.7
Taking details (TD)	12.9
Telephone not working (TNW)	0.7
Verify status of owner (VO)	5.3

Where should further resources be made available?

5. Bruddersford Brokers, a long established firm of insurance brokers in the Bruddersford area, found themselves being approached increasingly by clients seeking advice on health and safety matters within their workplace. The clients were anxious not only to make sure that they were complying with current legislation and hoping to prevent accidents which would result in claims under their employers' liability policies, they were also anxious to reduce their premiums by improving their claim record. Some were also genuinely concerned about the well-being of their workforce.

The partners realized that if clients were to be helped to improve their employers' liability claims record, then they needed to be provided with means of identifying the areas to which they should be dividing their health and safety measures or accident reduction policies. As it so happened, the firm had been approached by the local polytechnic and had agreed to take on a sandwich-course student from their business school. She was given the task of devising such an advisory service.

As a first step, she analysed the premiums received by the firm. Employers' liability policies brought in some 20 per cent of the total income and 94 companies were so covered, the total employers' liability premiums being £1,642,000. She extracted all the companies who paid £10,000 or more (Exhibit 1) as a first step. She then intended to analyse all the successful claims made by these companies over a period of three years to see whether certain types of injuries predominated, classified according to the location of the injury on the body. This would then form a basis for accident prevention policies. Time, however, only permitted a detailed breakdown of the three largest clients (Exhibit 2).

F.C. Ltd—involved in polymer processing, rubber and plastics technology.

L.G. Ltd—involved in civil engineering, building, opencast mining, tunnelling, etc.

J.B. Ltd—involved in wire drawing and engineering.

(*a*) Discuss these figures.

(*b*) What further work would you recommend?

Exhibit 1

Total no. of clients = 94 Total employers' liability premiums = £1,642,000

Companies paying £10,000 or more employers' liability premium:

B.W. Ltd	30,000	K.W. Ltd	66,000	U.V. Ltd	35,000
C.C. Ltd	100,000	L.G. Ltd	428,000	W.L. Ltd	21,000
C.M. Ltd	17,000	M.L. Ltd	13,000	W.W. Ltd	50,000
C.R. Ltd	14,000	M.R. Ltd	11,000	X.C. Ltd	32,000
F.C. Ltd	135,000	O.U. Ltd	28,000	X.Y. Ltd	75,000
G.J. Ltd	36,000	P.B. Ltd	82,000	Z.Y. Ltd	33,000
J.B. Ltd	121,000	P.R. Ltd	88,000	Z.Z. Ltd	10,000

Exhibit 2

Injury site	No. of injuries per site for:		
	F.C. Ltd	L.G. Ltd	J.B. Ltd
Head & face (excluding eyes)	14	38	10
Eyes	6	14	3
Arms	10	12	8
Hands and wrists	57	88	59
Torso	5	31	7
Back	10	33	6
Internal organs/diseases	8	10	2
Legs	11	57	11
Feet and ankles	31	57	26
Multiple	11	43	12
Dermatitis	3	4	5
Unknown	13	9*	10**

* Includes 6 fatalities; actual injury sites unknown.
** Includes 1 fatality; actual injury sites unknown.

Index